THE CONSEQUENCES OF FEAR

ALSO BY JACQUELINE WINSPEAR

THE
CONSEQUENCES
OF
FEAR

A Maisie Dobbs Novel

JACQUELINE WINSPEAR

HARPER

An Imprint of HarperCollins*Publishers*

Dedicated with admiration and gratitude
to my wonderful editor Jennifer Barth

FIRST EDITION

Designed by Kyle O'Brien
Art by Potapov Alexander / Shutterstock, Inc.

Library of Congress Cataloging-in-Publication Data has been applied for.

ISBN 978-0-06-311176-9

21 22 23 24 25 LSC 10 9 8 7 6 5 4 3 2 1

"Fear makes us feel our humanity."

—Benjamin Disraeli

PROLOGUE

St. Ermin's Hotel, Caxton Street, Westminster, Friday evening, October 3, 1941

R ight, son, this one's going to that address in Leverstone Road—you go over Vauxhall Bridge and after a few lefts you're almost there. Know where it is?" The porter pointed to the handwritten address on the envelope as he handed it across the desk to the boy, who grasped it, ready to leave for his next destination.

"Reckon I know it," said the boy, glancing at the address. "It's on my way home."

"Not so fast, young Freddie Hackett. You might have to leg it back here with a reply before you can run all the way to your gaff. The bloke you give this to will let you know." The porter glanced at the boy over half-moon glasses, pulled a fob watch from his waistcoat pocket and nodded as he checked the time. He regarded the boy again. "Now you mind how you go, laddie—this run's a good couple of miles, so let's hope he don't have a return message. You're quick on your pins all right, but them bloody Gerry bombers are at it again."

"I'm like a cat, Mr. Larkin—I can see in the dark." The boy grinned and held out his hand, wiggling his fingers.

"Don't you worry—I wouldn't forget this." The porter reached into his pocket and brought out a shilling, then flicked it toward the boy. The boy caught it between two fingers, slipped the money into his jacket pocket, fastened a safety pin to keep the pocket closed, and pushed the envelope into his trouser band, covering it with his pullover. Then he was gone.

Poor little bugger, thought Larkin as he made his way back into the foyer. *Poor little legs running all over the blimmin' place.*

"The runner get off all right?"

Larkin looked up as a large man in a well-cut pinstripe suit descended the sweeping staircase leading to the upper floors of a grand building that seemed designed to give an impression of strength and yet genteel hospitality, as one might expect of a hotel with a series of upstairs rooms requisitioned by clandestine government services.

"Yes, sir, Mr. MacFarlane. He just left."

MacFarlane ran a hand across hair that was fast balding, and nodded. "You don't like it any more than I do, Larkin—sending boys not old enough to shave off along the streets of London when bombs are falling."

"Can't say as I do, Mr. MacFarlane. But that one has got some speed to him, make no mistake. I reckon he could run a marathon, could young Freddie Hackett. The Air Raid Precautions bods who recruited him when they went round the schools, well, they said he was the fastest runner they'd seen—and with enough speed on him to go to the Olympics one day."

"Good—we can all be there to watch him get his gold—and beat Hitler's bloody Germans," said MacFarlane.

"Not a chance. By the time this war is over and they get around to having an Olympics, I'd say his best will have passed him by—that's if he comes out the other side, poor little bugger. He's only twelve."

"And he's not the only one out there, Larkin. Not the only youngster doing war work."

The porter nodded and tapped an evening newspaper he'd picked up from a nearby table. "Seen this? Turns out Hitler has said that the Germans have all but destroyed Russia and that they can beat all possible enemies no matter how much money they've got, even billions. What do you reckon to that, Mr. MacFarlane? Sticking his neck out a bit, don't you think?"

MacFarlane raised his eyebrows as he answered in a low voice. "Probably trying to wave a red cape at the Yanks, is my guess. Trying to pull them in so he can say he's knocking them into the next world." He looked at his watch. "Right, I'm leaving. Got to see a man about a dog and then I'm off to Baker Street."

Larkin smiled as MacFarlane turned and made his way toward the side entrance. *Got to see a man about a dog.* See a pint or two in the Cuillins of Skye more like, thought Larkin. He could just as easily have had his drink in the Caxton Bar at the hotel, but who could blame the bloke for wanting to get out to his favorite pub for a bit of a breather? After all, it wasn't as if he had anyone at home, waiting for him. And he worked all hours, if Larkin's ledger was anything to go by.

The boy raced across Vauxhall Bridge, looking up every few paces as he ran, feet light on the ground and not even breaking a sweat. He was the best and always had been. He'd won every race at school—the teacher told him he would smash the stopwatch wide open one day. He ran fast because the winner always got a sweet, and he really wanted that sweet the teacher held in his hand. He would have run to the moon for a bit of chocolate. Sometimes he saved it for Iris, his sister—a special treat for their lovely little Iris. But most of the time he couldn't wait and would pop it in his mouth, ready to run again.

Two florins and a half-crown jangled in his pocket—he couldn't hear the jangling on account of the bombers, but he could feel the coins bumping against his hip. He slowed down toward the end of the bridge, looking left across the water in the direction of the East End. It was burning again and he could see fires south of the river, in Walworth and Bermondsey. And there was that sound the bombs made when they dropped, a sort of *crump-crump-crump*, and he could hear the bells from ambulances and fire engines. Those were the only sounds on his run over Vauxhall Bridge.

The bombers didn't come over like they did in the Blitz, like a swarm of big death-dealing insects blackening the sky, but they still came and they still had it in for London, and all over the country. He sometimes read the papers while he was waiting for a message, so he knew all about the other cities and towns that had copped it. He wondered if boys like him in Leeds and Portsmouth had to run through the night with envelopes tucked in their trousers. But he reckoned that if he kept running, he'd be all right: a moving target was harder to hit. It was stopping that scared him. It had been a warm couple of days, for October, but he didn't want to slow down to take off his jacket in case his money dropped out. If he didn't hand his earnings over to his father, he'd get the belt for his trouble.

He turned onto one street, then another on his way to the address on the envelope—he never had to look twice at an address—and at once the sky lit up again. *Crump-crump-crump.* That's when he saw two men ahead, illuminated by a Bomber's Moon and falling incendiaries. He didn't like what he saw—there was shouting, and then the men were struggling, hanging onto each other, fighting, and he didn't want to run into any trouble. This blimmin' bombing was trouble enough.

He slowed down, but felt a finger of fear, of warning, shimmy down his spine. A doorway offered refuge, but was he too close? Could they see him? Bloody hell, he might as well have asked for the lights to go on all over London. He flattened himself against the wall. If the house behind him hadn't been a bombed-out shell, he would have knocked on the door and begged to be let in. He heard his heart beating in his ears and hoped that whatever was going to happen, happened soon— bombs he could tolerate, but people trying to kill each other when the Germans were trying to slaughter everyone in the blimmin' country, well, no, he couldn't understand that at all. People going for each other like that, it scared him something rotten.

Freddie crouched down in the doorway. One of the men appeared to have the upper hand now. He'd taken the other man and whisked him round, and had his neck in the crook of his elbow. Blimey, that bloke had big hands. Another flash of light and he saw everything, as if someone had turned up the gas lamp. The big bloke was wearing a raincoat, his dark hair swept back. If he'd had a hat, he wasn't wearing it now. More flashes and the man was illuminated again. Who was that film star he looked like? Freddie had gone to the pictures one Saturday morning, spending the bit extra Larkin had given him out of his own pocket. Old Larkin was a good sort—it was as if he knew what it was like for Freddie at home. Victor Mature! That was his name. Lon Chaney was in the picture too. It was called *One Million B.C.* But this bloke looked nastier than old Victor—and, blimey, that's a scar.

More flashes of light, more *crump-crump-crump* as bombs fell. Freddie wanted to get moving, but was now paralyzed by the violence before him. The big man with the dark hair pulled out a knife—Freddie saw it glint in the flashes of light coming from the skies. And then it was done. He saw the man push the knife straight into the other man's left side, then pull it out, and with a snarl across his face, he plunged the weapon into the man's heart. It wasn't like one of those pictures at the Gaumont. This poor sod went down with his eyes wide open, blood pouring from his mouth, and the murderer—oh dear God, he had just seen a real murder—pulled the knife out of the dead man's body and wiped it across his chest. For a second, Freddie thought he saw two men standing over the body, but his eyes had gone all blurry, so he wiped the back of his hand across his face to stop himself seeing double and looked up again in time to see the man—the killer—calmly put the knife in his pocket. He looked about him, then he'd gone on his way. Just walked off, steady as you like, into the darkness.

The boy leaned over and vomited onto the dusty red tiles outside the remains of the door. And he'd wet himself. He felt his bottom lip tremble and his hands were shaking. *Oh Christ, I hope the envelope . . .* but it was all right, it was dry. Not like his trousers.

Freddie Hackett sat for a while longer, trying not to sob. The envelope had to be delivered soon, or there would be trouble. But trouble would come when he got home and his father found out about the mess he'd made of his trousers. If he was lucky, Arthur Hackett wouldn't be home when he got there. And perhaps they'd dry with the heat of his body. That's what his mum said when the washing hadn't dried properly on the line out the back. "Never mind, love," she'd say. "It'll dry out with the heat of your body." He sometimes wondered why she bothered at all, scrubbing the clothes and putting them through the wringer, only to see smuts from the trains all over them when she brought in the laundry.

Another minute, that's all he'd need, and he'd be ready to start running again.

After a while the patch on his trousers didn't feel so wet, so he emerged from the doorway. He jumped up and down to get his legs moving, as if he were letting a motor car idle in neutral so the oil could get around the engine before putting it into gear, and then he started running again, making sure to look the other way as he passed the body of a man he'd seen murdered while bombs fell across London, probably killing a few hundred more when they landed. Or a few thousand.

It took another ten minutes to find the address, a row of houses still standing in a street that had otherwise been razed to the ground. He looked up at the Victorian terrace house and reached for the door knocker—but the door opened without him even touching the brass ring. A man holding an oil lamp put his hand on Freddie's shoulder and pulled him in.

"I don't want the air raid patrol round here because someone's seen a light coming from my house," said the man.

Freddie looked up and saw a scar move. No. Two scars moved, one on each side of his face, and there was another little one under his eye too, or was that the way the lamp flickered, making a bit of skin seem extra white? Freddie didn't like scars—they frightened him. But were they scars, or was it just the man's face? It didn't matter, because right now this bloke scared him something rotten, even though he was smiling. Freddie was as frightened as he had been in that doorway, because he could have sworn on his grandmother's grave that this was the very same man he'd just seen murder another bloke. He was standing right there, in front of him—a killer.

"You're a brave boy, running through all that. Which way did you come?"

Freddie might have wanted to vomit again, but he was no fool and took care not to reveal his route. "Oh, I took a short cut I know after the bridge—down Chamois Street and then round the back of Watsons' factory."

"I don't know that way."

Freddie shrugged, looking down at his feet because he didn't want to see the man's face again, not if he could help it. "Any message to go back, sir?"

"Just a minute. You can wait in there by the fire." The man pushed open the door to the parlor, where a small fire was beginning to catch. "Looks like you could do with drying out. Nasty out there when those bombers come in. I'd shit myself every night, if I were you."

Freddie entered the room and held his hands out to the flames. If he moved closer the growing heat might finish the drying on his trousers. Funny that, having a fire—it's not as if it was chilly in the house. Mind you, he never felt the cold much, even in winter. But there were papers in the grate, scorched, as if the man had been burning documents. Freddie knew that wasn't unusual—he'd often seen people do that with a message he'd just delivered. They'd take a match to the paper, or open the door to a stove and push it in with a poker. But there was this room, and it was strange too, he thought. His family didn't have much, but his dad had an old armchair, and there was a straight-backed wooden chair for his mum, while he and Iris had orange crates to sit on. And there was a bit of scraggy carpet on the floor that his dad told him had "fallen off the back of a lorry." This room was almost empty. No pictures, no mirror, no plant in the window—his nan always had a plant in the window to stop the neighbors nosing in. Well, she did until she and Grandad were killed when the house was bombed out.

The door opened and the man nodded toward the passage.

"No return message. You can go. Get on home, boy, to your people." Freddie rushed past, ready to scamper out of the house. "Hey, not so fast, Jesse Owens. Take this." The man pressed a half-crown into his hand, the long lines on his face appearing to have a life of their own as he smiled and patted him on the head.

Freddie ran down the road, stopping once to slip the half-crown into his sock. If he positioned it right, it would sit nicely on top of the soft bit where there was a hole in his shoe. It would even him up a bit. This coin was one he was keeping. He'd earned it for Mum and Iris tonight, and it wouldn't be piddled up the wall outside the Duke of Northumberland pub when his father turned out in his cups.

As Freddie ran, doubt began to creep in. The man with the scars on his face had been very generous. Almost kind. Could he have imagined it all? Could he have been wrong about witnessing a murder—might he have been mistaken, and the second man just sort of fell? His mum would tell him off for reading too many comics if he told her about it; she'd tell him he had a very active imagination. His mum was a clever one and said things like that. But even though she used long words and read library books in the evening when his dad was down the pub, she never minded him spending a few pennies to go to the pictures of a Saturday morning, if he wasn't running. She said he deserved a little dose of fun. Last week his dad had come home drunk and found her hiding a book behind the clock on the mantelpiece as he walked in the door. He had taken that book down and shoved it in the stove. Freddie had seen the flames leap up as he stabbed it in with a poker, then he'd pulled out that poker and gone for his mum with it. When Freddie leaped up to get between them, the poker landed across the back of his head. No one had any fun when his dad was around.

Next day at school he'd told the teacher his hair was bloody on account of tripping backwards on a run. His teacher gave him a funny look, but he still won the sweet for sprinting that day when the teacher took the boys out for PT. Not that there were many of them to beat, because a lot of his mates were still evacuated. In fact, half the school buildings had been taken over by the army, the blokes from the Royal

Engineers who sorted out unexploded bombs. One of them had told him that the Germans were deliberately dropping some bombs that didn't detonate straightaway, because they knew it made everyone terrified. People would see the bomb sticking out of the ground or down in a big hole, its sharp fins a sign of the threat lying in wait for someone to make just one false move. And then they were frightened to even breathe while soldiers moved along the cordoned-off street, one careful step at a time, to reach the bomb, climbing down into the hole to take out the detonator—sometimes it was so tricky the bomb went off, and those lads never came out again. Blood on the streets wasn't such a strange thing to see anymore.

As terrified as Freddie had been half an hour ago, he felt a bit braver now, and couldn't resist retracing his steps, just for a quick look. He legged it along the streets until he reached the spot where he'd seen the struggle between two men. But where was the other one? Where was the dead body? *Crump-crump-crump.* Bombs were falling across London, but Freddie could not hear them. He looked around, then knelt down, squinting as the skies lit up above him. Where the blimmin' heck was the body? As he stared at the ground, hoping that an incendiary might drop just close enough for him to see a bit better, but not so close that he was hurt, it was clear to Freddie that there was nothing there. No blood, no nothing. He felt sick again, and he knew that if he didn't start running right this second, he might have another accident and then his trousers would really stink. That, and he wanted to go home, to see his mum and give her the extra half-crown before the old man walked in the door, drunk as a lord.

And as he ran, his legs pumping like pistons in the bowels of a ship, Freddie Hackett knew that he had to tell someone about what he'd seen, because he was sure it wasn't his imagination. He couldn't keep this to himself. He had to do the right thing, like his old grandad used to tell him before he was killed. The trouble was, he wondered who he could tell, because as far as he could see, there wasn't anything to prove the two men had even been there. He'd have to think of someone. Someone who could do something about it. Someone who would believe him.

CHAPTER 1

"W hen will you be back, Mummy?" The little girl's brown eyes were wide as she stood at the playground gates.

"On Wednesday, darling. You'll have just two sleeps, two nights of sweet dreams, and I'll be home." Maisie Dobbs knelt down and put her arms around her daughter. "And Grandad will be getting Lady ready for the show on Saturday, so you've got a lot to do. Your first gymkhana! Grandad will be ready to take you out to practice when you get home."

The child grinned, revealing a gap between her two front teeth. "Do you think we'll win a rosette?"

"I think you might. But remember, it's your first show, so just going along is winning, in my book."

"Will Uncle Mark come to watch?"

"Yes, he said he'll come for a Friday to Sunday, so he'll be right there with us cheering you on, Anna."

"I hope he doesn't cheer too loud. He cheers loud. He cheered loud when we went to see Tarquin playing cricket."

"Well, Anna, Uncle Mark just gets very enthusiastic about games—"

The sound of aircraft approaching interrupted Maisie. Looking up, Anna put her hands over her ears as a trio of Hurricanes flew overhead.

"I hope that doesn't happen on Saturday, Mummy—it might scare Lady."

"Oh, I think Lady is well used to that sound by now, don't you? Nothing much unsettles that little pony." Maisie smiled again as a teacher came out of the school and began ringing the morning bell. "Now then, off you go. You've a cheese sandwich for lunch and a nice russet apple. And you might find another surprise in there from Uncle Mark."

"Chocolate!"

"Wait and see, my darling. Grandad will be collecting you after school—and remember, two sleeps and I'll be home."

The girl gave her mother one final kiss and ran into the playground, turning once to wave before calling out to a friend.

As Maisie walked the mile home from the school to the Dower House at Chelstone Manor, her thoughts drifted to Maurice Blanche, the man who had been her mentor since girlhood. She had once been his assistant and was trained by him in the art of criminal investigation. In his day, Blanche was a renowned forensic scientist, yet he was also an esteemed psychologist and philosopher, and therefore much of his teaching was not simply the nuts and bolts of his work but the importance of seeing the whole person in the perpetrator of a crime as well as the victim. She thought of the many lessons learned in Maurice's company, and how she might imbue this child she loved so much with the very best of her mentor's wisdom. She sometimes wondered if her father and stepmother were doing a much better job, simply by being steady fixtures in Anna's life and enveloping her with a joyous love laced with discipline and a down-to-earth foundation— the very foundation that had anchored Maisie when she was a child, long before she ever crossed paths with Maurice Blanche.

"Oh, it's all such a rolling of the dice, the bringing up of children," her friend Priscilla had counseled. "And let me tell you, as the mother of three boys, I know what rolling the dice is all about!"

Yes, Priscilla knew all about that gamble, with one son in the RAF, and another having lost an arm as he brought home stranded soldiers from Dunkirk.

As soon as Maisie entered the kitchen, looking up at the clock as she closed the door behind her, it seemed her stepmother wanted to speak to her. There was always a signaling when Brenda had something on her mind—a certain stance by the kitchen table, two cups out and a pot of coffee already made. Brenda had once been Maurice's house-keeper, and it was after he bequeathed the Dower House to Maisie that a bond had formed between Brenda and Maisie's father. Maisie knew that Brenda had been the only person to ever give Maurice "a piece of her mind." Now Maisie thought that she, too, was about to be on the receiving end of a piece of Brenda's mind.

"I thought we could have a sit-down together before you raced back to London," said Brenda. "Your train's not for another half an hour, and George has offered to run you over to the station—Lord Julian said it's all right to use the motor for shorter runs, and it's quite warm outside already. They said on the wireless that it'll be seventy-two de-grees today, though it'll go down the rest of the month, and then we're in for some rain. This changeable weather makes everyone out of sorts. Anyway, I'm glad Lord Julian's put his foot down and stopped Lady Rowan going up to London in the motor car. People look to them to set an example."

"Well, yes, I can see his point there—and not to worry, the station isn't far for me to walk."

"Be that as it may, but I told Lady Rowan we'd be having a little chat this morning, so she's sending George, which means we have a bit more time."

Maisie looked at the clock again. She knew what was on Brenda's mind. Now it seemed it was on Lady Rowan's too. She took a seat opposite Brenda, taking the cup of coffee as it was poured for her. It was a rare treat to have someone in the house who could make such a good cup of coffee. Certainly Mark Scott—the American diplomat Maisie had been seeing—was appreciative when Maisie explained that her former employer had enjoyed a fresh, strong brew made from ground coffee beans and had taught his housekeeper how to make the perfect cup.

Maisie thought it best to claim the opening salvo. "Right, Brenda, I suppose I'm being stalled here for a grilling." She took a first sip of coffee, and added a sparing quarter-teaspoon of sugar.

Brenda spooned the same amount of sugar into her coffee. "It's something that's been on my mind for a while, but I haven't said anything, and your father wouldn't dream of interfering in your business. We live under this roof, though, and until we can go back to our bungalow when Mr. Beale and his family return to Eltham, it's only fair I tell you what's been said. Lady Rowan is worried too."

"What's been said about what?" asked Maisie.

"You know very well what I'm talking about. Mr. Scott."

"I thought you and Dad liked him."

"We like him very much—he's a good sort, and he is wonderful with Anna. More importantly, he seems very good to you."

"Yes?"

"Don't be like that with me, Maisie—you know very well what I mean. There's been talk about it in the village, and it doesn't reflect well on any of us, especially Lady Rowan, who has a reputation to consider. Not to beat about the bush, they're saying you've been living in sin with the American and you've let the family down to allow it to happen—what with you being a widow and Lady Rowan's daughter-in-law into the bargain. And having adopted a little girl on your own."

Maisie took another sip of coffee, remembering Maurice's counsel. *When emotions are running high, take time to center your thoughts before you speak.* She held her left hand against the place where the buckle on her belt would fall if she were wearing one. With the other hand, she set the cup on the saucer.

"First of all, I have never known Lady Rowan to care about anyone's reputation—not even her own."

"She cares about yours, and—"

"Let me finish, Brenda." Maisie paused, still resting her hand on her middle. "Mark and I have an understanding, a companionship. Nothing happens in this house to alarm anyone. Anna is well-balanced, and she loves Mark's company. I do not see any reason to change our arrangement—he comes to Chelstone when he can, and is a welcome friend to our family."

Brenda rolled her eyes. "That's all very well, Maisie—but people want to see a ring on that finger. I'm surprised you don't."

"We are happy with our situation, Brenda, and we are both engaged in important work." Maisie bit her lip.

"And exactly what is this important work? Do you think your father and I haven't noticed that things are different? Mr. Beale is taking on more, and you only seem to be involved in the bigger jobs—no bad thing, in my estimation—yet you're still in London two or three days a week, and then every now and again you go off for a week at a time."

"Not often, only when a case demands it—and Anna is settled now, she's used to it."

"No, I don't think she is."

Maisie looked at the clock again. She was just about to counter Brenda's comment when the telephone rang.

"I'll answer that," said Maisie, pushing back her chair. She fled along the hallway to the library, which this morning felt like a refuge. She had the Bakelite receiver in her hand before the third ring.

"Chelstone—"

"Miss—what time will you be in today? Reckon about eleven?" Billy, Maisie's assistant, sounded breathless.

"If the train's on time, yes, about eleven o'clock. I've to go out again at twelve, but we can discuss the cases when I arrive, and—"

"Good—I just want to tell this boy what time to come back to talk to you."

"What boy?"

"Oh, sorry, getting ahead of myself. Do you remember that boy, Freddie? Freddie Hackett? The one who comes with a message for you every now and again? Him."

"What's wrong with him?"

"Poor kid reckons he saw a man murdered a few nights ago. Knifed. Freddie said he wasn't going to say anything, but it's giving him night-mares."

"Murdered? Billy, that's a job for the police. Tell him to go to see Caldwell at Scotland Yard. Make it easier for him—telephone Caldwell and explain that the boy is under a great deal of . . . of . . . pressure, given his work as a message runner."

"That's the trouble, miss—he went to the Yard, and apparently they sent a copper out to the spot where he said he saw it happen and the copper laughed at him. Told him he'd been seeing things—there was nothing there. Apparently there was some checking of records, but the only confirmed dead were from the air raids. And one drunk. Mind you, we know they're short-staffed at the Yard, what with the number of police in the services now and no one to nab all them criminals on the streets. Anyway, young Freddie remembered being sent over here with a message and seeing your sign at the front, so he thought he'd come back to tell us about it. I always gave him an extra shilling for his trouble, so I reckon he trusts us. Poor kid, running all over London in shoes more holey than righteous."

"Billy—you believe him, don't you?" Maisie twisted the receiver cord around her fingers.

"I do, miss. You'll see him, won't you?"

"Of course I will." Maisie looked up—a knock at the front door signaled that George, the Comptons' chauffeur, had arrived to take her to the station. "Children should always be believed until proven otherwise," she added. "Tell him to come back at a quarter past eleven. I'm leaving for the station now—see you in a while."

As she left the house, her document case in hand, Brenda came to the door. "Don't forget this," she called out, handing Maisie her gas mask. "And think about what I said. It's time. You deserve more than a bunch of flowers and a box of American chocolates once a week."

Maisie leaned forward and kissed her stepmother on the cheek. "See you on Wednesday, Brenda. I'll telephone this evening, but it might be a bit later than usual. I've promised to pop over and see Gabriella Hunter after work. Remember Miss Hunter? Maurice's old friend? She wrote last week for the first time in ages, and she sounded a bit lonely so I thought I'd call on her." She didn't give Brenda a chance to respond, but ran toward the motor car, where George was standing with the passenger door open. "And I think we all like those chocolates, don't you?" she called over her shoulder.

Yet as George closed the door and Maisie waved one last time from the back seat, she wondered if perhaps she should have confided in Brenda regarding Mark Scott. But no, that would never do. Even if she had understood Maisie's concerns, Brenda would only have worried.

———

Maisie arrived at the first-floor Fitzroy Square office just before eleven o'clock. As she unpinned her hat and ran her fingers through her short black hair, layered in a way that enhanced the natural waves that curled around her ears, Billy brought her up to date with events at the office.

"There's two cases of theft—I'm not sure we can do much about it, but I'm talking to the people about getting their locks changed and securing their windows. I tell you, this looting is terrible—and according to a couple of the coppers I know, they say it's all getting worse and the government bods are keeping it on the q.t. because they don't want it in the press that crime is getting out of hand. They just want everyone to carry on thinking that we're all working together against blimmin' Hitler over there, and not against each other." He paused. "And there's another case come in for us—a bloke who reckons his wife is having an affair with an Australian officer assigned to the RAF."

"Oh dear," said Maisie. "I don't like those cases. Nine times out of ten, whatever we find out, it seems the couple who were so unhappy end up happy again and we are the bringers of good news or bad who are vilified for doing our job and being the messengers."

"Bread-and-butter work, though, miss. It's bread-and-butter work, and we've still got another three small jobs, you know, basic security worries, that sort of thing. Nothing I can't look after by myself—mainly it's a case of settling people who've got themselves a bit worked up about what might happen to their houses while they're down the shelter, or a bit of direction about what to do with their valuables. Of course, they're the well-heeled people who can pay for the likes of us to make them feel better."

Maisie and Billy pored over papers for another ten minutes, with Maisie claiming tasks that she could fit in with her "other" work—a role that Billy would never inquire about, though he knew his employer was now involved in war service with a government connection.

Maisie glanced at the clock. "Freddie should be here in a minute, so best we put away these files. If I remember correctly, he's an observant chap—he was looking everywhere last time he came with a message."

"Oh, he's a quick study, miss—but I reckon he's scared too."

The doorbell rang, two sharp, shrill bursts.

"That'll be him, miss—I'll go down."

Maisie finished putting files in a drawer, but instead of going through the folding doors that led into her own office, she pulled up two chairs in front of Billy's desk, then changed her mind and positioned three chairs in front of the floor-to-ceiling windows, so they could all enjoy a view to the outside world. Maurice had often observed that to give someone another aspect as a backdrop to conversation—perhaps a more pleasing landscape to look out upon—encouraged a broadening of perspective. It could slow down the heart rate, stimulate memory and temper the nerves, allowing the interview subject to open both heart and mind. And there was something about Freddie Hackett that Maisie remembered—a feeling that the boy had a good heart and a wounded soul. She had felt it as their hands touched when he passed her the manila envelope from Robbie MacFarlane; a sensation across her chest that almost caused her to gasp. Yes, that was the memory she held of the young Freddie.

"Here he is, miss," said Billy, opening the door and holding out his hand as if he were the master of ceremonies introducing the next act at a music hall. "The best runner in all of London."

Freddie Hackett blushed and took a step forward. He was only a few inches shorter than Maisie; as a man he would stand just shy of six feet tall, she thought. He wore trousers that might once have been his father's, for they were baggy and held up with a leather belt. His collarless shirt was clean enough, and over it he wore a knitted pullover in a Fair Isle pattern, which Maisie thought must have been uncomfortable, given the weather. He shook hands with Maisie, wiped his left hand across his forehead, and nodded as if deference were natural for him. As he returned her smile his pale blue, almost gray eyes reflected the light, changing his countenance in a way that made him appear so very young.

"I'm glad to see you again, Freddie—but I'm very concerned about what it appears you have witnessed. Come on, come over here and tell us all about it." She tapped the back of the chair to the left, not wanting to put Freddie between his interlocutors. "It's such a lovely day, and I like to see out over the square after having to put up with the blackout before the sun's even down for the night."

Freddie nodded, and took his seat. Billy sat next to him, and Maisie took the third chair.

"Now then, Freddie, it seems you had a terrible shock. I know you've told the story to Mr. Beale here, but I would be obliged if you'd tell it again so I can get a clear picture of what happened to you. Sometimes people hear things differently, so we want to make sure we have all the right information to help us decide what to do next."

The boy nodded, cleared his throat and began recounting the events of the night he saw a man murdered. He described the man to whom he had delivered the envelope, running his fingers from his cheeks to his mouth and under his right eye as he recounted what he had seen as the door opened and he looked up at a face that he was sure he had seen not twenty minutes earlier—and his belief that the man before him was indeed the killer.

"And the thing is," he added, having described returning to the spot where the crime took place, and not finding a body, "the thing is that I've thought about it all a lot, and I reckon that the bloke what did it is not English. And he had a knuckle-duster as well as that knife he used to do in the other bloke."

"Can you describe what it was about the man that made you think he was a foreigner?"

Freddie nodded and cleared his throat again. Billy pushed back his chair and moved toward a filing cabinet by the desk occasionally used by Sandra, who came in to deal with office administration.

"Carry on, son," said Billy. "I'm just getting you a cream soda to wet your whistle."

"I'd like one too, while you're up," said Maisie, returning her attention to the boy. "So he was a foreigner."

The boy nodded again. "It was the way he said certain words, though he sounded right posh. I've had to deliver to the Frenchies before, and I reckon he was French."

"Yes, I understand," said Maisie. She knew the boy was a runner for the various secret services, and would likely have been tasked with delivering messages to the Free French, who had their own intelligence sources. They were not happy with the fact that the British were landing agents in France.

Billy handed the boy a bottle of cream soda and another to Maisie. "What about the knuckle-duster, son?" asked Billy.

The boy lifted his hand. "If you wear one of those, it leaves marks right across there." He ran a finger from the opposite hand across his knuckles. "You can always tell when a bloke's had one of them on."

Maisie leaned forward and with a soft touch swept the boy's fringe away from his eyes. It was a mother's touch, gentle, and as the boy looked at her, his gray-blue eyes filled with tears.

"And how would you know that, Freddie?" she asked.

He looked down as if to study his worn hobnail boots, then looked up again.

"Seen it on my dad's hands." He caught his breath and looked beyond the window, focusing on the autumnal canopy of trees shading the square. "Felt it too," he whispered, taking a deep breath as he turned back to Maisie and Billy. "So's my mum. But he keeps his hands to himself on nights I bring home the money. If I miss school to work, it upsets my mum, but it stops him going for her when I earn a few shillings, so it's worth it. I can always read a book while I'm waiting to run a message. Mum likes to know I'm reading." He looked down at the bottle of cream soda, lifted it to his mouth and drained the contents.

"I'll take that, son," said Billy, reaching for the empty bottle and handing him his own bottle. "You've got a thirst on you, so have this one—I've not touched a drop."

"Is your school near the place where you saw the man killed, Freddie?" asked Maisie.

"Not far." Freddie Hackett began to sip from the fresh bottle of soda.

"I have to go to another appointment when we've finished, however it won't take long for Mr. Beale and I to accompany you to the spot so we know where it is, and then I'll have to get on my way. After that he's going to take you straight round to the school, and he'll square things with your teacher, so don't worry about it." She paused. "Where does your father work? Near home?"

"He works when he gets work. He couldn't join the army, even the Territorials, on account of his wounds from the last war. He's got a war pension."

"That won't amount to much," said Billy.

"I don't want anyone going round there to see my dad, miss. Please don't turn up at our gaff or anywhere looking for him—and don't you, Mr. Beale. I've got to consider my mum and Iris."

"Don't worry, Freddie," said Maisie. "We won't be going to see your dad, but I will be popping into Scotland Yard a bit later on, to have a word with a detective I know, and he'll ask for more information, just in case he wants to talk to you. But I'll make sure he doesn't go off to see your mum and dad without you knowing."

The boy seemed relieved as he stood up. "I'd better go now."

"Right you are, son. Let's be on our way." Billy pushed back his chair and put his arm on the boy's shoulder as he turned to Maisie. "We'll go and get a taxicab while you lock up, miss."

CHAPTER 2

T his is it," said the boy.

Maisie tapped on the glass, instructing the taxicab driver to stop. Freddie Hackett clambered out of the cab, followed by Billy, who held out his hand to Maisie.

"Watch them puddles, miss—there was a shower or two last night," said Billy.

Maisie turned to the driver. "Would you mind waiting here, please? We'll only be a few minutes."

She paused to look at the bomb sites around them, where a few remaining houses stood like solitary teeth. Mounds of rubble were piled along the side of the street and between homes, enabling the thoroughfare to remain open for horse-drawn carts and other vehicular traffic—a sign that life was carrying on in a city under siege.

"Over here, miss," said Billy, who had found a long, thin piece of discarded iron and was poking away at granulated cement several inches thick that was covering the pavement. Freddie Hackett knelt at his feet.

Maisie joined them. "It didn't take you long to find it, Billy—the victim was definitely a 'bleeder,' wasn't he?"

"All I can say is, the copper who came out with young Freddie here couldn't see to the end of his nose." Billy stopped moving the sand around and rested on his haunches next to Freddie Hackett. "Look at this. Big old puddle of blood. I don't know where the constable's head was, but it wasn't on the job."

He stood up and continued to prod with the iron rod, revealing more of the dark brown stain that was expanding as he cleared away sand and dust.

"There's no doubt that someone made sure this was well disguised with cement dust," said Maisie. She leaned over and touched the stain, then stood up and looked around her. She began to walk backward and forward, peering down while expanding the breadth of ground covered.

"What's she doing?" asked Freddie.

"It's what they call a 'grid search,' son—instead of just wandering around looking for something when you don't know what you're looking for, you sort of mark out a grid in your mind so you don't miss anything within a certain distance to and from a central point—this here is the central point."

"Sort of like geometry at school."

"Yeah, son, sort of like that. But then you look for something that just doesn't seem right, something that stands out or is a bit odd, as if it doesn't belong."

Maisie continued her search until she had walked every inch of a twenty-foot square around Billy and the messenger boy, which entailed negotiating a good deal of rubble. She looked up toward the bombed-out buildings and piles of masonry and squinted, standing for a few minutes before beginning to make her way back, adhering to the grid she had just walked while still concentrating on the ground. Then she stopped, and reached down.

"What is it, miss?" asked Billy. Freddie stepped toward Maisie, but Billy stopped him. "Hang on, mate—we don't want to disturb anything."

Maisie felt for the small drawstring cloth bag in her pocket, and drew out a pair of tweezers. She leaned forward with the tool and picked up half a cigarette.

"Looks like someone's old smoke to me—and I don't know who'd have a mind to throw away half a ciggie. It's hard enough getting them on the black market," said Billy.

Maisie nodded. "And that's exactly what this is—a half-smoked cigarette." She drew her attention to the boy. "Freddie, was the murderer smoking?"

The boy closed his eyes tight, furrowing his brow so that at once he seemed like an old man in a youth's body. He nodded and opened his eyes. "I was just remembering—and I reckon he was smoking when him and the other bloke started having a barney, and then he flung his smoke down before he started on him."

Maisie turned to Billy. "It's a French cigarette."

"Blimey."

"And there's something over there, on that pile of rubble—do you think you can reach it for me, Billy?"

"Right you are," said Billy, walking to the edge of the pavement, where mounds of broken bricks, cement and the remains of what were once homes had been shoveled away from the road.

"Can you see it?" Maisie watched as her assistant scanned the area she'd indicated.

Billy smiled. "Got it, miss—it's a wallet." He stepped down and handed the old, worn wallet to Maisie.

As she suspected, there was nothing inside; no identification, no money, no photographs. She closed the wallet and brushed sand away from the back and front.

"There it is," said Maisie.

"What?" said Freddie Hackett.

"It's a bit damp, but you can see the words 'Fabriqué en France' embossed into the leather on the back. It was made in France." She took a handkerchief from her bag and wrapped it around the wallet, along with the somewhat soggy half-smoked cigarette. "Of course, it could have been bought in London or anywhere else, but it's an interesting discovery. I would imagine that either it dropped from the victim's jacket in the struggle or was thrown there. Did you see the men on that pile of rubble at any point, Freddie?"

Freddie shrugged. "They were all over the place, going for each other, so they could've stumbled up there." He closed his eyes. "I was so scared, Miss Dobbs, I saw arms and legs everywhere. Then there was the knife . . ."

"It's a terrible thing to have seen, Freddie." She paused, adding, "Well, an interesting find anyway. You never know, whoever removed the victim might have taken the contents of the wallet and thrown it over there. People's personal belongings are scattered everywhere after a bombing, so anyone finding it wouldn't have given it a second thought."

The driver of the taxicab sounded the horn and leaned out of the window.

"Oi—you gonna be 'ere all day, love? You're tallying a nice little bill, you know."

"Just one more stop, sir," called Maisie in reply, turning to Billy. "Here's what I'd like you to do. Could you go with Freddie to the school, let them know he's been a sterling example of a young man doing his duty and reporting a crime and that he should have no punishment for the morning's absence?"

"Right you are—it'll be my pleasure."

"I'll see you back at the office later." Turning to Freddie Hackett, she gave the boy her full attention. "And you, young man, are very brave, and you've shown great fortitude. I want you to keep in touch with us—you know where to find Mr. Beale and we know where to find you." She paused, looking into his eyes, and rested a hand on his shoulder. "Freddie, you seem skilled at remaining safe, but I want you to be vigilant—be even more aware of your surroundings wherever you go. In fact"—Maisie reached into her shoulder bag for her purse, and picked out a shilling's worth of pennies—"I'd like you to stop at a telephone kiosk and place a call to Mr. Beale after school each afternoon for the next few days. He'll give you two numbers in case there's no answer at the first. Do you know how to use the telephone?" The boy shook his head. "All right, we can sort that out," continued Maisie. "Mr. Beale will find a kiosk on the way to the school, and he'll show you what to do and how to speak to the operator. Is that all right?"

Freddie nodded.

Maisie took a silver coin from the purse. "And here's a florin to give to your mum."

The boy's eyes widened as he looked up at Maisie. "Yes, miss. Thank you very much, miss." Freddie reached for the money and put it in his sock.

Maisie inclined her head. "Why do you put the money in your sock, Freddie?"

"So it's safe, for my mum." He looked away from Maisie, then down at the reddish-brown stain on the ground. "My dad gets my running money, and if he's there when I come home, he goes through my pockets to make sure I've given it all up." The boy faltered for a moment, as if searching for the words in his mind. "And then he goes down the pub."

Maisie nodded, and felt her throat catch. She looked at her assistant. "All right, Billy—be on your way. I'll see you later."

She watched the man and boy walk together, Billy ruffling the lad's hair as they made their way along the street, then waving and calling out "Afternoon, mate" while touching his cap to acknowledge the costermonger who passed them with his barrow. The boy looked up at Billy and smiled, leaning in a little closer as Billy's arm rested on his shoulder. Maisie sighed and returned to the taxi, stopping to give the driver another address before climbing aboard. She wanted to see the house where the alleged murderer had accepted a message from the boy runner.

Once again, she asked the taxicab driver to remain on the street to wait for her. She was already late for MacFarlane, but she expected to be in time for the two interviews she was to conduct later. The driver would have to cool his heels just a little longer.

"I hope you've got a few bob on you, miss, because this little jaunt won't come cheap."

"Don't you worry," said Maisie, looking down at her notebook. "You can stop just down there."

"Not a lot of life around here, is there? I reckon them houses will be condemned, if they're not already. It's a wonder they haven't gone up in smoke before now—though likely as not there's no gas, because the supply would have been shut off."

Maisie looked up at the three-story Victorian house as the cabbie pulled alongside. "Yes, you're right," she said, remembering that in Freddie's recounting of the meeting, when he met the man he thought was a "foreigner," he had described him carrying an oil lamp.

She stepped from the cab and walked toward the house, up three steps to the front door, then lifted the blackened brass knocker. There was no answer to either the first or a second knock, so she applied pressure to the door. It moved just a little, allowing her to push it open and step into the passage, revealing a house that was familiar in design. Thousands of houses built in the mid- to late 1800s were constructed to more or less the same specifications, give or take a room or two. The entrance passage—and it was never referred to as a "hall" because only the upper classes had an entrance hall, whereas the lower classes referred to the same, albeit smaller entrance as a "passage"—had a parlor to the right, sometimes followed by a dining room, and at the end of the passage was a kitchen and scullery. Larger houses might have a cellar accessible via a door under the staircase—which was directly ahead as she entered—but this house had only an under-stairs cupboard. She anticipated two rooms above, and then another narrower staircase leading to an attic room. The WC would be outside, either at the bottom of the backyard or just to the left of the door that led from the kitchen to the yard—and it was a yard, a limited space with flagstones, which could never be called a garden.

While the house seemed to have all its walls, she noticed large cracks across the ceiling and fallen masonry along the passage. She turned the key on a wall-mounted gas lamp; there was no telltale hissing, so the supply had indeed been cut off. She moved into the parlor. There was nothing of note to be found. And that, she knew, was a find in itself. The grate had been cleaned of ash, and the floor had been swept. There was nothing in the house to suggest a family had been here and then left in a hurry. Blackout curtains were drawn back. *Blackout curtains.* Hadn't Freddie Hackett said the man pulled him in quickly because he didn't want to get a mouthful from the air raid patrol, because light was visible through the open door? She looked at the long, wide crack across the ceiling and walked around the perimeter of the room once before stepping into the passage. Treading with care across fallen masonry, Maisie again focused her attention on the ceiling above, then the floor beneath her feet. If she were not mistaken, the collapse of part of the ceiling was recent—perhaps last night—and had fallen onto a swept floor.

There was nothing in the small dining room or the kitchen. No crockery left behind—not even broken china. The shelves were empty, and though she could see marks on the floor left by a freestanding kitchen cabinet, she suspected it had left the house with the family who lived there before bombs drove them away. She imagined them leaving with their belongings on a hand cart, and wondered where on earth they might be—housing in London and other bombed cities was becoming hard to find.

She made her way upstairs. Beds and wardrobes had been abandoned in the upper rooms, which did not surprise Maisie. If a family were moving into smaller accommodation, some furniture had to be left behind. There were no sheets, yet on one bed a counterpane remained. She pressed down on the mattress as if she were in a furniture store, testing it for firmness.

"I feel like Goldilocks," she whispered, looking around her at the water-stained walls and even more cracks across the ceiling.

She climbed the second staircase to the attic room. Perhaps if the country had not been at war for two years, the gaping hole in the roof above might have delivered a shock. Instead she merely sighed as she picked her way across fallen tiles and beams toward a bed in the corner. The fallen roof was recent—again, it could have come down last night as rain fell, forcing already weakened beams to give way—and there was a musty odor signaling mold growing around the walls. A counterpane had been pulled up, as on the bed in the room on the floor below, but that wasn't what had drawn her toward the bed. She knelt down and picked up a scrap of manila paper with a small metal clip still attached. It was a fragment from an envelope of the type used in many offices and government departments, the sort secured by two prongs that poked through a hole in the flap and then split apart to hold it in place. It was clear that the flap on the envelope to which the fragment belonged had also been glued to ensure security, as the scrap of manila paper still had the metal fastener in place. It was likely the envelope had been opened in a hurry and the recipient was not aware that a piece had flown off. Easy to miss in the half-light. Easy to miss if you had been tasked with clearing the house of recent signs of life and you didn't want to venture a second time into a room with a weakened roof whilst it was raining. She knew that even the most experienced criminal or even a highly trained agent could make a simple error. Hadn't she been told as much during her training when she was first recruited into the realm of intelligence in 1938, when she accepted an assignment that took her to Munich? It was always the minor blunder that could catch you out: the bus ticket dropped from your pocket, or the shred of clothing caught on a nail, or the way you picked up your knife and fork. She slipped the fragment into the handkerchief with the cigarette end and the wallet.

Nice of you to be prompt on a Monday," said MacFarlane, squinting at his watch. "What time do you call this, eh?"

"It's now half past two, and I'm still in time for my interviews, Robbie." Maisie smiled. "And there's no need to get snippy, just because you've lost your spectacles."

"Still can't get used to the bloody things." He shook his head and slid two folders across the desk. "Can never find them where I saw them last. And don't you laugh—you're not so far off yourself, Maisie. Another few years and you'll be wearing a glass bike on your nose too."

Maisie had known Robert MacFarlane for some years, since their

paths crossed when she was in search of a madman intent upon causing chaos and indiscriminate death across London. At the time Mac-
Farlane was a senior detective with Scotland Yard's Special Branch,
but was later promoted into a shady area of intelligence when he
became the linchpin between Scotland Yard and the Secret Service.
Now he was an important cog in the wheel of the Special Operations Executive, the SOE, with a special brief to once again smooth
relations with the Secret Intelligence Service, who were none too
pleased when the SOE was formed in July 1940, following a clandestine meeting at St. Ermin's Hotel, where the prime minister, Winston Churchill, had given the order to "set Europe ablaze" with acts
of irregular warfare.

Maisie checked her own watch, then opened the first folder, trying
not to squint as she read notes in a tiny hand, therefore avoiding another ribbing from Robbie MacFarlane.

This was the job that Brenda had referred to earlier. She had no
idea what Maisie was doing for the government, just that she had a
role and that it was part of her national service—and hadn't everyone
been encouraged to do their bit? To answer the call if they had a skill
that would benefit the war effort? Brenda herself was a member of the
local Women's Voluntary Services, donning the green uniform several
days each week before going out into the community to help anyone
burdened by the loss of a home, a husband or a son. Sometimes German bombers returning to their bases in France would release a final
bomb in a rural area, so while country folk did not suffer the same
losses as towns and cities, they knew how it felt to be on constant alert,
especially if they were close to an airfield or factory. Kent had been
hard hit—the Battle of Britain had been fought in the skies above the
county, so the people were used to the presence of army, of dogfights
over their fields and farms, followed by the odd Luftwaffe pilot jump-

ing from a burning aircraft and landing in a tree or in someone's back garden with his parachute trailing behind him.

Maisie was well aware that Brenda believed her war work might be somewhat similar to her own since the night Priscilla—Maisie's dear friend and London ambulance co-driver—had almost died saving children from a burning building. Maisie had rushed to Priscilla's aid, sustaining burns to the backs of her hands as she dragged her wounded friend from the inferno. Though not as serious as Priscilla's facial scarring, the lesions were still visible. She never returned to driving the ambulance, nor would she have been allowed to; it was understood that a trauma once experienced would adversely affect an ability to do the job without trepidation in future.

Maisie had told Brenda the truth to a point—that she was now helping in a government office and that Billy had taken up more work in her private investigation business. Better to tell a half-truth rather than a lie—lies could become hard to maintain.

It was MacFarlane who had summoned Maisie to a Baker Street address earlier in the year, to inform her that her expertise was now required for the war effort. Her particular role was top secret, however, and had to remain so, even after the conflict had ended. The job was for the SOE, interviewing prospective resistance agents at various points in their training to assess their continued fitness for the role and to predict how they might respond under increasing pressure—the very high-stakes pressure of assuming a false identity while living in a German-occupied country. And those agents would not simply be a part of a community, they had to work—as waiters, as children's nurses, or as secretaries and farm hands—while at the same time coordinating support for local and regional resistance operations, where they would conduct acts of espionage and sabotage against the enemy, or send vital information to London.

Agents had to be prepared to enter France at night, leaping from a Lysander aircraft as it rolled along a field lit by torches. The aircraft would often take on board a returning agent after the drop-off and had to be in the air again within three minutes of landing, so speed was of the essence. Or the agent would land in France via a parachute drop, bury the chute and then be ready to travel by train to meet a contact, all the while remembering to speak nothing but French and confident in their role and new identity to show their forged documents to any German guards without taking flight if stopped. The agents had to be prepared to die—to withstand torture, and to take their own lives with their issued cyanide pill if capture was imminent. They called it their "L-pill"—for it was indeed lethal.

In short, a resistance agent was required to be a certain type of person, and the task of recruiting them fell to the scouts who brought them into the SOE, followed by experts who interviewed them and pronounced them suitable candidates. They were then handed over to the seasoned agents and military personnel tasked with preparing them for their remit. If they passed every test, they would be sent overseas—and France was not the only destination—where they would risk their lives for a country that would never admit to knowing who they were, and would disown them if they were captured.

Maisie felt the weight on her shoulders, a sensation that was not just metaphorical, but manifested in a painful sensation of pressure that ran from her neck down to the base of her spine. She sat up in her chair, assuming strength in her backbone.

"Shall we get on before the first of these two interviewees comes in?" MacFarlane nodded toward the folders. "They've both advanced through every component of their training, so this is the final once-over before they leave. If you have any doubts, well, at least we know what we might expect and plan accordingly."

Maisie nodded, and opened the first folder. Upon seeing the name at the top of the sheet of paper inside, she felt as if someone had touched her neck with an ice pick along the very place where she had been wounded by shrapnel in the last war. It was a chapter of her life she had relegated to the distant past, yet since war was declared in 1939, she sometimes felt as if it were only yesterday. It was a time before she became a psychologist and investigator, before she knew what it was to solve a crime, but more than anything, before she knew who she really was.

She closed the folder and opened the second. She exhaled deeply before looking up at MacFarlane, who was pushing back his chair as if to stand.

"What do you think you're doing, Robbie?" Her tone was sharp. "I cannot interview either of these candidates, and you know it. It's a . . . a . . . a conflict of interest. I know both of them, and the fact that it's fallen to me to interview them is a setup—isn't it?" She tried to quell her feelings. It was hard enough doing this job—hard enough being dispassionate about her role, which she accepted because she knew she could do it well; if she stopped one unsuitable young man or woman from certain death, then it was a job well done. The whole remit was difficult without having prior knowledge of the prospective agents. Hard enough without having affection for both of them. "Is this some sort of trial? A test of my honesty? Of my suitability for this job? Because if that's what it is, I would just as soon step aside for someone else to do it so I can go back to my daughter and to doing my part to solve the odd crime a couple of days a week, because heaven only knows your friends at Scotland Yard are up to their eyes in a backlog they can't clear, aren't they?"

"Calm down, Maisie. Unruffle your feathers."

"Unruffle my feathers? Robbie, don't start—"

"Not like you to become so heated, is it?" MacFarlane sighed, leaned toward Maisie and tapped the folders. "I—we—thought you would be able to set aside your prior knowledge of our candidates and give us your best assessment of their continued potential. Even at this late stage and after all they've gone through in training, I want to know they are completely ready to get out there and do their bit for our French brethren and the rest of bloody Europe, especially us, because we're far from being out of the woods with old Hitler. With his luck, he could come walking on water across the Channel tomorrow." He paused. "Will you see them?"

Maisie pushed back her chair and walked to the window. She looked down at the street and folded her arms in front of her as if to protect her heart. Secrets, secrets, secrets. She sometimes felt as if she would drown under the weight of other people's secrets. Even this part of her own life had to be hidden—from her child, her father and stepmother, her best friend and her lover. She was always on her guard, and those she cared for most could only know so much—they could only know part of her, not the whole. And she feared she might lose herself in all the secrecy—it had happened before. She sighed and turned to MacFarlane.

"I'm angry, Robbie MacFarlane, but I'll do it. Just get someone to bring me a strong cup of tea first, would you? And for god's sake have them make it hot and put it in a big mug and not a soppy piece of china."

"Who do you want first?"

Maisie nodded. "Miss Pascale Evernden."

Pascale was Priscilla's niece, the daughter of one of three brothers lost in the years from 1914 to 1918. Peter Evernden had been an intelligence agent in the Great War, and while operating undercover in

France had fallen in love with a young woman who worked alongside her mother to commit acts of espionage against the occupying army. Pascale's mother was assassinated by the Germans when her daughter was just a baby; Peter, who had been moved into Germany to gain valuable information for the British, was killed the same year during a food riot—at the end of the war the German people were starving, as were their soldiers at the front.

Peter Evernden had never known he had a daughter. Maisie had uncovered the truth while investigating the supposed death of an aviator in France during the last war—the flying ace had delivered Priscilla's brother to the location where he would go about his work. Pascale had been raised by her grandmother, Chantal, but not only had she inherited her father's aptitude for languages—she spoke French, English, German, Spanish and Italian in several different dialects—she was also the image of her aunt. Since learning the truth of her parentage, Pascale had spent summers with Priscilla, becoming close to the family, and she also took her father's name. Chantal remained at her chateau, which had been requisitioned by German officers in 1940, and as far as anyone knew, not only was she still alive but even at her age she was an active member of the Resistance. Before the war, Chantal had insisted Pascale attend finishing school in Switzerland— she thought the girl too much of a tomboy and a little too wild—and it was from Switzerland that the young woman had made her way to England when Chantal ordered her not to return to France when it came under German occupation.

The second agent Maisie was scheduled to interview was a woman she had known for over twenty years. The candidate, Elinor Jones, was beloved by Priscilla, her husband and their three sons and was considered no less than a cherished member of their family.

Now, along with Pascale Evernden's, her life was in Maisie's hands.

CHAPTER 3

The poised young woman who sat before Maisie wore a well-cut costume of black wool barathea, with only the slightest hint of embellishment on the hip pockets, which bore gray silk stitching in the shape of a butterfly. A silk blouse was just visible as a white edge to the jacket's V neckline. Her black shoes were polished and she wore silk stockings—which were becoming somewhat difficult to find in the shops. Her dark hair was twisted into an elegant chignon.

Maisie cleared her throat, took a deep breath and closed the folder on the desk in front of her.

"Pascale—"

"Tante Mai—"

The two women had spoken at once.

"Go on," prompted Maisie.

"I didn't know you worked here, Tante Maisie," said Pascale, addressing Maisie by the name she had been accustomed to using for her aunt Priscilla's best friend.

"First of all, let's adopt a more formal address while we're in this building, shall we? And there was no reason for you to know I worked here—no one in my immediate circle, including my family, is aware of my work for this department." Maisie looked at Pascale directly, remembering the girl she had first encountered as a thirteen-year-old in France, galloping toward her on a black horse before fearlessly clearing a five-bar gate and circling her mount to a halt in front of Maisie. "I know that at the outset of your training you were required to sign forms holding you to the Official Secrets Act, so you should know I am part of that swearing to secrecy. You must not reveal to anyone that you have seen me here. Is that clear?"

Pascale nodded. "Yes. Yes, it is—Miss Dobbs."

"Good." Maisie avoided Pascale's gaze. She was finding it even more difficult to maintain a formal tone than she had anticipated. "I take it your aunt has absolutely no knowledge of your candidacy for this position."

"I never told her. I've hardly seen her since I came over—well, as you know I stayed at the house with them for a short time, but they were in Kent at the cottage. After a little while I moved into digs with another girl—but you know that. Then I was busy with my job as a translator. Well, until this job came along. And I don't have to worry about money." The young woman brushed a stray hair back behind her ear. "I have funds."

"Indeed." Maisie opened the folder. "Hmmm, yes. The flat's in Notting Hill. Not terribly far from Mrs. Partridge's London house."

"And yours."

"Quite." Maisie raised an eyebrow. "Now, perhaps you can tell me how you came to the attention of this section."

Priscilla's niece looked down at her hands, then back to Maisie. "I thought you might know."

"A few details are outstanding, so perhaps you can fill in those gaps for me."

Pascale cleared her throat. "I was staying at Tante Priscilla's house— she wasn't there and neither were the boys or Uncle Douglas. He was with her in Kent. Then Elinor came home to her room."

Elinor had once been the boys' nanny and had worked for the family in France and again in London. She was Welsh, but had taken French lessons and become proficient in the language while living in Biarritz. Elinor was much loved by Priscilla, Douglas and their sons, so even when the boys were past the age of needing a nanny, Priscilla had insisted that her room in the Holland Park house would always be kept for her, a bolt-hole when she came home on leave from the First Aid Nursing Yeomanry, which she had joined at the outset of war. Priscilla had been with the FANY in the Great War, which only increased her affection for the former employee.

"Elinor is a bit older than you—do you get on?"

"We do, actually. When I was there, she wanted to speak in French all the time. She said she needed to practice with a native. I've always liked Elinor, and I was more than happy to accommodate her, so of course we became friends. I've always thought she was a terrific woman, probably because anyone who could manage my three cousins deserves a medal."

Maisie once again raised an eyebrow.

"Well, all right," said Pascale. "She managed me pretty well too— I was a bit difficult when I first began coming to London, and Elinor seemed to know how to calm me down. There was so much to . . . to absorb. This new family and finally knowing who my father was, and seeing Tante Priscilla was like looking in a mirror and seeing an old version of myself."

"I wouldn't tell her that," said Maisie. "But go on."

"So when she started conversing in French, I wanted to know why, and she said, 'Oh nothing really. I just don't want to lose it.'"

"Then?"

"I didn't believe her."

"And?"

"I followed her and watched where she went, and I saw other people coming and going, and I . . . I suppose I put two and two together. She was in uniform but not doing any of the things that Tante Priscilla told me she'd done when she was with the FANY."

"It's a different war, Pascale." Maisie held the young woman's gaze. "So you watched, you made a guess at who was doing what and where, and you decided it might be an idea to be heard speaking fluent French in front of some of the people you'd seen leaving that building."

"I saw a man leaving one day and I thought I would follow him. I thought he looked important."

"He is," said Maisie.

Pascale smiled and nodded. "Anyway, I knew we were walking toward that shop where they sell books and papers from other parts of the world—not that they have much stock these days—so I greeted the vendor in French. He's originally from Brittany and I've chatted to him before, but this time I did it a bit louder. I made sure the man could hear me, because I had a feeling he would approach me, and I was right."

"People with your linguistic skills have been discovered on trains, in shops, hospitals and just doing their shopping, so that doesn't surprise me."

"And here I am."

"Here you are." Maisie paused, and smiled. "Now then—let's get down to business. I have some questions for you—some I would like you to answer without any consideration, just off the cuff. The others I want you to think about—I'll give you a minute."

"Fire away." The young woman pulled back her shoulders as if reminded to do so by a finishing-school teacher.

"Before I do that, Miss Evernden, be aware that you just effectively revealed the name of another agent. You assumed I knew about Elinor

Jones, so it's just as well I'm not a member of the Gestapo trying to find out who you are and what you and your friends are up to." Maisie paused. "I could strike you off right now for that, and you know it."

Pascale looked down at her hands, then at Maisie again, and replied with a tone of defiance, "I will never give away anything to the Gestapo. Never. The Germans killed my mother."

Maisie felt a lump in her throat. She knew Pascale Evernden was as brave as Priscilla, and to her advantage she usually had a cooler head on her than her aunt at the same age. Usually. Not always. Maisie knew her decision already, because apart from the slip—she would never make that mistake again—Pascale would pass the remaining hour-long inquisition with flying colors, of that she had no doubt. She wasn't so sure about the next interviewee, who had a softness to her character that was always close to the surface, which explained why she was so loved. But it might be too close for this work—and that would render her vulnerable.

Elinor!" Maisie's greeting for the next candidate was quite different from the one she accorded Pascale Evernden. She took both Elinor's hands in her own. "Elinor, it's lovely to see you—but first, I must add that we are now in a formal interview, so it's Miss Dobbs and Miss Jones."

"You've always been Miss Dobbs to me . . . Miss Dobbs," said Elinor.

Maisie laughed. "Quite right—now the formality is all on my shoulders." She extended a hand toward the chair on the other side of the desk. "Please sit down, Miss Jones."

Once seated, Maisie opened the second folder and took a moment to run her finger down the first page—she had already read every word on the report and had no need to remind herself, but the move could unsettle a candidate, and Maisie wanted to see how easy it was to disquiet Elinor Jones.

Elinor remained relaxed, so Maisie continued.

"Tell me how you were recruited, Miss Jones."

Elinor cleared her throat. "Well, as you know, I joined the FANY, and I thought I'd be learning to drive an ambulance, like Mrs. Partridge in the last war. She recommended me for it, you see, when I said I was going to join up."

Maisie nodded. "Go on."

"Anyway, we had to list any skills we had, and I speak French. To a point it became easy when I was working for Mrs. Partridge in France—remember I had to learn English as a child because my first language was Welsh. And of course, I was still a girl myself then, so it was easier."

"I seem to remember there was a young man in Biarritz."

Elinor blushed. "Well, he was a good reason to learn at the time. But then I went to a lady who gave lessons, and of course the boys nattered away in French all the time and I didn't want them thinking they could pull the wool over my eyes by slipping into French every now and again. They were right scamps then, those boys."

"I know they were!" said Maisie.

"I can't believe it when I see Tom in uniform—and he's training other pilots now. And what with Tim at Cambridge and Tarquin planning to—"

"So you added proficiency in the French language to your list of skills," interrupted Maisie.

"Yes. Then I was transferred to the same department as that Mr. MacFarlane—and I remember seeing you on the stairs there last year, but I wasn't supposed to say anything to anyone, which is why I couldn't talk at the time. I felt bad about that, Miss Dobbs. Anyway, then they brought me over here and I had some interviews with different people and my training was approved."

"Radio operator."

"Yes."

"And now you've been given your final tests and certified as ready to join a unit in France."

"I think the training has gone well. I work with another girl—she'll be my contact here, so she had to learn to recognize my fist. That's what they call the way you tap out your message—everyone's different you see, and—"

"Yes, I'm familiar with the work," said Maisie. She leaned back in her chair and regarded Elinor Jones, remembering her as a girl who had often appeared barely older than the three gregarious boys in her care; young charges she had marshaled into a level of obedience their mother could never quite achieve. "Miss Jones—all right, Elinor— Elinor, you have been recruited for very dangerous work. Are you fully aware of the risks? The average life of a radio operator in France is proving to be about six weeks at best."

Elinor blushed and nodded, yet as Pascale had done before her, she straightened her back. "Miss Dobbs, our country is in dire straits. Our ships are being torpedoed by U-boats right, left and center and we are close to the danger point with regard to food supplies. I know that and you know that, but most of the country is in the dark about how terrifying things really are. Hitler is trying to starve us out. If I can do just one thing to slow down his progress, then I shall do it. Even if I have to die trying."

The words on the page in front of Maisie blurred. Blinking away the moisture in her eyes, she cleared her throat.

"Right, let's get started, shall we? I have some questions for you—

some I would like you to answer without any consideration, just off the cuff. The others I want you to think about—I'll give you a minute. All right?"

"Fire away," said Elinor, leaning forward.

There had been little reason for Maisie to venture into the area around Mecklenburgh Square since conducting the investigation into her first case, a brief she had accepted with a sigh of relief after setting up in business on her own in 1929. That first case opened the door to more work, and began to soothe the panic she had felt several months earlier when Maurice informed her of his intention to retire. Instead of taking over his office, he recommended she should rent premises of her own in order to establish her independence. "It's time to spread your wings, Maisie—time to fly alone. You are more than ready to leave the nest. The work we've done together will remain with you; however, if you stay here, I believe it would stunt your ability to do your job effectively and in your own unique way." Maisie had put off making the move until the last minute, because everything about the change in circumstances was daunting, not least the responsibility of affording rent on the rooms she'd found in Warren Street—rooms that seemed sad and tired in comparison to the well-appointed office on Wigmore Street where she had worked as Maurice's assistant.

Her fears regarding the future were assuaged when the first client came to her, a man named Christopher Davenham, who believed his wife to be in the midst of an affair with another man. Maisie had followed Mrs. Davenham from the couple's home in Mecklenburgh Square to a cemetery where the woman laid flowers on the grave of the man she had once loved, a soldier who had returned from service in the Great War with terrible facial wounds. That visit to the square in

1929 had itself been a walk down memory lane for Maisie. When she was younger, some months after Maurice first became her mentor and began directing her studies so that she might gain a place at university, he had brought her to see various friends and associates who lived in and around the square, which had become an enclave of writers, artists and philosophers, both women and men, who had clustered in the area in search of like-minded intellectual neighbors.

Now she had returned to see Gabriella Marie Hunter, a woman who had once told Maisie that she preferred the companionship of her books and papers to most human fellowship, though in her recent letter she had admitted to a certain "yearning for the company of someone who knew Maurice." The letter inspired Maisie to pay a visit sooner rather than later. She had always liked Gabriella, and—if truth be told—despite the woman's admission regarding her devotion to her work, she thought Gabriella was wise in matters of the heart. With the exception of her beloved family, matters of the heart had always been Maisie's Achilles' heel, so she welcomed the opportunity to seek the older woman's counsel.

Hunter's connection with Maurice had been seeded in childhood, though she was a good deal younger than Maisie's former mentor. Both were the offspring of a union between France and Britain: in the case of Maurice, his Scottish mother had married a Frenchman; Gabriella's mother was French, her father English. They were drawn together by their shared backgrounds when Hunter was a student and Maurice her professor. Maisie had sometimes wondered if they had been lovers, but always put the thought out of her head. Imagining Maurice in the intimate presence of a woman would have been akin to speculating about one's parents having a wild, passion-filled affair—though the suspicion remained. Maisie suppressed a laugh as she took hold of the bellpull and waited.

A housekeeper answered the door with a curt "May I help you?"

Maisie smiled. It was her break-down-the-portcullis smile, for she suspected the woman might be overly protective of her employer. "Good afternoon. My name is Maisie Dobbs, and I'm an old friend of Miss Hunter. She wrote asking me to call—I sent a postcard by return to let her know I'd pay a visit this afternoon, though I am later than promised—and of course, the postcard might not have arrived." She reached into her bag for a calling card and held it out to the housekeeper. "Here you are."

There was an instant change in the housekeeper's demeanor upon reading the card. She ushered Maisie into the hall, where she asked if she would care to take a seat while she inquired if Miss Hunter might accept her visit.

Maisie smiled as the housekeeper departed along the narrow passageway toward the second room on the right, which she knew was Gabriella Marie Hunter's study and library. She rarely took advantage of her position but on occasion found it useful to eschew the card introducing her as a "Psychologist and Investigator" for one of the personal calling cards her mother-in-law had given her upon her marriage to James Compton. It announced her as "Lady Margaret Compton"—a position underlined by the impressive Compton family crest. Maisie knew Gabriella would find it rather amusing.

Gabriella Hunter came to her feet and held out both hands as Maisie entered the library and the housekeeper took her leave. "Maisie, dear—it has been far too long." She kissed Maisie on each cheek and extended a hand toward an armchair next to the fireplace. A needlepoint screen with a geometric pattern in bold primary colors stood in front of the cold grate. Maisie knew not to expect the austere working study, which as a rule would be associated with an academic. This was a room where walls that were not covered with stacks of books were painted in a pale peach color and complemented by curtains of the same hue, just a shade or two deeper. The combination gave Hunter's surroundings an aura of calm. The Art Deco armchairs would have been as out of place in a gentleman's club as they would in the home of a dowager who favored cabbage roses. Each chair was upholstered in heavy pale-cream fabric, with lines of brown piping fanned to resemble a shell. Wide rounded arms set off by the same piping dominated the two armchairs, which gave the impression of enfolding a person as they settled into the thick cushioned seats.

Maisie sat down, at once feeling as she had in those days when she and Maurice would sit before the fireplace in the Dower House library. There was a certain anticipation of deep and worthy conversation, a feeling that she would be stretched intellectually. As with the exercise of any muscle, though, she could expect some strain, and there would be an almost painful pleasure in the outcome.

Gabriella Marie Hunter was a woman with bearing, though she now used a cane to steady herself. She wore a plain navy blue day dress of linen and silk—a blend Maisie recognized, for although it had the look, movement and texture of silk, there was a heavier weight to the fabric. A single strand of pearls adorned the woman's neck, with delicate matching pearl earrings. A silver watch appeared to be draped rather than buckled on her wrist, and Maisie remembered that Gabriella told her once that she hated the feeling of anything tight fitting, confiding that she had never, nor would she ever, wear a corset. Her still-slender frame seemed not to need the confining article of clothing.

With hair a blend of different shades of gray, as if an artist had taken a fine brush and painted long sweeps of silver next to charcoal, and a cut reminiscent of the same short bob she had worn some forty years earlier, Gabriella Hunter was the epitome of elegance.

"Tell me how you've been, Maisie—how is your heart? Mended? Scarred? Still rather an open wound? Losing James was such a terrible shock—though I knew you would find yourself again."

Just like Maurice, straight to the point, thought Maisie. "The scarring is fainter now, Gabriella. And I have a daughter." Maisie reached into her bag and brought out a photograph she kept in a leather case. "Her name is Anna. I adopted her last year—she was an evacuee, an orphan, and . . . and I came to love her."

Gabriella took the photograph while reaching for the spectacles that dangled from a chain around her neck, a deft move that did not disturb her pearls. "Oh yes," she said, as soon as she was able to inspect the photograph. "She even favors you." She handed the photograph back to Maisie. "And I suppose she always was yours, in a way. Human beings and animals have a tendency to find their way home, even when it's thousands of miles away and they have never set foot in the place before." She paused, looking at Maisie over the spectacles, and was about to speak again when the housekeeper returned to the room bearing a tray with tea and cakes.

"Ah, excellent, Mrs. Towner," said Hunter. "Just put the tray on the table here, and I am sure Mai— Lady Margaret will pour for us."

The housekeeper's eyes widened, and she appeared about to protest when Maisie came to her feet.

"Thank you, Mrs. Towner—I'll pour tea and serve the cakes," said Maisie. "My goodness—you must be psychic—my favorite Eccles cakes! Lovely—though I am sure they will spoil my dinner!"

The housekeeper blushed and hurried from the room.

"You've intimidated her, Maisie. She's always been in awe of a title—and perhaps enough of a snob to be impressed."

"She's a miracle worker to get the ingredients for the cakes."

"Squirreled them away even before the war—she said there was no harm in stocking up." Gabriella Hunter reached for the cup of tea as Maisie passed it to her.

"So, Gabriella—are you in good health? Your note seemed to suggest that all was not well." Maisie thought it best if she, too, got straight to the point.

"Oh dear—I shouldn't have worried you. It's this war. I keep reading that life goes on and hearing that the young are having a whale of a time in the clubs, dancing the night away even though a bomb might drop and kill them all—I don't even know if it's true, but it makes me want to be twenty again. Mind you, I had more on my mind at twenty, but I feel quite . . . quite bereft of good company, even though I have often said I prefer my books. And I miss conversation. I thought you wouldn't mind if I had a taste of life outside the confines of my house, just for as long as it takes to have a cup of tea."

"I'm delighted you wrote, Gabriella. Now then, what are you working on? I see a great pile of papers over there, so I know you've something on the boil."

"I can't say much at the moment, but it's an interesting topic that has been on my mind for a while. It blends a very close look at literature following the last war with my own experiences in France and the Levant, and my understanding of it all, but I have to be—"

"Circumspect?"

"Definitely. Very much so. Which is why I don't want to immerse you in the minutiae today—perhaps another time. I do want to know about your life though. Tell me, is there a young man?"

"Gabriella, I am not exactly young anymore, so no, there is no young man." Maisie took a sip of tea. "Though there is one who is just a bit older than me."

Hunter set her cup and saucer on a side table. "Do I detect a hint of something else?"

Maisie shrugged, putting down her own cup and saucer. "Oh, Gabriella, I don't know. He is a lovely man, with a wonderful sense of humor, and he just adores my daughter. But you see . . . well, he's a diplomat of sorts. An American, working at the embassy. I'm not sure exactly what he does, and of course I cannot really tell him what I do, so—"

"So you've fallen into a dark tunnel of your own secrets."

"I suppose so, yes."

"And where secrets reside, so does fear—it's the unknown."

"Yes. That's right. And I know that if anyone would understand what it is to live with secrets, it's you, Gabriella." Maisie rubbed the backs of her hands, relieving an ache in the lesions across her knuckles. "Sometimes I can imagine a road ahead for both of us, and other times I don't even know when I'll see him, and whether he'll be at my flat when I get home—or vanish for days."

"And I'm sure he could say the same about you."

Maisie nodded. "To a point, though he knows where I am when I'm at Chelstone."

"Your work is for the government?"

"For the most part now. Yes."

Hunter looked out of the window. Maisie thought it was as if she were staring into the past.

"If I look back, Maisie, I think kindness is the most important thing. There were interludes when—well, that can wait for another time—but suffice it to say I believe love must be cradled gently, as if you have something very precious in your hands that you do not want to break. I wish I had been more careful as a younger woman. Not necessarily young, but younger, at a time when I had confidence that love was still possible . . ." She turned her gaze back to Maisie. "Anyway, the war will be over one day, Maisie—what you do now will pave the way for how you will live in peace. Remember that, my dear. Never let fears get in the way of happiness, because fear can lead to such irrational reasoning, and we can make dreadful mistakes, saying things we can't take back." She seemed at once melancholy. "I've been guilty of such errors, in my time."

M aisie entered her garden flat in Holland Park by the side entrance. As she slipped the latch on the gate, she could already hear a blues number playing on her gramophone, and the smell of cooking coming from the kitchen. A wicker table was set for two on the lawn, for the weather had changed again and it had become an unseasonably warm evening. She could hear Mark Scott singing along as he cooked spaghetti—she knew it would be spaghetti. It was always spaghetti when Mark was in charge of supper. Maisie wondered if the man had been weaned on Italian food, though she would not have thought to use herbs in the way that he used herbs—beyond a little sage and rosemary in the Christmas turkey stuffing, she didn't know anyone who used herbs. Now Mark Scott was in her home, and herbs had become a staple in the kitchen.

"Hi hon," said Mark, coming to the door, his shirtsleeves rolled, his tie loosened. He looked at his watch.

"You're early," said Maisie, allowing him to wrap his arms around her.

"Actually, Maisie, you're late. Don't you remember when I called and said I'd be getting away on time to cook dinner for us tonight? I figured I had some time owing, and I wanted to see my lady. But I guess she didn't want to see me so much."

"Mark, I am so sorry—really, I just had a lot to do today, and a new case came in, and—" She stepped back and looked up at her lover. Her smile faded. "You're going back to Washington."

"Maisie, you can read me like a book. But look, it's not for long—not like the last time when I hadn't a clue whether I'd be away for days or months. I'm flying over just for a week—well, maybe more. Maybe less. Have to see. Usual route via Lisbon—to be on the safe side. But I'll miss the half-pint's gym-thing."

"Gymkhana," corrected Maisie. "She'll be upset, but—"

"But then she'll be so excited by it all, the fact that her old Uncle Mark isn't there won't matter a bit." He sniffed the air. "Oops, better check the dinner, don't want to burn the pan again—and I mean 'again this evening,' because that's the second sauce I've whipped up for you."

"Oh, you didn't throw away good food, did you, Mark?"

"Maisie, it was burned. I can't put burned food on the table because it isn't good, even though as you will probably remind me, there are people wanting for something to eat in this country." He paused with a sigh that seemed to signal exasperation. "Anyway, as you can see, I thought we'd just have enough time to eat outside with a candle to light the way—it's warm enough, though they say the weather will break tomorrow. I tell you, if you Brits didn't have weather, you'd never talk to each other."

Maisie thought of Gabriella Hunter's words of advice. *Love must be cradled gently.* She smiled. "Yes, of course. Forgive me, darling—I wasn't thinking. It's been a long day." She followed Scott into the kitchen, where the aroma of fresh garlic and tomatoes simmering teased her appetite—she realized she had not eaten since a hurried slice of toast at Chelstone before leaving for the station, and an Eccles cake that she could not finish at Hunter's house. Now she realized she had admonished Scott for wasting food when she was guilty of the same thing.

"So, what calls you to Washington?" she asked, taking off her jacket and hanging it on the back of a chair. She leaned against the doorframe and accepted the glass of chilled white wine he passed to her.

"Oh, you know, embassy business." Scott smiled as he clinked his glass against hers and leaned in to kiss her cheek.

She closed her eyes and breathed in his aftershave. The ship was righting itself again, and they were on an even keel.

"I don't suppose it's got anything to do with Hitler's speech last week—about Germany being in a position to 'beat all possible enemies' no matter how much they spend. We all know that was a dig at the United States." Maisie paused. "Sorry. Careless talk costs lives."

"Sure does," said Scott, turning back to the stove. He set down his glass and began serving spaghetti and sauce into two bowls. "Grab the bread from the oven, hon—it should be warm now."

"The advantage of knowing you, Mark, is the food—and Anna just loved her chocolate treat this morning."

"Now she tells me—I guess I know Anna only laughs at my jokes for the chocolate." Holding the plates, Scott nodded toward his glass, and they made their way to the garden, Maisie carrying the glasses and bread.

"You've got that look on your face, Maisie," said Scott, as they were seated and he raised his glass once again to touch hers. "You're either worried about me—and I doubt that—or someone else. Is it Anna or your dad or Brenda or Rowan or . . ."

"You're going through the family list until you see my face change, aren't you?"

Scott laughed.

"I'm just a bit tired," said Maisie. "As I said, long day."

"All the days are long right now—for everyone." He set down

his fork and reached for her hand. "Maybe you should head back to Chelstone—you don't need to do whatever you're doing, Maisie. It would be good for you, for Anna. Maybe even for us."

"For the time being, Mark, I have to make a contribution and do my bit as much as everyone else. It's just that the bit I'm doing worries me at times, and today was particularly draining."

"That bad."

Maisie nodded. "Risking other people's lives is always bad." With her free hand she lifted her glass and took a sip of wine. "Forget I said that—I shouldn't have."

"Said what? It's gone already, sweetheart." He smiled at her. "It's gone from my mind, never to return."

Maisie held on to his hand. "I'll miss you, Mark—when you're away."

"Me too, you too," said Scott, holding her gaze for a few seconds. "Come on, eat up—there's more in the pan. And let's talk about something else. How's your dad? Is his knee still giving him trouble? What does that old beau of yours say about it . . . the orthopedic guy?"

She released his hand, taking comfort in his deliberate attempt to bring the talk around to normal everyday things. Steering the ship forward. They discussed her father's arthritic knee, the fact that Lord Julian was defying all attempts by the grim reaper to claim him, Anna's progress at school, her squealing laugh when she was happy, and Brenda's opinions, which seem to be gaining strength every day—though Maisie did not mention the morning's conversation with her stepmother. Mark Scott enjoyed talking about life at Chelstone, about Maisie's family, about Priscilla, her husband and boys, to the extent that Maisie sometimes thought that he felt a certain comfort, a sense of belonging, in claiming her family for his own.

The lightness of conversation lulled her, as if she were at the edge of a lake and each subject was a dragonfly skimming across the water on a warm summer's day. She knew without a shadow of doubt that she was in love with Mark Scott. But the past had taught her that war was never a good time for love, though Gabriella Hunter's words echoed in her mind. *The war will be over one day, Maisie—what you do now will pave the way for how you will live in peace.*

CHAPTER 4

Maisie did not go straight to the office the following morning, but instead made her way to Scotland Yard, where she asked to see Detective Chief Superintendent Caldwell. Having waited in a drafty corridor for fifteen minutes, she was informed that he could spare her a minute or two of his time.

"I know the way—you've got your hands full here," said Maisie to a relieved police constable, who had a line of people waiting for attention.

Caldwell was standing outside his private domain as she approached, walking through an outer office where two detectives were at work. "I take it this is not a social call, Miss Dobbs—I just hope you're not about to land more work onto my overflowing plate." He held out his hand for her to enter the room. "Take a pew—just throw those files on the floor, I won't get to them for a week anyway."

Maisie regarded the man before her—stocky, his perspiring brow furrowed and his hands ink-stained. He seemed flustered and tired at the same time, his tie askew and an unshaven shadow around his chin. The office was small, with a desk at one end underneath a high window that offered little natural light. There was just enough space for Caldwell to squeeze around the desk to take his seat. Several drawers on the two filing cabinets had not been closed—or perhaps they were jammed open—so the door into the office offered only sufficient room for a person to shuffle in sideways while holding their breath. There were piles of papers on the floor and visitor chair as well as the desk. Caldwell's jacket, hanging on the door, partially obscured the glass that would allow him a view into the outer office, if the door were closed.

"I can come another time," said Maisie.

Caldwell grinned. "Blimey, I must look rough if you're offering to walk out of here before having your two penn'orth of my busy day." He leaned on the desk, rubbed his eyes and sighed. "Want a cuppa? I can get one of the blokes to bring us some stewed tea and even find the odd biscuit of suspicious vintage, if you like."

"I'll take the tea, not the biscuit," said Maisie.

"Thank the Lord for that—an excuse to get something wet and warm down me."

Caldwell stood up, kicked a wastebasket to the side and walked to the door. He called out to a younger man in the corridor, "Oi! Watling. Two teas, splash of milk," and turned back to Maisie. "No bloody good asking for sugar anymore, is it?"

Maisie laughed. "I was going to give it up anyway."

"Well, I wasn't." Caldwell took his seat again.

A young constable entered holding two mugs of tea in one hand, and a plate with four plain biscuits in the other.

"Blimey, biscuits! Fresh-looking biscuits! And on a plate!" said Caldwell, clearing a space on the desk. "You'll be the commissioner in a few months if you go on like that, Watling."

The constable put down the mugs along with the plate of biscuits, and blushed. "Anything else, sir?"

"No, off you go, lad. Close the door behind you."

With the door closed, Maisie reached for a mug of tea and changed her mind about the biscuit.

"Young Watling's safe from call-up," said Caldwell, taking up the other mug. "Turned down by the services on account of being color-blind. Normally we might have done the same, but we need all the help we can get." He took two biscuits, pausing to dunk one into his mug of tea and popping it into his mouth before it disintegrated. He drew a handkerchief from his pocket and wiped his mouth. "Now then, let's get down to business. What do you want? Is it something to do with that runner seeing things in the blackout?"

Maisie nodded. "Yes, it's to do with the runner, but I don't think he was seeing things. I believe he witnessed a murder, though there is no body."

"Tricky one, that. No body." Caldwell took a deep breath and dunked his second biscuit, eating it with the same speed as he had the first. He coughed, thumped his chest, and took a generous sip of tea. "I tell you, this job is nothing but a recipe for terminal heartburn." He paused. "Look, we are scrambling here at the Yard. I know you've probably heard this from other quarters, and probably even me, but all that nonsense about Londoners all pulling together and crime going down is just that—nonsense. There's a black market to deal with, crime through the roof, looting, and suddenly human life isn't worth what it was. And I haven't got enough men to sort it out because they're all in the army now—or the air force, or navy. So when I send someone to look for a body and they can't find one—even though the Germans are making mincemeat out of us—I have to assume there was no bloody body in the first place."

"I think there was, Superintendent Caldwell. I know your men are pressed for time, so I went along to the place where the boy said he had seen the murder take place, and I found blood."

"There's a lot of it about. And bodies, and bits of bodies." Caldwell exhaled audibly. "You know what one of the firemen found the other morning? He goes into a shelter and finds everyone dead. Not a mark on them. Twenty people, women and children, and they are all dead. The bomb knocked all the air out of their lungs and they died instantly. Gone, just like that." He snapped his fingers.

Maisie could see emotion overwhelm the usually derisive policeman. "We're seeing terrible things, aren't we?"

"I don't know if we'll ever get over it, Miss Dobbs. What I've seen since war broke out will stay in my head forever, I'm sure—and I'm a copper. We expect to see things most people don't." He shook his head. "Right then. Back to the boy. You say you found blood?"

"Yes, and it looked as if it had been covered with the crumbled cement and sand that's left when the rubble has been cleared off the road—most of the area is a bomb site."

"What was the lad doing there?"

"Running a message."

"Who for?"

Maisie widened her eyes.

"Oh, all right," said Caldwell. "But is there anything you *can* say?"

"I'm afraid I can't—but I wondered if you might know which mortuary a body from that part of Vauxhall might be taken to, if it were found by the ambulance service. I haven't been driving since last year—since . . ."

"Since your mate copped it. Don't blame you. How is she?"

"One more operation to go—in December, a couple of weeks before Christmas."

"Poor woman."

"Anyway," said Maisie, anxious to press on. "We would have taken the bodies to Lambeth, but I wanted to know if you'd received any word from the pathologist that a death by stabbing had been recorded."

"What's it been? Four days? We should have been told, but—"

"But when someone's dead, they're dead, and the pathologists are overwhelmed."

"I hate to say it, but yes. Or—and believe me, I hate encouraging you in your little quests, Miss Dobbs—if what you say is true, the body could have been removed by someone else or taken down to the water and dumped there with some ballast tied to the feet. It's not as if we're short of lumps of rubble in London, is it?"

Maisie shook her head, sipped the last of her tea and stood up. "You're right—but I had a few moments to spare and thought I'd drop in to see what you thought. Could you do me a favor and perhaps telephone the pathologist at the mortuary in Lambeth and—"

Caldwell caught her eye. "Are you as convinced as you say you are, Miss Dobbs? I've worked with you a few times now, and despite all I say to wind you up at times, I know you know what you're doing. I know doubt when I see it too—and there's a little bit of doubt in your eyes."

Maisie sighed. "He was a tired boy at night in a bombing raid. On one hand I have to believe him because I have some more . . . anyway, on the other hand I know it's possible to see dragons lurking in the shadows when you're scared."

"What were you about to say then? You have some more what? Evidence? Now then, let me just—"

"Sir!" The door opened following a single knock, and the young constable entered. "Sorry to interrupt you, sir, but we've just had the river police on the blower again, and they want to know when you'll be down to look at the body that was hauled in by the crew trying to bring up the Spitfire that went down into the water last night. What with the crane and two dredgers, there's people gathering to watch. They've been trying not to attract attention to the murder victim, but they're getting worried about it, sir. I told them you were held up, but they said there's already a reporter snooping around, though so far he's only been interested in the Spitfire, which they'll be hauling out as soon as they've got the chains around it. Shall I call down for the motor car?"

Caldwell raised his eyebrows. "Thank you for that, Watling, lovely timing as usual. I'm going to be having a word with you about the importance of maintaining confidentiality in the department."

"Sir?" The young detective constable's brow furrowed.

"Oh, never mind. Yes, call Digby to bring the motor round, because we're not walking down there."

"Yes, sir." The constable turned to leave and knocked his elbow against a filing cabinet. "Ow!"

"Watch it, Watling—that thing cost money. I'll have your wages docked for that."

Maisie watched the constable as he returned to his desk. She inclined her head, then turned to face Caldwell. "A body coming up from the river, Detective Superintendent?"

Caldwell sighed. "Yes, Miss Dobbs—a body. We got the message a little while ago. Knife wounds to the abdomen and heart, just the sort of thing you've been asking about—no more information than that at this stage. What with the disturbance caused by bringing up the Spitfire, it must have dislodged the deceased. I didn't want to say anything, because we've been under attack for over a year, and it could be anyone."

"Bombs don't usually land with knives on board, Caldwell."

"All right, all right—you'd better come with me. The pathologist is there now to see to the poor boy who went down with his Spitfire."

A crowd of people had gathered around the police cordon along the Embankment, though it was clear their main focus was the Spitfire about to be winched out of the murky waters of the Thames.

"This is why I wanted the motor," said Caldwell. "We could've walked, but then we'd have had trouble getting through that lot. Last thing I want is a blimmin' press bod collaring me for a comment because he's heard there's more than one body coming up."

Maisie nodded and followed Caldwell as he made his way around the perimeter of the cluster of people gathered, an audience of onlookers who responded with a collective gasp as the crane began the task of lifting the aircraft onto the barge. Water streamed from the fuselage, the cockpit cover open and hanging away from the aircraft. The pilot's upper body lay slumped across the outside, as if he had tried to climb out but drowned in the attempt. Maisie put her hand to her mouth and felt her eyes sting. A woman screamed. The crowd seemed to huddle closer together.

"Poor bugger," said a man. "Poor bugger doing his bit for us lot, and he ends up down there."

Muttering, the crowd nodded heads, many dabbing their eyes with a handkerchief brought from a pocket in haste.

"All right, everyone—let's give the boy some peace." Caldwell nodded to a couple of constables to disperse the gathering. "The lad went up there for us, and it's only right we respect him now. Time to go on your way and get your work done before Goering's lot come in for another go at us. Move along, ladies and gentlemen. Let's get him out of there and into somewhere dry."

People began to leave with bowed heads, and as they passed Maisie heard a woman whispering to herself, "The Lord is my shepherd, I shall not want . . ." She turned to watch as men clambered onto the barge and began to remove the young aviator's body from the cockpit. They carried him as if he were the most precious cargo, lifting him with a gentleness they would bestow upon a newborn babe, before laying him to rest on a stretcher. Maisie recognized the pathologist as he covered the body with a tarpaulin, before two ambulance men loaded the stretcher into a waiting ambulance and drove off, followed by a Royal Air Force chaplain.

"Over here, Miss Dobbs—our bloke is over here," said Caldwell. "They fished him out before anyone could see what was going on. The audience was more interested in that poor boy in the Spitfire anyway."

Maisie followed Caldwell, though in truth she wanted nothing more than to go home and try to contact her godson, Tom, a pilot in the Royal Air Force. She loved Priscilla's sons as if they were her own.

The pathologist was already inspecting the body when Caldwell and Maisie reached his side.

"Caldwell, good day for it. Rain's holding off." The pathologist looked up at the detective, and then to Maisie. "Oh, Miss Dobbs— nice to see you again. Keeping well?"

"Yes, thank you, Dr. Jamieson. All's well—though witnessing a Spitfire being winched out of the water rather took my breath away."

"Me too. A bit of emotion never hurt anyone in this job—I don't hold with this idea that you have to be hard. Having a feeling for the dead opens the mind."

"Blimey," muttered Caldwell.

"And don't take any notice of that one." Jamieson smiled as he nodded toward Caldwell.

"You sounded just like Maurice," said Maisie, kneeling down beside the pathologist.

"Hardly surprising. The man who trained you also trained me. Now then—let's get down to business."

"Oh yes, let's," said Caldwell, rolling his eyes as he drew back his sleeve and looked at his watch.

"Right," said Jamieson. "I'll be doing a full postmortem back at the lab, but you can see where the blade entered here, and here." He pointed to two livid serrations of the flesh. "Nasty weapon, make no mistake. And it is a weapon—not your average kitchen knife. One right there to the celiac artery and the next to the heart. The killer was a professional. He knew where to go and he did it fast."

"Time of death?" asked Caldwell.

Jamieson shook his head. "You should know by now, Detective Superintendent, that being in that murky brine for any length of time messes up the usual indicators, but I'd say his luck ran out a few days ago and he was thrown in the drink within a very short time of death, possibly an hour, maybe two, judging by the decomposition."

"Identity card? Ration book? Engraved watch? Anything to indicate who he is . . . was?" asked Caldwell.

Jamieson shook his head. "Nothing."

"Dr. Jamieson, may I assist with the postmortem?" asked Maisie.

"Of course, though I won't be able to start until later this afternoon—about four? The body will be going to my lab near Victoria station."

"I know where it is. I'll see you then," said Maisie.

"Don't mind me, will you?" said Caldwell. "I'm only the copper around here—and I want to be the first and only one to hear what you have to say after you've taken off your aprons. Is that clear?"

"Very clear," said Maisie. "I'll come right over to the Yard with the notes as soon as Dr. Jamieson releases them—that all right with you both?"

The men nodded.

"Right then—let's be on our way," said Caldwell. "Drop you anywhere, Miss Dobbs?"

"Thank you for the offer, Detective Superintendent. I think I'll walk from here."

Maisie bid good-bye to the two men and began to walk away, looking back in time to see Jamieson unfurl a tarpaulin across the body of the unknown murder victim, with the same tenderness he had accorded the fallen airman.

The terrace houses on Collington Street in Lambeth were known as "back doubles" and shared walls on three sides, so that only one room had a door and windows. The front row of houses faced the street, and the attached houses behind them looked out upon a shared courtyard, where a series of WCs were lined up against a wall. The first-floor rooms where Freddie Hackett lived with his family were accessed via the courtyard. As the Industrial Age gathered pace, and accommodation was needed for the families who rushed in from the land to find work in the factories, back doubles had been built by the thousands in towns across Britain, using cheap labor and even cheaper materials to house the lowest-paid workers. By the turn of the century, decades before the Hacketts moved into their two rooms, grateful to have a roof over their heads, the back doubles were known to be unsafe, unsanitary and soul-destroying, yet with their low rents they were all the poor could afford.

Even before she stepped out of the taxicab, Maisie knew the geography of Freddie Hackett's home, because she had grown up in a house almost exactly the same.

She entered the courtyard by a side gate and looked around at the sad dwellings, at doors with paint peeling away and smoke-stained windows. Laundry had been hung on lines across cracked and broken flagstones where even weeds struggled to grow. Maisie could hear women talking, peppering their washhouse conversation with the odd chuckle, the sound of fabric being pushed across corrugated wooden boards as if in defiance of their lot. It seemed a futile task, as layer upon layer of dust settled across every home in London, continuing to fall long after each night's bombing raids. The women pegged out clean laundry on the washing line, only to bring in clothing and bed linens that could do with another wash.

As she reached the door, Maisie read a note nailed to the frame.

For Hackett, knock three times. For Dunley, knock four times.

There were holes where a door knocker had once been screwed into place—doubtless it had been torn off and sold for scrap. She rapped on the door with her knuckles.

There was no answer, so she knocked again.

"Just coming!" The voice came from within, and Maisie heard someone running down the staircase, which she knew was located just inside the door.

The door opened just as a second voice came from the downstairs dwelling.

"Is that for me, Gracie? I thought I heard four knocks."

"No, Mrs. Dunley—it was three. Someone for us."

"Could have sworn I heard four. Is it the police again, after your old man?"

"No, Mrs. Dunley. I've got to go, Mrs. Dunley."

The woman at the door turned to Maisie. She was about Maisie's height, with hair drawn back in a topknot scarf, and wore a pinafore over a gray dress that was clean and pressed but had seen better days. Her blue eyes seemed to reflect the dress, making them appear to change hue as light shafted in through the open door, and she had a warm smile—though neither of those attributes could mask the attention a bruise on her cheek would attract.

"May I help you?" she asked, holding a hand to her cheek.

"Mrs. Hackett?" Maisie didn't wait for confirmation—Freddie Hackett was his mother's son. "I wonder if you could spare a few minutes of your time for me—it's about Freddie."

The woman gasped, her hand still on her cheek. "Oh, you're not from the school board, are you? Has he been playing truant? I mean, he's a good lad, but you know he does important work—he was chosen to run messages, you know."

"It's all right, Mrs. Hackett—I'm not from the school board, and I know your Freddie is a good lad. I'd like to ask you a few questions because he came to me for help after he'd witnessed something that happened on Friday evening while he was running a message." Maisie took her professional calling card from her pocket and handed it to the woman. "I knew him before, because he delivered messages to me on a couple of occasions."

The woman nodded, but the frown remained. She studied the card, stepped aside and held the door open. "We're up the stairs," she said, closing the door and leading the way.

A dustpan and broom with worn bristles were leaning against the wall at the top of the staircase, and Maisie could see that Mrs. Hackett was a woman who tried to keep her home as clean as she could, even if that home comprised just the two upper rooms of accommodation that had never seen better days. She led the way into the small, damp back room that was both the kitchen and living area. Maisie assumed the other room was a bedroom—and she knew that compared to the accommodation that some had to settle for, this was considered more than adequate. Whole families were now living in one room, as the continued bombing destroyed more and more housing stock.

Freddie's mother pulled out a chair from the table and, as if she needed to explain her living circumstances, began to speak. "We're lucky to have this place, you know. We were bombed out of the last house—well, it was only two rooms, a bit bigger than this, I admit. Then we heard of this one through someone I met when I took my youngest to church one Sunday, and as I can give Mrs. Dunley a bit of help now and again when she needs it, we got this place—and a home is a home, however it comes. The children have to bed down on the floor, but you know, kiddies will sleep anywhere, won't they?" She stopped speaking and rested her hand against her face again. "Would you like a cup of tea? I have to go out again soon—my other cleaning job, across the water—but I've time for a quick cup, then I'll nip down and check on Mrs. Dunley before I go off to work."

"If you're brewing up, I'll join you." Maisie had learned years ago that a slight change in her diction to suit the moment was often all she needed to relax the person she had come to question. She didn't have to sound like a local, just meet them halfway, so without realizing it they felt as if she were a friend and not a stranger. But Freddie Hackett's mother sounded as if she, too, had modified her locution to match that of her neighbors.

"Right then." Mrs. Hackett smiled, only taking her hand from her face when she turned away from Maisie. The kettle was already coming to the boil on the gas ring atop a small stove.

"Mrs. Hackett, I'm sure you know that Freddie witnessed a man being attacked—it was while he was out running a message."

"I do, and I told him to go to the police—but they weren't interested. Said they had enough on their plates without running around after a lad with a big imagination. Apparently they checked the area and found nothing—so now they think my Freddie is either soft in the head or a liar. And I know for the fact that my boy is neither. He's a good son to me."

Hackett turned around holding a teapot in one hand and two cups in the other, revealing the full extent of the deep purple bruise. She placed the teapot and cups on the table and reached up to a shelf for saucers and a small jug. Stepping across to the window, she picked up a half-full milk bottle where it was kept in a pail of cold water, decanted some into the jug and set the bottle back in the bucket. There was something about the small, chipped willow-pattern jug that touched Maisie, as if Freddie Hackett's mother were clinging to a crumb of gentility—perhaps a connection to the past, or a longing for better times.

Studying the woman as she poured tea, Maisie continued. "Has Freddie shown any signs of anxiety since Sunday? For example, have his hands been shaking, or is he scratching his face or rubbing his hands together—any movements you've not seen before?"

"Nothing new, no." The woman shook her head, and Maisie could see tears well up in her eyes. She looked down and placed a cup of tea in front of Maisie.

"Nothing new." Maisie sipped her tea, thanked the woman, and continued. "Mrs. Hackett, I wonder, has he ever shown such signs? You said 'Nothing new'—but is there a behavior already established?"

"He's a brave boy, my Freddie—going out in the dark and running those messages so we have money coming in. Yes, he's doing his bit, but I think he's too young for that kind of work, even though he's always been light on his feet." A single teardrop ran across her bruised cheek, which she swept away with the back of her hand. She looked up at Maisie. "He scratches his arms. You can't see the scratches because of his shirt sleeves, but sometimes he does it and draws blood."

"That's a sign of nerves, Mrs. Hackett. How is he progressing at school?"

"Oh, he's very good. Does his best. I've no complaints—and it's not as if he's got much longer, is it? He'll be out to work when he turns fourteen. What with his running job, it's not surprising he gets a bit anxious, because he goes straight from school to an office across the water, where he has to be ready to take out messages to the other office, so he goes from Baker Street to a building on the Albert Embankment and along to another place near Parliament, from one to the other. Sometimes they have him running a bit further—even back across the water, if need be."

Maisie remembered how her South London–born father always referred to anything on the other side of the Thames as "across the water"—the famous London river was always known as "the water" to locals.

"Why do you think he's anxious, Mrs. Hackett?"

"Same reason we're all a bit nervous, Miss Dobbs—we've seen the bodies, haven't we? We've seen our neighbors killed, even the little ones. We've got our hearts in our mouths half the time, haven't we? All scared out of our wits every single night."

"Yes, of course—I just wondered if there was anything more specific to Freddie." She took a different tack. "Were your children ever evacuated?"

Hackett shook her head. "I was going to let them go, but I heard such things—terrible things happening, out there in the country. All them children living with strangers, coming home and not knowing which way is up. No, if one of us goes to meet our maker, then we all go together. We're a family. And being as there are so many children away, the school is only small now, so the children are doing all right. The army is in the other half of the school—the bomb disposal lads. That's who I feel sorry for."

"And your husband's not in the service?"

"No, he's—he wasn't fit for service, on account of his wounds from the last war. He gets work where he can, though. You'd think there'd be more for him, what with so many men away, but no, it's only piece-work he can get—you know, a piece here and a piece there, paid by the hour with never a promise of more than that." Hackett looked at the clock on the shelf above the stove. "Speaking of work, I'd best be getting on."

Maisie stood up. "Mrs. Hackett, I've a taxicab outside and I'm go-ing back across the water. Come on, let me drop you off—save you running to catch a bus."

"Are you sure? That's very kind of you, Miss Dobbs, and I'm much obliged. I'll get my coat."

Maisie took the cups to the sink, rinsed them under the cold tap and placed them on the draining board. A single framed photograph hung on the wall by the door, of Freddie's mother on her wedding day, her hand resting on the arm of her groom. Maisie looked closer and, glancing along the passage to see if she had a moment, reached into her bag for the magnifying glass that was always part of what she thought of as the "kit" she kept with her for use during an investiga-tion. Lifting the glass to the photograph, she leaned toward the image, focusing on the man Grace had married.

"Ready when you are, Miss Dobbs!" Hackett's voice echoed along the landing.

Maisie put away the magnifying glass and joined Mrs. Hackett on the landing.

"Sorry to keep you, Miss Dobbs. I just had to nip out to the WC, and of course I have to lock the doors up here or Mrs. Dunley comes up for a poke around—she's a bit nosy. I'll pop my head around her door to make sure she's all right, though." She lowered her voice, leaning in toward Maisie. "She pretends she can't move very well, but you can rest assured, the minute I leave, she'll be up these stairs and trying the door handles."

Maisie smiled, and as she looked at Hackett, she noticed that the woman had applied powder over the bruise, though it was still visible.

"How on earth did you do that to your face?" asked Maisie.

"See that broom there? I tell you, it happened so fast! I was hurrying and stepped on the brush. The handle popped away from the wall, and whack! Straight across my cheekbone! Freddie was here and ran down to the pub to see if they had some ice for it. Bless that boy."

"That's just the sort of thing I'd do, Mrs. Hackett," Maisie said as they made their way down the stairs. "We women are always rushing, and there's always something in the way."

"At least you don't have children to worry about too."

"Oh, but I do," said Maisie. "I have a little girl. I just use my maiden name for my work."

Maisie waited in the taxi while Grace Hackett checked on Mrs. Dunley. Once the vehicle set off, Hackett picked up the conversation. "Is your husband in the services?"

Maisie caught her breath. She had noticed Hackett glancing at the third finger of her left hand as she asked the question. "No. I'm a widow, Mrs. Hackett—but we're doing well, my daughter and I. Very well indeed. Now, where would you like to be dropped off?"

Later, having given Mrs. Hackett—who had invited her to "call me Grace"—a lift to an address in Belgravia, the location of one of her several jobs, Maisie asked the driver to drop her at Victoria Station. She wanted to walk around for a while to settle her mind before joining Jamieson at his laboratory. She had a few thoughts to dissect before assisting the pathologist. For a start, Maisie was sure the broom handle had not taken a swipe at Grace Hackett's face. She had seen enough wounds on both the living and the dead to know a bruise sustained as a result of a fist to the cheek and how it might differ from that of an accident. But of greater interest was the image of the man Maisie assumed to be Freddie Hackett's father. Focusing on the photograph of Grace with her new husband on their wedding day, Maisie could see he had sustained his own facial wound: a long, prominent scar across his right cheek.

CHAPTER 5

Outfitted in a white laboratory coat, mask, and rubber gloves, her hair fingered back under a white scarf, Maisie scribbled notes on a clipboard as Jamieson spoke. On occasion she stopped him to ask a question, or to point out something for him to look at again. She liked Jamieson; there was something in his bearing that continued to remind her of Maurice—the way he touched the body, even whispering, "Sorry about that, old man," as if the cadaver before them still held life and warmth.

Every part of the deceased was inspected and condition noted, right down to an ingrown nail on the big toe of the right foot.

"The shrapnel wounds are telling, don't you think, Dr. Jamieson?" asked Maisie.

"Yes. I saw so many just like this in the last war—and the water has brought more shards to the surface of the skin. I daresay he picked out a few splinters each week, and the constant reminder probably gave him nightmares about the day he got them." He sighed. "Trying to look beyond his condition, what age would you peg him, Maisie?"

Maisie looked up. Jamieson had never used her Christian name before. She stared down at the body again. "I'd say he was a young soldier during the last war, not too many years on him at the time, and perhaps only a little older than the century. Let's settle on about forty-two, something of that order."

"My thoughts exactly." He looked up at Maisie. "And please, do call me Duncan. It seems silly to stick to formalities in the presence of the dead."

Maisie could feel her face flushing. On the contrary, she would rather have stuck to the "formalities."

Jamieson continued. "Anything else you've noticed?"

Maisie cleared her throat. "This man had quite a life—or quite a job. Look at these scars here—on the arm, and the thigh. And this one across the palm of his hand. He has been in a few scrapes—fights, I should say, and weapons were involved. Either that or he was terribly accident-prone." She stood back and began to chew the side of her lip.

"What is it?" asked Jamieson.

She sighed. "Look, this is going to sound incredibly . . . well, it's speculation, but I believe this man might have been some sort of fighter. And I don't mean a boxer or wrestler. This body is like a child's drawing book—there's scribble everywhere and every mark looks like the result of a deliberate wound. I suspect he was in combat well beyond the last war, and that he found himself in some very tight corners." She set the scalpel and clipboard on a metal trolley alongside the postmortem table, and folded her arms. "I even wonder if we are dealing with a seasoned killer."

"The murderer was the one who knew how to kill, Maisie—swiftly and with ease."

She nodded again. "Oh, I can see that." Slipping her pencil into a pocket, she picked up a scalpel from the instruments tray and used it to point to the two knife wounds. "This is precision work, as you observed when we first saw the body. But I wonder if the murder could have been the result of two sharks fighting, two trained killers who would go at each other to the death. Or might one of those two killers—this one—have been unsuspecting, with no reason to fear the other man?"

"Now you're venturing outside my territory, Maisie. I'm strictly the corpse man. I can tell you about the weapon, the trajectory of the knife as it was plunged into the body here and here, and I can tell you that this chap liked a drink or two—or three or four—if I'm not mistaken. Nasty-looking liver—could be the result of too many French aperitifs and a good number of other spirits. More than that is beyond my purview. But it's always interesting to hear someone like you begin to see the story."

Maisie frowned. "French aperitifs? Have you assumed he's French?"

Jamieson shrugged. "That's where I speculate, I suppose." He shook his head. "No, it's not. I can trust you with my thoughts because you're a product of Maurice Blanche's teaching methods. First, I was a doctor at a casualty clearing station, and then later a field hospital during the last war. For the most part the soldiers under my supervision—my patients—were British, but we had a number of French, Australian, Canadian, South African men—and even the odd German brought in. In time, I didn't even need to be told the nationality—I just knew. Ask the other doctors and they would say the same. I expect you would have known too—after all, you were a nurse in the last war, if my memory services me well."

Maisie nodded. "Go on."

"And the other thing is that I found myself speaking to him in French before you arrived. Obviously not because he could have answered; it was a matter of instinct. That probably sounds frightfully strange, but as you know, it makes the job so much easier if you have a word or two for the poor bastard in front of you."

Maisie put down the scalpel and picked up the clipboard. She noted a couple of additional points from their observations of the body, making a brief mention that the deceased was believed to have been of French origin.

"I think I can guess why you transferred to forensic pathology," she said.

Jamieson laughed. It was a hearty laugh, a laugh that Maisie thought seemed to come from the very heart of him.

"I'm sure you can, Maisie. I just didn't want to lose another patient, another lad screaming for his mother or his sweetheart, or begging me to please end it for him so the pain would go away. At least with the dead I can't do any worse than has already been done. I don't have to live with the screams anymore, or the fear of making the wrong decision and losing someone who hasn't had enough time to know what life is all about." He looked down at the body of the man Freddie Hackett had seen murdered. "He may have been a killer, Maisie, but we cannot judge the reason why."

W*e cannot judge the reason why*. Now back in her Fitzroy Square office, Maisie was sitting at her desk letting a pencil run through her thumb and forefinger before dropping onto the blotting pad time after time as Duncan Jamieson's words continued to echo. A professional killer, possibly a Frenchman, was dead and another on the loose. The witness was a boy tasked with running through burning streets to deliver messages—"doing his bit" and likely becoming as shell-shocked as any soldier she'd seen in the last war. And he was a boy whose father bore a scar, as had the killer he'd described.

We cannot judge the reason why. She allowed the pencil to drop through her fingers once more and hit the desk, but this time she let it bounce onto the floor as she pushed back her chair. She stood up and walked to the window, folded her arms and looked down at the courtyard below, to the small area where just last year a German spy had grown flowers and vines to disguise the aerial that allowed him to send radio messages to his superiors. Maisie had reported him to Robbie MacFarlane, and as far as she knew he was already dead. Executed. Months later she had rented the downstairs flat so that Billy could use it on those nights when he was not able to return to his family. His wife, Doreen, and daughter, Margaret Rose, were now living in Frankie and Brenda's bungalow in Chelstone village, while Maisie's parents had moved full-time to the Dower House. Billy would return to the office before the blackout, and she knew that she, too, should leave soon to go home to her Holland Park flat. But she lingered, pondering her next move. It was like a game of chess.

The telephone began to ring, interrupting her thoughts. She picked up the receiver.

"Fitzroy—"

As always when the caller was Robert MacFarlane, his voice boomed into the receiver before she could finish reciting the number.

"Maisie! There's a motor car coming over to take you to your abode so you can throw a few necessaries into a suitcase—and make it a small one, you won't need much. You're booked on the sleeper to Edinburgh. Best time of the year in my bonny Scotland."

"But Robbie . . . it's Anna's—"

"Don't fret, lassie, I'll have you back by Friday night, and you won't miss the wee girl's show-jumping debut on Saturday. And from what I hear, your gentleman friend left today to return to the Colonies, so I know you're not booked up. Anyway, we're needed as a matter of some urgency—got a group being pushed through the first part of their assessments, the paramilitary training, and we've got to get them double-checked, approved for whatever it is we think they'll be best at, then on to the next stage as soon as we can. Make sure you bring a pair of trousers and some boots. And a woolen jacket—as you know, it can get a bit nippy up there."

"We're both needed?"

"I'll see you at the station, Maisie—we can have a dram or two over our supper on the train. Thank the good Lord the sleeper is running again."

"I'd better be back in London by Friday, Robbie—come what may."

"I promise."

The continuous tone on the line signaled that Robbie MacFarlane had ended the call in his usual manner, which amounted to slamming the receiver into its cradle.

"First time I've heard you promise anything, if my memory serves me well," said Maisie to the empty room as she placed a finger on the switch bar, then let go and began to dial. After several rings, Brenda answered the Dower House telephone.

"Good afternoon."

Maisie smiled when she heard the clipped tone of her stepmother's "telephone voice." She knew the woman on the other end of the line would always be as protective of her privacy as she had been of Maurice Blanche's need for seclusion when she was his housekeeper.

"Hello, Brenda—sorry to bother you, but there's been a couple of changes to my plans this week," said Maisie, running the telephone cord through her fingers. "First of all—"

"First of all, Maisie, I do hope this is not going to disappoint Anna— I don't think I could bear to see the hurt on my granddaughter's little face when I tell her that Mummy won't be there at the show to see her ride."

Maisie raised her eyebrows. It was a day of firsts—she had never heard Brenda refer to Anna as "my granddaughter," although she was sure she would have done so while chatting to other villagers. She smiled as the words seemed to swaddle her in comfort. "No, I'll be there, but I won't be home until Friday evening."

"Is it to do with Mr. Scott?"

Now she could almost feel Brenda bristle as she spoke. "No, he's . . . he's not here at the moment. And I have to go to . . . to go somewhere else. Not too far, but I won't be able to get back until Friday. Which means that I will be home as soon as I can."

"What about him?"

"Him?"

"Mr. Scott. Will he be coming? I would like to know if he's also going to return from wherever he's been, so I can make up a room."

"No, he won't be in London for another week or so."

"Right then. Will you telephone to speak to Anna later? She's still down at the stables with her grandfather."

"I'll call from the station—she'll be back by that time." There was a pause, one Brenda did not fill. "Well, I'll be off then. Give my love to Anna and to Dad—and to you, Brenda."

"Mind how you go, Maisie," said Brenda.

Once again Maisie was left holding the receiver, having heard another person end the call without saying good-bye. She exhaled as she replaced the receiver in its cradle.

"Seems I'm in more trouble with Brenda than I thought," she said aloud. She looked at her watch and wrote a message for Billy before picking up her jacket and leaving the office, locking the door on her way out. A black motor car was waiting for her, engine idling and a young ATS driver standing alongside the rear passenger door. The ATS—the Auxiliary Territorial Service—was the women's branch of the army. The driver smiled as Maisie approached, saluting as she opened the door.

"Miss Dobbs? Traffic is light today, so I should have you home in next to no time."

Maisie thanked the driver, taken aback by the salute.

———

As the motor car pulled up outside the front entrance to Maisie's garden flat, another black vehicle approached from behind.

"Wonder what he wants," said the ATS driver, glancing into her rearview mirror. "One of them Yank motors just pulled up behind us."

Maisie glanced up at the rearview mirror and met the eyes of her driver, who had raised an eyebrow. She smiled at the young woman and turned to look out of the back window. "Yes, I wonder," she said, and was about to open the door when the driver stepped out of the vehicle and opened it for her. Maisie alighted from the motor car as the driver of the other vehicle approached, bearing a small package.

"Miss Dobbs?"

"Yes, that's me."

"Special delivery—from the United States embassy."

"Oh, thank you," she said, accepting the proffered parcel. The driver touched his cap and returned to his vehicle.

As Maisie watched the motor car pull away, the ATS driver issued a reminder. "Sorry, ma'am, but we really don't have much time."

"Oh yes, of course."

Maisie rushed into the house, gathered sufficient clothing for two days, including the items specified by MacFarlane, and pushed the parcel from Mark Scott between two woolen cardigans.

Negotiating streets still in the process of being cleared of debris from the previous night's bombings, the young driver looked back at Maisie every time the motor car was required to come to a halt, before being waved on by police. Finally, she addressed Maisie.

"You don't recognize me, do you, Miss Dobbs?"

"I—I beg your pardon?" said Maisie, once again meeting the woman's eyes in the rearview mirror. "I thought you looked somewhat familiar, but—well, to tell you the truth, everyone looks different in uniform."

"It's been a while, to be fair, and we only met briefly. I wasn't in uniform then—but I was on my way out the door of that terrible office."

"Of course! You were working for that dreadful man—the company where Joe Coombes was an apprentice."

Maisie saw the driver's eyes take on a mischievous sparkle as she smiled. "That's it, Miss Dobbs. Charlie Bright at your service—though it's Corporal Charlotte Bright now. And I was really glad to get away from that miserable sod in that gawd-awful office. What a—well, I shouldn't say, Miss Dobbs. It wouldn't be very ladylike."

Maisie smiled. She thought not being ladylike probably didn't worry the corporal at all. "And now you're a driver."

"I've done other jobs since I enlisted. For a while I was in the ack-ack batteries, working the cameras with my friend Mavis to get a position on enemy aircraft. We'd joined up together. I almost copped it one night—I'd sprained my wrist, so another girl was on duty with Mavis, and they were both killed. Broke my heart, it did. I thought I'd never stop crying, I miss her so much. She was a real laugh, was Mavis. But you've just got to get on with it, haven't you? We all have, you know, to get on with it, because the Germans aren't giving us time to mourn."

"And how did you become a driver?"

"I asked until I got, is more or less how I did it. Went on the training course—and it's not that it takes a lot, driving a car, or a lorry, is it? I've done both—put me behind the wheel of anything and I'll take you anywhere you want to go. Anyway, then I was funneled into more training for this posting."

"Why was that?"

"Um—well." Bright seemed to check herself. "It was just for a few more things I had to learn. I mean, I've got to look after important people like you, haven't I?" Catching Maisie's eye in her mirror, she gave a wink and then concentrated on the road again.

"So you must know Mr. MacFarlane," said Maisie.

"Everyone knows Mr. Mac. It was him who told me to come over to your office to collect you and then take you to your flat. He's a bit of a tease, old Mac, but a good sort. You don't want to see him in a temper, mind. That's why I always get his jobs, and I drive him too now. He knows I don't care who he is, he doesn't get away with having a go at his driver just because he's annoyed about something somebody else did!"

"Good for you, Corporal Bright. It's always best to stand your ground with Mr. MacFarlane."

"Here we are, Miss Dobbs," said Bright, as they approached the station. "I'll bring your case in for you."

"Not to worry, Corporal. It's not heavy."

"Right you are, ma'am." Bright brought the motor car to a halt. "Just a tick."

Corporal Charlotte Bright stepped out of the motor car clutching a brown envelope. She opened the rear passenger door and saluted as Maisie exited the vehicle and stood beside her.

"I don't know if I warrant that sort of recognition, Corporal."

"Miss Dobbs—I'm attached to Mr. MacFarlane's department. Everyone in there deserves a salute as far as I'm concerned. Mr. MacFarlane will meet you on the train." She handed Maisie the envelope. "This is for you—he said to have a dekko at it before he sees you."

"Thank you, Corporal. Safe driving."

Corporal Charlotte Bright smiled. "Mr. MacFarlane says he doesn't trust anyone else to drive him, Miss Dobbs. So you're safe with me, if I drive you again."

Maisie smiled again and took her leave, though she stopped to look back as Charlotte Bright closed the passenger door and used a cuff pulled up over the heel of her palm to wipe a smear from the handle. A couple of young army recruits were passing, but slowed their pace to make their admiration of her ankles obvious and to pass comment. Though Bright appeared to ignore them, Maisie thought it was rather clever, the way she stuck out her foot and tripped up the one closest to her so he lurched into his friend and they both fell to the ground. Corporal Bright acted as if she hadn't even seen them go down when she took the driver's seat once again, closed the door of her motor car and moved off into traffic without looking back. It occurred to Maisie that she should probably feel honored that MacFarlane had sent one of his best drivers. She was sure the ATS corporal's special training encompassed an ability to protect her passenger in any adverse situation, and given her impression of young Charlotte—"Charlie"—Bright, she had no doubt the young woman could take care of herself, and woe betide anyone who was foolish enough to underestimate her.

Maisie opened the envelope to find her travel warrant plus a clutch of notes, then made her way toward the departures board to find her platform. As she walked through the station she was framing a conversation she planned to have with Robert MacFarlane—or would she? Was he expecting her to mention Corporal Bright? Was he waiting for her to bring up the fact that he had just put another young woman she already knew into her orbit?

Putting all thoughts of MacFarlane and the journey to Scotland aside, Maisie began walking toward a telephone kiosk. Stepping in, she dropped her suitcase at her feet, took a handful of coins from her pocket and began to dial. The telephone at the Dower House rang only once before it was picked up.

"Mummy! Mummy-Mummy-Mummy—is that you?"

Maisie smiled. Anna had a habit of repeating herself when she was excited or nervous.

"Yes, my darling, it's me! I'll be back on Friday night, did Grandma tell you?"

"Yes-yes-yes! It's a long time. And Emma hasn't been well."

Emma was another adoptee in the house—an elderly Alsatian Maisie brought home following the death of its owner. The dog and Anna had formed an immediate bond.

"Oh dear—what's the matter with her?"

"Grandad says it's her poor old heart, but just to let her rest, so I've been reading her stories."

"I'm sure Grandad is right—he knows a lot about all animals."

"But what if she dies? What if she dies, Mummy? What will we do if she dies?"

"Now then, let's not think like that." Maisie felt a sensation in her chest, as if the flow of blood to her heart had become constricted. "Which story does she like best?"

"I think the one you read to me about Peter and his magic ship— *The Ship That Flew*. I couldn't read it all to her, but I remembered the story so I just told her without the book."

"That's a very good story, Anna. Now then, can you put Granny on the line, so I can talk to her? And remember to count the sleeps before I come home—there's only three!"

"Three sleeps! I'm going to read to Emma again—here's Granny Brenda."

Maisie heard the telephone being passed from the child to the adult, and Brenda instructing Anna to put her slippers on.

"Brenda, what's all this about Emma?"

"Oh Maisie, what a time for you not to be here. I know you have to do your bit, and there's plenty of others doing the same, but . . . but little Anna is going to be crushed before the week's over. Your father says Emma is on her last—we knew she was old when she came to us, and it's only been the love of a child that's kept her going. Follows Anna everywhere, that dog." There was silence on the line. "Maisie— Maisie? Are you still there?"

Maisie nodded, the words caught in her throat. "I should come home right now."

"Look, my dear, I'm sorry I was short with you earlier—we're all a bit out of sorts, I suppose. What with this horse show—and I'm surprised they're doing it, but I suppose life has to go on, doesn't it? Even though it's wartime. And you have important work. I don't know what you do, but I know it's important. Don't fret about the littl'un. She has our arms around her, and when that dog's time comes, we'll hold her even tighter."

"Brenda—Brenda—I think I've had enough." Maisie felt her voice crack again.

"You just do your job and come home. You'll have time to think about it all when you're back under your own roof. You can go into that library, pour yourself a nice cream sherry and put out a glass of malt as if Dr. Blanche was in the room, and you can sit for a while and weigh it all up. You'll know what to do."

"How . . . how did you know I always pour a glass for Maurice? How did you know that's what I do?"

"Because I do it myself sometimes. Just sit and think to myself, 'What would Dr. Blanche say about that?' I don't do it as much as I used to, when I was the housekeeper, because I've your dear father at my side now. Frankie Dobbs is a wise man, Maisie—and he's watching out for Anna, so don't you worry. If you're not here when that dog goes, we'll look after her."

"Thank you, Brenda—thank you so much." Maisie looked up at the station clock. "Look, I'd better run—"

"Take care, Maisie."

Maisie wiped the tears from her eyes, drew back the kiosk's concertina door so she could check the departures board, and closed it again to make one more call. Again with her pile of coins at the ready, she began to dial, pushing button A to connect when Billy Beale answered. She heard the coins fall into the box, and began to speak.

"Billy—Billy—it's me."

"Where are you, miss? I thought you'd be here by the time I got back to the office."

"I'm at the station—it's important business, Billy. I'll be back on Friday afternoon, I would imagine, though probably going straight to Chelstone. Look, I've not got long, but I want you to do something for me. I want you to find out everything you can about Freddie Hackett's father."

"His dad?"

"Yes, that's right. We know Arthur Hackett is a drinker, and we both think Freddie gets the sharp end of his temper when the man is in his cups—and Freddie is fiercely protective of his mother and sister. But I paid a visit to his mother today, and if a photo in their kitchen is anything to go by, Hackett has an obvious scar on his face. I'd like to know more about his history—even military history, and I'd really like to know where he got that scar. If you can sniff around and ask some questions of Freddie's teacher—pay a visit in confidence just as if you were checking up on him, making sure he's all right—that might give us something to go on too."

"She already knows me, miss, from when I took Freddie back to the school, so that'll be easy. I know what to do."

"Good. And one more thing—very much on the q.t.—find out from one of your newspaper friends what he knows about the French in London. And I don't mean ordinary refugees—but military. Free French and anything else he knows about, say, French civil servants in London. I can get official information from MacFarlane, but I'd like to have any other snippets that come to the surface."

"Right you are, miss. Consider it all done. I've written my report for the day—about the new clients."

"I'll try to telephone tomorrow, Billy. Can't promise though."

"I'll be coming back down to the village on Friday. I miss my girls."

"I'm sure they miss you, too. Perhaps you and I can have a chat on Sunday." Maisie looked at the station clock. "Ooops, got to dash, Billy. Talk to you tomorrow, I hope."

Maisie picked up her case and ran toward the platform for the train soon to leave London for Edinburgh's Waverley Station. Once aboard, Maisie was shown to her berth. Having stowed her suitcase in the luggage rack above the bed, Maisie loosened her jacket and took off her hat. She ran her fingers through her hair and shook her head. In another few minutes she would hear the guard's whistle and the train would begin to move. Soon enough the steward would come to check the blackout curtains were in place. At the front of the train, the locomotive would have a canopy across the engine that was required to be fitted onto all trains now, so that after dark sparks from the furnace would not be visible from the air, marking it as a target for any Luftwaffe pilot looking for an opportunity to add another notch to his Messerschmitt's tail.

She slumped back in her seat and closed her eyes. The words had tumbled from her mouth without thought. *I think I've had enough.* But had she? What would she do all day if she were to pass the business to Billy and return to Chelstone full time? Anna was in school from nine until almost four, and for her part she knew she wasn't the sort to idle away her days.

When the war was over, it might all be different—she might buy a house in London, a larger property but still near Priscilla. She would enroll Anna in school nearby, and make sure she was there to collect her daughter every single day when the school bell rang at four o'clock. But she had Frankie and Brenda to think about. Her father was over eighty years of age, and though he claimed to be "as fit as a fiddle," she had noticed the little things—the half-stumble here, a comment not heard there, a recent conversation forgotten. And now she had a job where the driver of a motor car sent to collect her had to be someone who could protect her if it became necessary, and perhaps even kill to do so.

CHAPTER 6

Despite the fact that it was wartime, there remained a certain pride of place evident in the dining carriage, a sense that standards were there to be maintained even at the worst of times. Comfortable seats, crisp white linens, and table napkins folded flute-like in the center of cutlery positioned just so were a hallmark of the service expected by the well-to-do traveler. Fortunately, the clackety-clack, clackety-clack of wheels on rails rendered private conversation inaudible to fellow diners.

"According to the notes I received, we have twelve recruits all told. Who else will be there?" Maisie lifted her spoon and immersed it into a bowl of mulligatawny soup as she waited for MacFarlane's answer.

"Twelve British recruits, and we've a couple of Frenchies, an Algerian—or is he a Moroccan? Something like that. And a French Canadian."

"Won't there be a problem with the accent? I mean, the Canadian will probably sound as if he has a French version of a North American twang, compared to the locals. And the recruits from French North Africa have an accent—though I expect that's where they're going once trained." Maisie stirred the spoon around the edge of the steaming soup before lifting a spoonful to her lips.

MacFarlane ripped a piece of bread from the roll on his side plate, and shook his head. He answered while continuing to chew. "We've been through that—they've all passed muster as far as language is concerned, and as you know, our little bundle of tests in Scotland is to separate the wheat from the chaff. To see who's up to snuff and worth us putting in the time and effort training them to be heroes. And we've some others along for the ride too—including one from somewhere in French Indochina, plus a Belgian or two. By the way—"

"Yes, by the way," said Maisie, setting down her spoon. "I thought it was interesting that a certain Corporal Bright was sent to drive me to the station."

"She's a good lass, young Bright. Got some spirit about her."

"I know that."

"And don't read anything into the fact that you already know her. Oh, and while we're on the subject of women who are working for their country, I thought you would like to know that both Evernden and Jones are under orders to proceed to Hampshire, and they'll be across the Channel within a day or two. They're lucky—they're going out on Lysanders, so they won't be up there in a Halifax bomber with a parachute each." MacFarlane shuddered. "Brrrr—gives me the shivers. I could hop off an aircraft that's just landed and still moving a wee bit, but leaping out while it's a few hundred feet up in the air—I tell you, I take my hat off to every one of them."

Maisie felt a chill settle across her arms and around her shoulders. "I always said I would never ask anyone to do something I wouldn't be ready to do myself, but . . ." She shook her head. "But now more than ever, I feel as if I've pushed them into an abyss of terrible danger, and it's not only because I know them. I feel for their parents, their families, if . . . if the worst happens, they will never be allowed to know the truth." She bit her lip. "Perhaps it's being a mother . . ." She felt her words falter as she imagined Anna grown, and perhaps not knowing where she might be.

"Whether man or woman, they all know what they're doing, Maisie—if they go down, they know how it will be reported to the family."

"And that's the terrifying thing—Pascale and Elinor, for example, should be having the best days of their lives, but instead they're putting them on the line for us, and the moment they're in situ, if they're captured or killed, we're to deny all knowledge of them. They're on their own over there, and there's little we can do if they get into trouble." She paused, took another spoonful of soup, and pushed the bowl away.

"You'd better finish that, lassie—none of us is so full inside that we can turn away good food. There's people who'd be grateful for your leftovers."

"Sorry—you're right." She pulled back her bowl and took another spoonful of the cooling soup. "The fact that our hands are tied if their cover is blown, and they fall into the hands of the Gestapo—it's something I think about every time I have to assess whether a recruit is finally ready to be sent over there. And as I told you right at the beginning, when you came to me about this job, if I have reason not to pass someone for work in France or wherever they might be in line for, then you must give me your word that they will not be sent over." She paused to finish the soup. "But it's not just that. I don't like being so far away from Anna. I'll do the job I'm here to do—I'll watch the new recruits as you and the other instructors try to kill them to see what they're made of, and I'll interview them and write my reports, but please, I just can't be so far away from my daughter again."

"You've forgotten that at least two of the women we approved for departure last week have families, Maisie. They're doing what they're doing so their little ones don't grow up in a world led by an ugly fascist mob."

Maisie leaned back into her seat. "I know."

"Wouldn't you do the same for your child? Isn't that why you answered the call to duty, even though you hate every minute of it, as we all do?"

"I want Anna to live in a good world, Robbie. A better world."

"Aye, and with that I rest my case—oh at last, here come the lads with our pie. I thought the kitchen carriage had worked its way loose from the rest of the train and gone off down another line!"

Maisie thanked the steward who removed the soup bowls, while another served them plates of meat pie and mashed potato covered in gravy, and poured a healthy measure of red wine almost to the top of each glass.

MacFarlane touched her glass with his own before she had even reached for it. "That's what I like to see—a decent pour to the top of the glass. It won't be in there long enough to breathe."

"Robbie—what about Corporal Bright? Why did you send her to collect me? You knew very well our paths have crossed before—you've said as much, and I know for a fact that nothing much goes by you. I'm sorry to go on about it, but it seemed more than just a coincidence. I don't think you're being honest with me."

"Look, Maisie—I know her father, it's as simple as that. He's a sergeant over at a police station near the Elephant and Castle, so when he told me she'd finished her driver training with the ATS, I made some inquiries, pulled a few strings and snapped her up. She's my best driver—and for you, Maisie, only the best will do." He pointed to her meal, encouraging her to start. "Anyway, the fact that you knew her is, indeed, no more than a simple coincidence, so there's your honest answer. Now then, eat up, because I don't want to miss the pudding course, and if I leave it too late, it'll sit on my chest all night."

Maisie picked up her knife and fork and began to cut into the pie.

"Maurice always had something to say about coincidence, you know—he said coincidence is a messenger sent by truth."

"You've mentioned that before, Maisie, and not just once. You know as well as the next person—as well as the next detective—that in our business there are always coincidences. They settle like flies on dead meat in any investigation. Personally, if I look back on some of the useless alleys I've been led along while following a trail left by coincidences, I'd say they were dispatched by an evil little gnome bent on sending us off down the wrong line of inquiry." He scooped up a forkful of mashed potato, holding it above the plate as he continued. "Some of these so-called coincidences mean something, and some don't." He put down his knife to take a hefty gulp of wine. "Right, now that's out of the way, can we get stuck in to our dinner before it gets cold? And I want to talk to you about our plans for the next couple of days—we've got our work cut out for us. Oh, and one more thing—I've arranged for you to fly home. You'll be getting a lift on an RAF flight from Prestwick down to Biggin Hill. All being well, Corporal Bright will pick you up and take you straight to your country seat, Your Ladyship."

"That's enough of the title, Robbie. Mind you, I'd have been shocked if you hadn't pulled that out of your hat at least once over supper. But thank you for arranging the flight back—I appreciate it, much as I hate flying."

MacFarlane and Maisie were met at Waverley Station by a black motor car, though this time the driver was a soldier in the uniform of a Scottish regiment. The one-and-a-half-hour journey took them across a landscape she knew well from the months she had spent in Scotland during the years of her apprenticeship, when Maurice had arranged for her to train in the fundamentals of legal medicine so that she might deepen her knowledge of the fast-developing field of forensic science. While the vistas were different from those of the soft, undulating Kentish countryside, she had grown to love the beauty of Scotland, so the drive calmed growing feelings of conflict regarding her role with the Special Operations Executive. There was little conversation between MacFarlane and Maisie, and all too soon they arrived at a property that on her first visit she thought could pass as a fairy-tale castle if the country were not at war. The gray granite manor house with mullioned windows, small turrets near the roof and a round tower at each end would have seemed magical at any other time—and under any other circumstances.

The grounds were extensive, surrounded by rugged terrain that stretched for miles, with only one ancient bothy to be seen in the distance. The estate was the place where men and women recently recruited to join the Special Operations Executive came to be tested in every way imaginable and on every level—physical, emotional, moral, and spiritual. Only if they passed would they be sent for additional training and subsequently deployed to join a resistance group in Europe or—for just a few—Scandinavia. Most would be bound for France.

Maisie knew that both Pascale and Elinor had already endured the tests inflicted upon them, and they had passed every stage of scrutiny, even the terrible repeated rounds of sleep deprivation followed by interrogation. Had they not come through their trial by fire, she would not have been interviewing them prior to deployment. She knew very well that they could already be waiting in a different kind of manor house, a very English property in Hampshire where they would enjoy good food, fine wine and some laughs with others who had been readied for the same work, and they would sleep in comfortable beds—until one morning when they came down for breakfast and saw their names chalked on the board in the dining room, and knew that they were the next agents scheduled for departure. Maisie understood only too well that when the moment came, even if they had not experienced true fear before, then they would feel her tentacles reaching into the very center of their being. For a good agent, fear seemed to linger on a balance beam. If it was kept plumb in the center of the beam, fear would protect them; it would enhance their senses and alert them to danger. Fear could be an agent's greatest asset. But if fear increased and tipped the balance too far in one direction, then it could paralyze an agent, lead to ill-considered decisions, panic, and errors that might risk the lives of others and result in their own death. And if fear were diminished to a point of overconfidence, then they and an entire resistance line were as good as finished. Fear had to be handled with care, managed so it became a tool, not a weight.

Once the names were on the board, the clock was ticking. At nightfall the agents would be taken to an airfield nearby, where a senior member of the SOE would check their coat pockets and the labels in their clothing, just to make sure they hadn't left anything about their person that would identify them as British. A French lipstick might be slipped into a woman's handbag, or a bus ticket from a local French town for a man, or a pen sold only in France. The agent would wish them luck, and they would need every scrap of good fortune if they were to survive even the landing in a French field, where they would be hurried away by locals working for the Resistance before the Gestapo even knew they were there—if that luck had crossed the Channel with them. Despite the company, and despite the honor among those they would work with on acts of sabotage and murder, from the time they boarded the aircraft, they were on their own. As soon as they saw their name on the board in the dining room of the genteel country manor house, each agent began to balance the fear inside them. It was a delicate dance with fate.

Upstairs in her assigned room Maisie inspected the door lock, followed by the window latches. She took a moment to breathe in fresh air through the open window and look at the land beyond. Her quarters for the next two nights enjoyed a view across the craggy landscape, and she could even distinguish the bothy in the distance. Moving away from the window, she checked under the bed and in the wardrobe, the first steps in her complete sweep of the room. She had conducted a search on her two previous visits to the house, though she was not sure what she was looking for—perhaps a means of listening to her conversation, even though no one else came to the room and there was no personal telephone. Or there could be a tool for keeping a log of when she entered and exited the room. She would know when she found something amiss. Light fixtures and the two table lamps were checked. She knelt down to look under the desk, then stood up and pulled out each of the drawers. Nothing. She tapped the wooden cladding on the walls and even removed books from shelves situated to the right of the door—a secret means of entering a room would not be unusual in such an old house. Every wire was examined, every inch of carpet scrutinized, until Maisie was satisfied that there was nothing in the room to concern her. Not today anyway.

Now she had something else to attend to, something personal. A matter of the heart. She had resisted opening the package from Mark Scott while on the train. She had picked it up, turned it over and held it, but she wanted to wait until she was in a room and not ensconced in a railway carriage at night. She wanted to have something good to look forward to, prolonging the frisson of excitement she had felt from the moment the parcel had been handed to her, a sweet anticipation she wanted to draw out for as long as she could.

She unlocked her suitcase, moved clothing aside and drew out the brown-paper-wrapped package. Sitting on her bed, she turned it over. Taking a deep breath, she worked the knotted string free, slid her finger under the seal and pulled away the paper to reveal a plain black cardboard box, also sealed. She felt her heart beat faster as she opened the box, exposing tissue paper and a deep blue velvet presentation case tied with a purple ribbon. She held her breath for a few seconds and with care untied the ribbon and put it aside before lifting the lid.

The single diamond on a gold chain caught the light and took her breath away. It was not an ostentatious gift, not a huge stone meant to impress, but an elegant, graceful cut. A card had been slipped under the delicate chain.

"I cannot wait to be with you again—and soon. With love, Mark."

With love?

Did those words have meaning for Mark Scott? Or was it just a line that people used—and perhaps even more so when it felt as if affection had begun to evaporate? Maisie read the message again. And again. Holding on to the velvet box with the diamond necklace inside, she walked to the window and gazed across the land before her, resting her eyes on the swathe of green hills in the distance. Mark wasn't the sort of person to say words he didn't mean. If this were so, it meant she was loved by the man she had come to love in return. Now what were they to do? They were two people from different worlds, not so young any more, and she with a daughter to consider—a child she had vowed to put before everything else. Everything. But in a time of war "everything" seemed to take on a different hue, and keeping loved ones safe meant sacrifices had to be made. Men and women had died making that sacrifice in the hope that their children might live in a free world.

Maisie felt the fear settling in as if a great weight had taken up residence in the very center of her being and was working its way through her body. She struggled to hold the flood of emotions steady, knowing that what Gabriella Hunter had called "irrational reasoning" could so easily grow, filling her with an invasive, debilitating dread—a dread that had the power to lead her onto a path filled with errors. And perhaps more than anyone, she knew that the movement of fear along the balance beam could happen so fast. She closed her eyes, in that moment wishing she could wave a magic wand and have Maurice be right there in the room with her—that she could fall to her knees and say, "Tell me what to do. Tell me how I can be all the things I want to be. Please tell me now, how I can be with those I love and still, then, be of service?" What would Maurice say in return?

She set the deep blue box with the diamond necklace on the bed and delved into her shoulder bag to find a letter she kept tucked away in a pocket. It had been with her for years, the folds breaking apart where she had read and reread the message inside whenever she was assailed by doubt. She kept it close because she never knew when she might need to return to it, skimming over whole sentences to land on words that might guide her at a given moment.

Years ago, before he died, Maurice had written, "We have spoken on many an occasion, you and I, of the darkness I fear will envelop Europe once again." As she read words she could quote by heart, she felt the presence of her beloved mentor. ". . . You will be called to service . . ." She lingered on the sentence that always made her feel as if Maurice had laid a hand upon her shoulder to fortify her spirit: "I have great faith in your ability to assume challenges that stand between you and the quest for what is right and true."

But what is right and true now, at this very moment, Maurice?

Maisie bit her lip, folded the worn piece of paper, and slipped it back into the envelope. She returned it to her bag, then reached for the blue velvet case once more. Before removing the gift, she unclasped another chain, one she had worn for several years now. It held the wedding ring James Compton had slipped onto her finger the day she became his wife; she had removed the ring from her finger and worn it in this way from the day she accepted that she was a widow. She felt the chain loosen and caught the ring in her palm, studying it for some seconds before she unpinned the diamond necklace and removed it from its moorings before slipping the ring and chain into its place and closing the blue box.

Standing before the dressing table mirror, she unlocked the clasp and fastened the necklace, touching the stone as it came to rest just below her throat's hollow. She closed her eyes, then opened them to gaze at her reflection. Still with her fingertips on the stone she whispered, "With love," and waited to see if fear began to move away, and so relinquish its grip on her heart.

Checking the time, Maisie quickly changed into clothing more suited to walking across the hills—a pair of corduroy trousers, a roll-neck pullover, tweed jacket and sturdy brown leather shoes. There was no rain, so she would not need the rubber boots she had thrown into the suitcase at the last minute. Casting another glance at the afternoon's itinerary, she saw that following lunch there would be a walk with MacFarlane to inspect several points the recruits were to reach during the orienteering part of the induction, and review the challenges they would have to overcome. Once they returned to the manor house, she would have an hour to read the applicant biographies before her interviews were due to begin.

Maisie realized she was hungry. Before she met MacFarlane in the instructors' dining room, though, she needed to place a call. There was a telephone with a secure line in a small room adjacent to the instructors' mess.

"Priscilla? Priscilla, I need a favor."

"What on earth are you whispering for?" Just the sound of her friend's voice drained some of the tension from Maisie's shoulders. "You sound as if you're in a crypt. And where are you anyway?"

"Let's just say 'crypt' isn't far off. Look, I haven't long to chat, but I wonder if you could go over to the Dower House and see Dad, Brenda and Anna—I'm worried about Anna, and—"

"I'll do it. Right now." Maisie heard the unmistakable sound of Priscilla opening and closing her cigarette case, followed by the flick and snap of her lighter. "What's happened?"

"Emma is not well—apparently Dad has said it's her time and she'll probably have passed away in the next couple of days. And Pris, I'm not able to come home at the moment—I'm not due until Friday afternoon, so I'll be there for the gymkhana."

"Oh dear—Anna will be crushed when that dog goes. I'll get over there straightaway—see what Auntie Pris can do." There was a second's pause as Priscilla drew on her cigarette. "And speaking of being an aunt—you haven't heard from my niece, have you? I know she's living the life we all lived at that age, and hopefully keeping away from men in uniform, but I haven't heard from her in days. She's been very elusive for a long time."

Maisie closed her eyes as she prepared the lie. "I haven't seen her, actually—and if she's anything like Aunt Priscilla, you won't be hearing from her either! Of course, there is that translation job she's been very excited about, so I would imagine she's rather busy."

"Hmmm, takes after her father—he was always one to keep secrets. I couldn't keep anything quiet to save my life, yet as we know, my brother was a mystery unto himself. Even as a child you never knew what he was up to." She cleared her throat, and coughed.

"Didn't the doctor tell you to give up the cigarettes before your next operation? It will be the last, Pris, so you should really make the effort—smoking and going under anesthetic do not work together. You might as well get your lungs in good order now."

"I know, Nurse Maisie, I know . . . I'm stubbing it out. Hear that? Anyway, look, only one other piece of news—well, two. No three. First of all, we heard from Tim, and he seems to have settled in at university. Thank heavens for that! Now of course we don't really need to live in the cottage—we only came to be in the country while Tim was recovering from the amputation. God, doesn't Dunkirk seem like years ago? I think we'll go back to London at some point, but of course Tarquin has completely thrown any further schooling out of the window and loves working with the forestry people. I have a conscientious objector for a youngest son! Perhaps one day he'll study horticulture or something and become famous like Gertrude Jekyll. Finally, number three on the list. Speaking of my operation, there's a slight change in the date—it's now on the cards for December the eighth, a Monday. Expect to bring me a generous gin and tonic on the ninth."

Maisie laughed. "And knowing your doctor, he'll allow it!"

"McIndoe is a terrific chap—he's done a wonderful job on me so far. If I comb my hair just so, you might never know I had to be dragged from a burning house and left half the skin from my face on a fiery fallen roof beam!"

Maisie heard voices as the instructors gathered for preprandial drinks in the mess next door. "I've got to go now, Pris. I'll try to telephone later."

"I'll have a full report for you. Don't worry—if anyone can cheer up your darling child, it's her Auntie Pris!"

Maisie replaced the telephone in its cradle and left to join the other instructors in the mess. As was so often the case, she was the only woman in the company of men.

"Ah, there she is!" MacFarlane beckoned to her. "Maisie, let me introduce you—"

Maisie smiled, ready to greet a man who was a good three inches taller than MacFarlane.

"Major André Chaput—he's here for a couple of days and he likes a wee dram, good man that he is." MacFarlane moved aside as Major Chaput extended his right hand toward Maisie.

Revealing not a second's hesitation, Maisie was quick to disguise a tremor of shock as she looked up to greet the major and registered his face. She took the major's hand and spoke to him in French.

"Talented woman, our Miss Dobbs," said MacFarlane, laughing. "And when it comes to knowing what's going on upstairs"—he tapped the side of his head, a favorite gesture—"there's none to beat her."

"Is that so?" said the Frenchman, addressing them in almost unaccented English. "Then I shall have to watch what I say."

"Not to worry, Major—I'm only here to put our recruits under the microscope." Maisie stole a glance at the major's knuckles, where there was the merest hint of rough skin. She could hear Freddie Hackett's words echoing in her mind. *If you wear one of those, it leaves marks right across there . . . you can always tell when a bloke's had one of them on.*

As MacFarlane changed the subject to the weather forecast the following day, Maisie feigned interest, agreeing with his comment on the cloud formation before excusing herself to speak to another instructor she had met on a previous occasion. She looked back only once at the French major, who at that very moment was staring in her direction. Without doubt, the tall man with an officer's bearing might have warranted a second look in any milieu. The combination of pale blue-gray eyes—not unlike Freddie Hackett's—and dark hair slicked back in waves rendered him film-star handsome. At this very moment she didn't want to believe in coincidence, or entertain the possibility that she had just greeted a man who seemed to reflect the image she had held in her mind's eye from the moment Freddie Hackett had described witnessing a murder and delivering an envelope to a man he believed was the killer. Yes, she had to admit she was tired, more than a little at odds with herself and the work she was starting to detest—and couldn't those conflicting emotions conspire, leading to the dreaded irrational reasoning? Given her mood, she could be a prime candidate for it.

Such personal observations aside, it was the deep ridges on either side of Chaput's face that gave Maisie pause, and the small patch of paler skin just below his right eye. Try as she might, she could not help herself wondering at what speed those eyes might become cold, or the inquiring stare a threat.

CHAPTER 7

Maisie and MacFarlane set off across extensive lawns surrounding the Scottish manor until they reached a rustic gate. Magenta azaleas flanked the lawns, along with purple smoke trees and rich conifers. Ivy climbed the walls of the house, a deep green against granite that seemed to sparkle in the autumn sunshine. MacFarlane stepped forward, lifting the latch so Maisie could proceed before him, then picked up a path that led out through mixed woodland to the hills beyond.

Consulting the map she had carried with her, Maisie pointed into the distance. "So the recruits will exit here where we're standing and then make their way toward that rough crag over there."

"That's the first stop," said MacFarlane. "We'll stagger their departure, and this time they go alone."

"And they each have a different set of instructions?"

"More or less, though we give them a chance to cross paths, as we did the last time we were here. We'll find out what they do when they meet one another during their quest—will they ignore each other or say a few words and be on their way? Or will they exchange notes on what they're doing, which isn't allowed? We have people watching, looking for traits such as misplaced trust, fear, hesitancy—too much time spent lingering, and a lack of imagination or anticipation. As before, we're weeding out foolhardiness, though we want to see a certain spirit and an ability to overcome challenges we put before them—but there's always a middle ground."

Maisie nodded. "And where do you want me to wait?"

MacFarlane leaned toward Maisie and pointed to the map. "You'll have to leave the path here, then pass that bothy before continuing on to a stand of firs here. You'll find an old hide in that spot, so linger there and complete your observation record."

"Where will you be?"

"Waiting for them here." He pointed to a spot on the map. "We have . . . what did we call them last time? Obstacles. We have obstacles at each of these points, whether it's geographical or something else to push a few buttons upstairs." He tapped the side of his head once again. "Nothing like pushing those mental buttons, is there? They think they're going on a nice little Scottish ramble, but if they're not shaking in their boots by the time they get back, I want to know where we went wrong. I want to see an ability to overcome, to get on the right track again—in more ways than one—and I don't want to see over-confidence." He looked at his watch. "Want to take a nice little ramble now—before your interviews? It's been a long day already, Maisie, and I for one don't like waking up early on a train and then having to race out here as if I'm fresh as a daisy. It's a wonder I didn't drop off into my haggis at lunchtime, so I thought we could both do with a bit of fresh air to get the blood going again."

"Just a short walk then, Robbie—I want to go through my interview strategy one more time before we start."

"Strategy?" MacFarlane shook his head. "Strategy. Now there's a word. I wish there was a bit more strategy somewhere in this bloody war. Sometimes I think no one knows what they're really doing and we're all just winging it." He sighed. "Anyway—come on. Twenty minutes of this country air, and we'll be set up for what's left of the day."

He began walking, and Maisie fell into step beside him. "One thing I'd like to know, Maisie—what was all that about, in the dining room? I saw you give the Frenchie major an old-fashioned look. I've seen you do that a few times over the years, hen—what's on your mind?"

"His face is on my mind, Robbie."

"Taken a fancy to him, have you, Maisie?"

Maisie stopped and looked up at her tall, heavy-set companion. "What on earth are you talking about? For goodness' sake, Robbie—it's his whole physiognomy." She ran a finger down each side of her face. "If young Freddie Hackett, the messenger boy, had drawn a picture of the perpetrator of the crime he witnessed, or taken a photograph, the image would have been a dead ringer for Major Chaput. Right down to those lines on his face and that small white blemish under his right eye." She shook her head. "Oh, and I had a quick look at his knuckles after we shook hands—he has healing abrasions that could be from using a knuckle-duster."

MacFarlane seemed nonplussed, as if trying to picture the Frenchman, but then he began to laugh. "I'm going to put this ridiculous behavior down to battle fatigue, Maisie. For a start there was no blemish that I could see—perhaps just a bit of slightly whiter skin—and those lines are what Chaput's mother and father bestowed upon him. Mind you, he does have a touch of Victor Mature about him."

"Robbie, you know very well that an almost exact description of a suspect is a rare thing—usually there's something off somewhere, but not in this case. I can't believe you're ignoring me."

MacFarlane stopped walking and raised his hand. "Stop right there. Stop. Maisie, this is not like you, and if you continue I will have you pulled off this round of recruitment testing. And I mean what I say. As soon as I heard about the boy's claim, I spoke to Caldwell. I've had a word with Larkin too, and Freddie Hackett is a boy with a lot on his shoulders—and that's in addition to the load he carries for us, running through the streets. Even a touch of fear can lead to seeing things, Maisie, especially for children. Oh, and according to Larkin, the only treat he gets is the odd hour on an occasional Saturday at the picture house when his dad is still in the pub—the boy loves the flicks, especially a good old scary picture." He ran a hand across his balding head. "There has been no body found—apart from the bloke you saw dragged out of the drink—and there's no proof it was the same fellow Hackett thinks he saw killed. That one probably met his end in a fight outside a pub somewhere. There's no evidence of murder, even with you going back to where it was supposed to have happened and sniffing around with your Mr. Beale. There's absolutely nothing to indicate a crime has taken place, and there's nothing—nothing—anyone can do about it. In fact, the best anyone can do for Freddie Hackett is to give him an extra couple of bob for his mum when he comes trotting along with a message—which is what we all try to do." He placed a hand on Maisie's shoulder. "But I can't have you imagining things that aren't there, Maisie—not now, not when so much is at stake. I need you and that quick mind of yours on the job right here."

"I believe the boy, Robbie—and I also have my doubts about Major Chaput. If it were not for the almost spot-on descrip—"

MacFarlane was quick with his interruption. "Then you've given me no choice. I'm sending you back. I can't have you here sniffing around a senior representative of an allied intelligence section. I'm pulling you off the afternoon's interviews, and you won't be observing tomorrow's testing. I'll have a motor car here within the hour—you can go straight to Prestwick and from there to Biggin Hill and home. If there's no flight going down, you'll be put up in a local hotel until to-morrow morning. It will all be arranged as a matter of urgency, and I'll explain your absence as having to do with an alternative assignment.

Sounds better than a family matter, because we've all got family matters, haven't we?"

Maisie shrugged. "Suits me, Robbie. I detest this work anyway." She began to walk away, a sick feeling beginning to roll in her stomach. She knew she was acting as if she were a stubborn girl of fifteen.

"So much for doing your bit, eh?"

Maisie turned to MacFarlane. "Don't you dare—you know better, Robbie MacFarlane. I've done my bit, as you well know. I did my bit in France when I was seventeen." She lifted her hair to reveal the fading scar at the back of her neck, and let it fall again. "And ever since the last war I've been doing my bit, every single day." She held up her hands, fingers splayed, knuckles toward MacFarlane, streaks of thick white tissue still evident. "And those scars on the back of my hands are from the flames that seared my skin while I was trying to help Priscilla, who was doing *her* bit by saving two children from a burning house. And you know what my next *bit* will be? My next bit will be the well-being of my daughter, who comes before absolutely everything else. Oh—and I'll be finding out the truth about Freddie Hackett— that's a very big bit that I'm intent upon sorting out."

MacFarlane stared at Maisie. "Freddie Hackett, well, god bless his cotton socks—perhaps that's a case for children being seen and not heard."

Maisie felt the heat rush through her. "Don't goad me, MacFarlane, just don't, because I will tell you right now that any children crossing my path will always be seen *and* heard—and until I have evidence to the contrary, I'll err toward believing them. I'm surprised you would not take the same action."

"Temper, temper, Maisie! I wonder what the great Dr. Maurice Blanche would say about that little outburst."

"And please don't bring Maurice into this—don't you dare! Not only would Maurice have given me leave to make my own decisions, but he wouldn't have countered my observations in the first place. He might have asked me a few more questions, possibly to sharpen my surveillance skills, and he might have guided me toward another conclusion—my conclusion—but he . . . he . . . he would never have discounted me. Ever."

"One thing, Maisie. You may be going back, but you're not off the hook. You've signed papers. You agreed to a certain task on behalf of your country, and you still report to me. I'll be in touch."

She turned and walked away from MacFarlane, wondering how it had come to this; how a peaceful stroll along a rustic path in the wilds of Scotland had fast become a shouting match. Yet in one respect, and one only, she knew MacFarlane was right. Her lack of confidence in a representative of an allied intelligence section meant that she should relinquish her duties. But there was another question lingering in the back of her mind. Had she pushed MacFarlane deliberately? Might she have deliberately put MacFarlane in the position of dismissing her, because she wanted to go home?

As she crossed the lawns at a brisk clip, making her way toward the carriage sweep that led to the manor's front entrance, she remembered something that Maurice had pointed out many years before. It was to the effect that sometimes the mind takes the initiative without fore-thought, as does the body. The two might function in this way alone or in concert, and why they do it is simple—they are interceding to protect the heart.

There was no official aeroplane departing until the following morn-ing, Thursday, so after a sleepless night in a guesthouse arranged by one of MacFarlane's staff, Maisie was taken to the aerodrome at

Prestwick early to board a Halifax bomber routed to Biggin Hill. There was no comfort on the aircraft, just a hard jump seat and a bumpy journey in weather that had become even more changeable; her legs almost gave way after the Halifax landed and steps were brought to the door for her to disembark. A motor car was idling, waiting for her on the tarmac, and as soon as she began to walk away from the aircraft Charlie Bright stepped out of the motor car and opened the passenger door. She stood to attention and saluted as Maisie approached.

"Good morning, ma'am. Nice to see you again, Miss Dobbs. Should be an easy run down to Chelstone, and it's a lovely morning for it now the weather's cleared up again."

"Thank you, Corporal Bright," said Maisie. "Do you know the way?"

"A bit of help when we reach the village would be handy, thank you, ma'am."

Maisie was grateful the driver seemed to sense her need for a quiet journey and did not endeavor to make conversation, though she asked for more specific directions after they had passed through Tonbridge and were close to Chelstone. Soon they were driving through the village, followed by the gates leading to Chelstone Manor.

"It's this house on the left," said Maisie. "You can pull in to that approach to the back of the house."

"It's a smashing house, ma'am—my dad would love those roses around the door. His are all gone by now," said Bright. "And who lives in that whopping great manor house over there?"

"My late husband's parents live at Chelstone Manor. This is the Dower House—I was fortunate to inherit it from a . . . from a very dear friend and teacher."

"Blimey—I couldn't imagine being friends with any of my teachers." Bright drew the motor car to a halt. "There's your welcoming committee—what a beautiful little girl. Is she yours?"

Maisie smiled, a rush of pride filling her heart. "Yes—that's my daughter, Anna." Without waiting for Corporal Bright, Maisie unlocked the passenger door and opened her arms as Anna ran to her.

"Mummy, Mummy, Mummy—you're home, home, home! Poor, poor, poor Emma . . ."

"Yes, I'm home, my darling." Maisie enfolded her daughter in an embrace, then let her slip to the ground. "Come on, this lady has to be on her way again, so help me with my bag." She watched Anna return to the kitchen carrying her shoulder bag while she collected her overnight case and waved to Brenda, who was at the door. "Would you like a cup of tea before you go?" asked Maisie, turning to Corporal Bright.

"Thank you for the offer, ma'am, but I've to be on my way." Bright consulted her watch. "Got to get back to London—picking up Mr. MacFarlane at another aerodrome actually." She put her hand to her mouth. "Oh dear, shouldn't have said that."

"Not to worry." Maisie noticed Bright's frown. "What is it, Corporal Bright?"

"It just that the orders are a bit creepy—you know, Mr. MacFarlane coming back early as well as you, and I've to pick him up with the mortuary van following behind me." Bright stopped speaking, stared at Maisie and shook her head. "Oh blimey—I've done it now. You didn't know about the mortuary van, did you?"

Maisie held up her hand. "As I said, not to worry. I'll be speaking to him later today."

"Sorry, ma'am. It's not like me to make a slip like that . . . I assumed—"

"Just don't do it again, and you'll be all right. No need to make a confession to Mr. MacFarlane. Have a safe journey back."

Bright saluted again. "Thank you, ma'am."

"And please—Corporal Bright, there really is no need to salute. I am not in uniform, so it's quite unnecessary."

Maisie watched as the white-faced ATS driver reversed her vehicle back onto the driveway, then turned toward the gate and the main road, on her way to collect Robert MacFarlane, who, it appeared, was accompanying a body back to London.

M aisie sat in the conservatory with Anna and Emma, the old Alsatian Maisie had rescued following the brutal murder of her owner two years previously. Anna and Emma had become inseparable, the dog accompanying her charge to school every day, and waiting by the gate for her return. As Emma's breathing began to falter, Anna lay beside her, her arms around the dog as her life ebbed away. Maisie lifted the weeping child, while her father knelt down to wrap the animal in a white sheet. With her daughter's little body tight against her own as she sobbed, Maisie felt the pain of loss leach into her heart, and gave thanks for the argument that had brought her home to her family sooner than planned.

The following morning, Maisie, Anna, Brenda and Priscilla stood alongside the grave Frankie Dobbs had prepared for his granddaughter's beloved dog. It neighbored the place where he had laid his own dog, Jook, at the turn of the year. As he lowered Emma into the ground using the sheet and allowed it to fall across her body, Anna threw handfuls of petals from late-blooming roses onto the white linen, calling to Emma that she was the very best dog in the world and it was good that she had company because she was now with Jook and they could play together in the fields. With the impromptu funeral service complete and the grave filled in, a rosebush that promised scarlet blooms, come summer, was planted atop the grave according to Anna's wishes—

she had stipulated that the roses had to be a different color from those that would bud and open again next year on Jook's grave.

"I'll put the kettle on for a nice cup of coffee," said Brenda. "And I've made some Eccles cakes—a treat for all of us, to celebrate old Emma's life."

"I'm going with Grandad to see Lady before it rains again," said Anna. "Grandad says a job of work is what we need, so we're going to do a job."

Frankie winked at Maisie, then ruffled his granddaughter's hair. "All right, love. Have you decided about the show? What do you think about riding Lady?"

Anna shook her head. "I want to stay here, with you. And Lady's sad about Emma, so she doesn't want to go either."

"I think that's a good idea, Anna—we can all stay at home and tell stories about Emma if you like. Come back for something to drink soon, when you and Grandad have done your jobs." Maisie watched as Anna took Frankie's hand and they walked away in the direction of the stables.

"That child scares me at times," said Priscilla. "She's upset, grieving, and she's shed her tears, but she takes it all in her stride. I had a complete tantrum when I was that age and my dog died."

"It's a sad thing, when your child knows how to deal with death—but she's had practice. And she will feel Emma with her."

"That's what worries me," said Priscilla. "The thought of some ghostly canine roaming the house—brrrr, it gives me the shivers. Anyway, shall we get that cup of coffee? And look—I didn't bring any gaspers with me. I'm taking your advice and giving up filling my lungs with smoke . . . well, inasmuch as I can."

Maisie smiled and shook her head in mock disbelief. She consulted her watch as they arrived at the kitchen, knowing that in all likelihood it was only a matter of time before the telephone started ringing and MacFarlane was shouting down the line from a mortuary somewhere in London. She wanted to speak to Billy first, so as soon as Priscilla left the house, she went straight to the privacy of the library.

B illy—hello."

"Miss—you're back a bit early. Thought you wouldn't be home until Friday."

"Change of plan, Billy."

"How's the littl'un? I heard from Doreen that the dog was on its last."

"Emma died last night, but Anna is taking it as well as can be expected. She planned a little funeral, so that helped her—and now she's with Dad. He's lined up some jobs for her."

"Bit of work never hurt anyone. Anyway, I've got some information on Freddie Hackett's father, miss. Not a lot, because I could do with more time."

"Have you heard from Freddie?"

"Only once, from a telephone box yesterday. He sounded all right, but I was going to wander over to the school today, catch him and have a word as he's leaving."

"Not a bad idea—but be careful. You don't want his friends seeing you."

"Reckon most of his friends are still evacuated. There's not a lot of kids in that school."

"So what did you find out?"

"Arthur Hackett, the father, was in the East Surrey Regiment in the last war. He was at Plugstreet Wood, then copped a Blighty a bit later on, but had a shock when they sent him back to join another regiment after he'd recovered—he thought he was out of the army and the war for good. He had some attitude about it, by all accounts. Got a temper on him too—he had a fight with an Australian while in the field hospital, then went for another bloke too. Poor soul survived a shelling and was almost killed by Hackett."

"I saw both sides when I was a nurse, Billy—most of the men just did their best to help each other out, but there were some who carried the weight of their wounding in anger."

"Yeah, but I went a bit deeper and it turns out he's got previous as long as your arm. Was discharged from prison early in the war because they needed more men in uniform—but you'd have found it hard to come across a nastier piece of work than Arthur Hackett, and we've seen some in this business. He'd been sent down for robbery with intent to kill, plus he even attacked a copper when apprehended for another job. Had a little gang, but seems even they didn't like him. I'm still chasing down some contacts. I might have some more tomorrow, but there's a lot of information missing. Apparently the army records office was bombed a few weeks ago, and they're saying that loads of files are gone forever, some are now incomplete and they're lucky to have collected as many pages as they did before taking them all to new premises. I tell you, it's a right mess."

Maisie was thoughtful. "How on earth did that sort of man meet a nice woman like Freddie's mum?"

"Young girl meets war hero. He probably spun a tale and that scar told a story, though I bet it was the wrong one. He might have got that on a job and not over there in France. She falls for him—and we know a lot of these wide boys have the gift of the gab. And then there's the other thing to consider—there weren't a lot of blokes around of the marrying age, so when he asks, she says yes. I've got to confirm this, but apparently she comes from a better sort of family—not wealthy, or anything like that, but good, solid working people. He rubbed them up the wrong way soon after the wedding and now they can't abide him, plus her mum and dad were killed in an air raid. Her brothers would like to see more of her, but Hackett apparently doesn't let her see her own family. And look at the place they live in. I mean, me and Doreen didn't have much when we were in the East End, but my family were never in a grotty old back double. Anyway, I managed to talk to her older brother, who said that she's welcome back into the fold any time, but she's loyal to her husband."

"It's not an unusual story, Billy—as we know only too well. When men cut off a family, it means trouble." Maisie began to thread the telephone cord through her fingers.

"You still there, miss?"

"Sorry, Billy—I was just thinking." She shook her hand so the cord dropped away. "Look, I'm going to be back at the office on Monday morning. I have a feeling I'll be provided with some information shortly that will help us with Freddie's murder case."

"Find out something, did you?"

"It's what I might be on the verge of finding out that could add to our evidence, such as it is."

"Blimey, miss, that sounds important."

"I hope so, Billy. I hope so."

As Maisie was helping Brenda prepare a late lunch, the telephone began to ring.

"That'll be for you, Maisie."

"And I bet I know who it is!"

Brenda tut-tutted and shook her head. "That telephone hardly rings when you're not here. Just like it was with Dr. Blanche. When he was away in London, it was quiet unless it was him to let me know when he'd be back. But as soon as he was home, off it went, nonstop, all hours of the day and sometimes the night. No peace for you people."

Maisie laughed as she walked away toward the library.

"Hello Robbie," said Maisie as she picked up the receiver and put it to her ear.

"You just took the wind out of my sails. How did you know . . . oh never mind. There's been a development."

"What sort of development?" asked Maisie, taking care to keep her voice even.

"One of our recruits suffered a fatal fall during the first of the outdoor exercises, not long after your departure."

"A fatal fall? And why is that any of my business, Robbie?"

"You know very well why it's your business, Maisie. Come on, it's time to put our little row behind us."

Maisie allowed a few seconds of silence to pass before speaking. "Who is the dead man?"

"One of the French bods. A bit older than the others, so probably that was something to do with it. And before you ask, Major Chaput was in the library. We've witnesses to his presence."

"Who were the witnesses?"

There was another silence on the line, this time from MacFarlane.

"Robbie, it's not like you to go quiet on me. Who were the witnesses?"

"The Algerian and a French Canadian."

Maisie nodded, as if MacFarlane had been in the room with her. "Do you want me to say the obvious, or will you spell it out for me?"

"He's in the clear, Maisie."

"I don't doubt he is. But who is he really? And what about the little coterie around him—his witnesses, the Algerian and French Canadian? They're not with us, but they're sharing our training and they're out there with our recruits."

"The French are our allies, Maisie, and they're in a rough spot. We're not an occupied country with the bloody Nazis marching down our streets, though god knows it could happen any day—so we've got to help them any way we can. We're putting our people into their country to help lead their resistance, so it stands to reason they want their own agents going in too. We do the best we can to get the job done in collaboration. It's a fair arrangement all round."

"It wasn't a fair arrangement for the dead French agent, was it?"

MacFarlane's sigh was audible. "We're back to work on Monday, Maisie. I may have dismissed you on grounds that you have a conflict of interest between your work for one of your so-called customers and your country, but don't forget I still have a piece of paper attesting to the fact that you are under my orders."

"So you reminded me in Scotland. All right, Monday morning it is, Robbie. I'll be there at eleven and no sooner. I'm coming up from Chelstone, on the train."

"Go straight to the mortuary in Victoria."

The line was disconnected. Maisie replaced the receiver and sat for a moment, thinking, before leaving the library to return to the kitchen.

"I've put the kettle on, Maisie," said Brenda. "Let's have a nice cup of tea before your father comes back again with Anna. I've been meaning to ask you about that lovely necklace—I've not seen you wearing it before." She raised an eyebrow. "Mind you, it'd be nice to see that stone in a ring."

CHAPTER 8

"Maisie! Hello, darling!" Priscilla tossed her cigarette onto the rails as she walked along the platform, and upon reaching Maisie, leaned forward to kiss her on the cheek. "I should have let you know I'd be taking the same train up to town, but I only decided last night—it's a spot of luck though, isn't it? We'll have time for a nice long chat," said Priscilla.

Maisie smiled, glad to have her friend's company—she was becoming tired of her own thoughts, which had been circling time and again around the question of Freddie Hackett and what he might have seen, or thought he had seen, on the night a man was murdered. "Bored with being in the country, are you, Priscilla?"

"Bored with myself, actually." Priscilla sighed. "Douglas loves working at the cottage, with perhaps just the odd journey up to town to see the bods at the ministry to discuss his next story about the war, or to talk to his editor about the new book." Douglas, Priscilla's husband, had been assigned to work for the Ministry of Information for the war's duration. "But now I'm feeling better—and more to the point, relieved that Tim is doing well—as well as can be expected anyway. Now I just have to get back to civilization a bit more often. I've tried gardening, tried watercolor painting and I've even tried to cook, all to no avail. And please—one more evening spent at a meeting of local women and I will have to tear my hair out. I've even seen Rowan gritting her teeth—we are not your jam-and-cakes sort of people, and neither are you. Your stepmother does a lovely lemon curd though."

"You make me laugh, Pris—and I love you for it! But what will you do in London?"

"Well, the first thing I'm going to do is find out what's going on with my niece! I've loved those long summer visits ever since you found Pascale for me, and now she's a grown woman in London on a more permanent basis, it actually made me feel as if I had a daughter, instead of being the lone female among my four men. I do worry about her though, and I know she's terribly concerned about her grandmother, as you can imagine. I keep telling her that Chantal is more than a match for any German officer living at her chateau—the woman has steel for a backbone. But I—I suppose I just would like to see more of Pascale."

"Pris—Pris, as I said before, she's a young woman about town."

Priscilla sighed, took her cigarette case from her handbag, but put it back again. "First sign of trouble and I want to light up." She shook her head. "Of course I know how it is. You find a party every night, if you can, and you make the most of it because tomorrow might not come. That's what I did, anyway."

"There you are—don't expect to see her, Pris."

"Maisie—" Priscilla turned to her friend. "Maisie . . . can you look me in the eye and tell me you don't know what's going on? As my dearest friend—the friend who saved my life? The friend who I know will be at my bedside as soon as I wake up from my final operation on this dreadful scar."

"Oh no you don't, Pris—that's pretty low even for you. Don't start the 'poor me' line, when it's clear I have no idea what Pascale is doing with her life. I mean, has it occurred to you that she might be seeing someone and she doesn't want you to know because you'll have a very definite opinion that might not match her own? The girl is over twenty-one."

"So you don't know then?"

"No—and why do you think I would know anyway?" Maisie did not flinch from her friend's gaze.

"Because you know all sorts of things that are supposed to be on the q.t. Did you know she's not at her flat? Told her flatmate she had a work assignment in Scotland."

"Priscilla, I suggest you stop gnawing at that bone. You know she has a translation job, and I am sure she is very busy—and you were right when you said it could be hush-hush, which means it has nothing to do with anyone but Pascale and her employer. Ah, here comes our train."

They boarded the train, Priscilla taking a seat opposite Maisie in the comfort of a first class carriage, with its wide seats and mirrored bulkhead. Maisie felt her friend staring at her.

"What?"

"Have you heard from your James Stewart yet? Or is he out of sight, out of mind?"

"Pris—"

"Oh, never mind. I suppose any talk of your dishy American is considered careless!" Priscilla opened her newspaper and took out her cigarette case. "To hell with the bloody operation. I need another gasper—and don't worry, I'll move over to the window."

Maisie felt a sigh of relief as the train reached the buffers at Charing Cross Station. Not only had it been a long journey due to trains being held up as they progressed toward the bomb-damaged station, but Priscilla had been increasingly snippy. Yet upon arrival, after they had made their way along the platform and passed the ticket collector, Priscilla turned to Maisie and wrapped her arms around her.

"I'm sorry—I was just dreadful on the train."

"You're worried, Pris—and you've been through a lot. Give yourself time."

"What with Tom flying bloody Hurricanes, Tim becoming quite another person after losing his arm, and then taking it out on everyone around him—mainly me . . . added to which I have Tarquin going off to be a forestry worker. I worry that he'll be set upon by thugs and beaten to a pulp for being a conchie! Douglas is immersed in his work, and then there I am—the lost soul with a scarred face that even powder applied with a trowel doesn't hide."

"You look lovely. I would be the first to tell you if you looked dreadful—and you don't. Yes, I can see a bit of the scar if you move a certain way. But consider those boys in Mr. McIndoe's wards at the hospital."

"Heavens, yes. I should shut up and remember every single one of them every day, with their scorched faces and hands. I cannot imagine the terror of coming down in an aircraft ablaze—I was only stuck in a burning house. I don't know how I've the cheek to moan when I saw those wounded young men every day in the Victoria Hospital."

"And your sons are men now—they can deal with whatever is thrown at them. You've done a good job there, Pris—and Pascale is like you. She's competent and brave. Do not fear for her, Priscilla—it would be the last thing she wants or needs." Maisie looked up at the clock. "Oh dear, I must dash—look, I'll come over for supper this evening, if you like."

"I'll have Cook rustle something up—she's been keeping the house as if we were there all the time, and she's managed to get some groceries in. Seven o'clock?"

"I'll see you then."

"Where are you off to now?"

"A mortuary." She waved as she walked away.

MacFarlane was already in the mortuary's examination room with the pathologist when Maisie arrived; he nodded by way of a greeting as she entered. Duncan Jamieson was inspecting the deceased's body with a large magnifying glass and did not look up. Maisie placed her jacket and hat on a hook alongside a table, upon which she set her bag. She took a white laboratory coat from another hook, and a white mask from a pile on the desk. Proceeding to the sink, she scrubbed her hands and selected a pair of clean, disinfected rubber gloves pegged to a line above the taps.

"Apologies for the late arrival, gentlemen. Trains were delayed coming into Charing Cross."

Jamieson looked up and smiled. "Hello, Maisie. We've only just started, so you haven't missed anything."

MacFarlane caught Maisie's eye and raised an eyebrow. She turned away and looked down at the body, that of a man of about forty years of age, with dark hair and an olive complexion.

"I can see the bruising around the face," said Maisie. "And on the torso—it's very bad there. What did you find at the back of the head, Dr. Jamieson?" She hoped he noticed the more formal address.

"What you might expect to find on a man who died as a result of a fall from a craggy mountainside in Scotland." With gloved hands he lifted the dead man's head and turned it to the side. "Easy turn even with rigor mortis, due to the broken neck."

Maisie leaned in to inspect the crushed underside of the skull. "His neck was also broken?"

"Yes."

She turned to MacFarlane. "Robbie—where exactly did this happen?"

"You know where we were last week? Well, if you stand at that point and look across to the crag with a drop down onto the path—we assume he fell from that high point, probably climbed up onto the crag while trying to get his bearings."

Maisie met Jamieson's eyes.

"Robbie," said Jamieson. "We both know that this man died when his neck was broken, and then he fell."

"No, we don't both know that, Duncan." MacFarlane's tone was terse. "He could have twisted his neck as his head hit the side of the crag on the way down."

"For what it's worth, I agree with Dr. Jamieson," Maisie said. "You can see from here that the way the neck was broken, if that's what indeed happened, then this crushing of the skull would have happened on the other side of his head as he fell. And look at the bruises on his body—all on the right side, in line with the skull injury. The broken neck is telling a different story."

"I can confirm it when I get inside the neck," said Jamieson. He shifted his attention to Maisie. "Would you like to assist?"

"She can't. Sorry," MacFarlane interjected before she could respond. "Change of plan for Miss Dobbs—and the only neck I want to see open is on a bottle. Miss Dobbs' time is spoken for this afternoon. Report on my desk by five, Duncan?"

"I'll have it dispatched over to you," said Jamieson. "Thank you, M—Miss Dobbs."

"Dr. Jamieson."

Once outside the mortuary, having deposited aprons, masks and gloves in a bin by the door, both Maisie and MacFarlane took deep breaths before either spoke.

"Phew, fresh air!" said MacFarlane. "I can't stand the dance that happens when a living, breathing person goes from human being to corpse to cadaver. I'm all right until I see the likes of Jamieson brandishing a bloody scalpel, and especially over the head. Not thrilled about the abdomen either. You medical people are like a load of ghouls."

"None of us find it easy, Robbie. But it's necessary work because we are either trying to save the living or discover how the dead met their end. And I don't like how this one met his end." She stopped walking and looked up at the man she had known for years. "We know he was murdered, don't we? There's no way we can quickstep around that one, and at this point Jamieson's report is a formality—I doubt you'll even open it."

"Not beating about the bush, so I'll say you could be right on all points—there is that chance. But some things have to be kept under wraps." MacFarlane pulled back his cuff and consulted his watch. "I could do with a drink in a quiet corner, and there's an hour to go before last orders, so let's chat in a more convivial atmosphere."

At the Cuillins of Skye, MacFarlane's favorite public house—only the sign was evident, as the building was partially clad in sandbags—he pushed open the door to the slightly more comfortable saloon bar, which had several armchairs and a settee covered in matching green-and-red tartan fabric. The public bar, by comparison, was a noisier place, with sawdust on the floor and a lunchtime crowd that would soon disperse to return to work on the railway or at the coach station, or with one of the many crews clearing what they could of broken buildings and piles of rubble from repeated bombings. The pub offered the opportunity for some camaraderie, a chat with others, and a chance to forget about war, if only for the time it took to down a pint. Maisie often wondered if she would ever remember walking along a street before it was bombed, and what it looked like without broken buildings looming out of the detritus of war like shattered teeth.

"Cream sherry?" asked MacFarlane.

"A small one, thank you," replied Maisie.

MacFarlane returned with a large single-malt whisky for himself and a sherry for Maisie, placing the drinks on a low table between the armchairs they had chosen for privacy, close to the window and well away from the door. There were only two other patrons on this side of the pub, and they were seated at the bar.

"What was the dead man's name?" asked Maisie.

"Thierry Richard." MacFarlane's pronunciation of the deceased agent's last name was flat; he said "Richard" as if it were an English Christian name.

"I think it's pronounced 'Rishard,'" said Maisie. "And was he about forty?"

MacFarlane nodded. "Maisie, you were never a star when it came to languages—we found that out when we were training you for the Munich assignment, so you're the last person to chime in on pronunciation. Anyway, Major Chaput is understandably very upset—raging, would be a better word for it. Richard"—he pronounced the word correctly, with a slight pause as if to dare Maisie to fault him again—"Richard had been with the major since the last war. They were at Verdun together, and he was with him later, in Syria, during the French mandate."

"Really? So Thierry Richard would have been about twenty-five or twenty-six then, and the major—what? Probably not much older. Thirties?"

"Yes. The major is nothing if not loyal—and his men are loyal to him too. He hand-picked all of them, and we're counting on them. Working alongside the French is vital for our success over there—they're our linchpins with the local resistance people. We're still building trust."

Neither Maisie nor MacFarlane spoke for half a minute. Maisie was framing her next comment, though she knew there was no other way to phrase what she had to say. "Look, Robbie—going back to what happened with Dr. Jamieson. It was clear to him—and he's the expert—that Richard was murdered, and as you know, I could not help but agree with him. That's two Frenchmen killed within ten days, and there's one common denominator."

"My hands are tied, and I don't suspect him anyway."

"I can't believe this. Every bone in my body is telling me the Mac-Farlane I knew before this war would have had that man at Scotland Yard under caution right now. And you're letting it go. Surely you'd concede that it's more than possible that the man who received the delivery of an envelope from Freddie Hackett was Chaput."

"I don't know anything about the message, who it was from or where it was going—don't imagine I know everything that goes on in every different intelligence section. A lot of envelopes are dispatched with only a number on the front anyway, and no name for the messenger to remember, and they are coded. But here's what I know—children see monsters in the dark, Maisie. They get a bit scared, and the next thing you know, there's a big hand waiting to grab their feet and drag them under the bed. There is no evidence to suggest Major Chaput had anything to do with killing another Frenchman, or anyone else for that matter. And even if I did want to question him, this is not the right time. We have a sensitive and very important alliance to protect, and that's with the Free French here in London. We need them, and we need their people who are over in France—if all that falls away, then we might as well start stocking up on bratwurst."

Maisie sighed in frustration. "This goes against everything I have ever believed about honoring the murdered dead; making sure that if the deceased were looking down upon us, they would know that while their earthly form is being mutilated by the pathologist's scalpel, some-one else cares enough to find the killer and bring them to justice." She paused. "But having said that, I see your point. I understand. Some things have to fall by the wayside during wartime. And on every level it seems to me that there's an abdication of respect for human life." She lifted her sherry glass and took first one sip, and then another.

"I know that tone, Maisie," said MacFarlane, picking up his glass and draining the contents in one deep swallow. He slapped the empty glass down on the table with such force that the man and woman sitting at the bar turned around. "Sorry!" said MacFarlane. "Dodgy wrist—dropped my glass." He laughed, though his smile evaporated when he turned back to Maisie. "That, hen, is the tone telling me you are going to be the dog that won't let go of this particular bone. I can see it in your eyes."

"I will drop the bone if you insist, Robbie."

Another silence. MacFarlane rubbed his forehead, then looked up at Maisie. "I don't insist because I expect you to do the right thing with regard to my position—let me remind you that I'm the one who carries the can if you cause trouble with our French brethren. I know you're trying to do your best for the Hackett lad, but at the same time I want to know if you discover anything—anything. Make that immedi-ately, not a day or two after the event. And leave 'Rishard' to me. You weren't there. You didn't witness a thing, and you only saw the body, not the place of death where he was found. I hope I can depend upon you to watch what you're doing."

"I will. Yes. You can count on me to be discreet, Robbie."

"Aye, and I reckon I can also count on you to land me in a diplomatic straitjacket." He cleared his throat, and came to his feet. "By the way, you might like to know that both those young ladies you're particularly interested in are now in France. So far, so good. Miss Jones sent over her first radio communication this morning. We'll be giving them orders via a message tucked inside a BBC broadcast tonight."

Maisie stood up, making sure her voice was low. "And Miss Evernden?"

"She's where she should be. We've no reason for any concern about her."

"I appreciate your letting me know, Robbie."

"You're off the hook in the meantime, Maisie. No more recruits to analyze. I'll be in touch though."

"Of course."

"By the way," said MacFarlane, opening the door for her, then joining her on the pavement outside. "You want to watch that Jamieson. I think he's sweet on you."

Maisie pinned her hat. "Robbie—for goodness' sake, you think everyone's sweet on me."

"Just observing. I'll be off now. Be careful, Maisie—just be careful. You're on your own time for a few days, but you're still on my watch."

Maisie took Billy into her confidence, inasmuch as she could, discussing with him a certain element of synchronicity that had occurred during a recent meeting. She was not specific about the details, that the meeting in question took place in a manor house in Scotland where recruits for a secret intelligence section were being put through their paces.

"So what you're saying, miss, is that you think you know who killed the bloke in the street, the murder young Freddie witnessed." Seated at the long table in Maisie's office, Billy leaned forward, his notebook open.

"I—I believe so. But here's the thing—assuming the body retrieved from the Thames is that of the man Freddie saw murdered, both the pathologist and I believe that at least one of the two men—either the man with the knife or his victim—was a professional killer, and I wouldn't rule out the second either. The pathologist agrees that the victim might have been an assassin, based upon wounds to his body—they were consistent with someone who has been in serious scrapes." Maisie went on to recap the postmortem findings on the man who rose to the surface of the river at the same time as the Spitfire. "I know that at first blush it sounds like a wild suggestion based upon supposition, yet in my experience speculative comments from experienced pathologists reflect what may at first seem like a guess, but they're really an intuitive response rooted in their depth of knowledge."

"And what do you think of this French major, the one you met at a party?"

"I'm not sure. He's not one for talking—though his command of English is excellent. He is an observer, though."

"What do you mean? An observer?"

"He keeps his eye on everyone around him, all the time. Now, to be fair, that's his job—it's the mainstay of anyone working in his position," said Maisie, aware that she could only share so much information with Billy. She was sure he had more than a passing clue about the real nature of her work, though. "But his level of awareness seemed rather intense. He seemed as if he was always expecting the devil to walk in, or to appear among the company."

"Maybe he's afraid of something himself—fear could be his devil, couldn't it? Do you want me to see what I can get on him?"

"I think you'll have trouble there, Billy. We've a diplomatic angle to consider, and I don't want MacFarlane around here shouting his head off." She pointed to Billy's notebook. "Now then, any more on Freddie Hackett?"

"Sporting a nice blue-and-purple bruise across his left cheek, apparently sustained when he fell while running an errand. He might have got a bloody nose in the same so-called fall."

"Oh dear Lord." Maisie rubbed a hand across her forehead, before consulting her watch. She stood up. "Right, I'm going over to the school—I should be just in time for the children to be leaving."

"You would stand more of a chance of catching Freddie by going straight along to the Albert Embankment—when I talked to him on the blower, he told me there's a big office along there where he'll usually go first, then the porter tells him where to run to next, perhaps Baker Street or that fancy hotel. He'll be setting off as soon as that school bell goes, so he can pick up his first job. He'll probably be running from there to Baker Street again. And I wouldn't be surprised if he didn't sneak out of his classroom to get there on time."

"Billy, would you come with me? You're the father of boys, and he trusts you."

Billy nodded. "I'm glad you asked, miss. I like the boy and want to do right by him. For a start, I know about a certain nose I'd like to rearrange, if I lay eyes on the owner's dial."

Freddie Hackett?" repeated the porter at Freddie's regular first stop. "Hasn't turned up yet—the little bugger is late and I've got something to go out in a hurry. Mind you, it's the first time. He's usually here bang on four. He pops home after school to see his sister, if he can, then he comes straight here, and I don't think he was told yesterday that he'd be starting off somewhere else today. I usually send him to the caff down the street for a bacon sandwich as soon as he gets here—we've got a kitty here to make sure the messengers get something inside them, what with all that running. Poor little Fred—probably the only decent food he gets in a day."

Even before the porter had finished speaking, Maisie and Billy had begun to move toward the door, with Billy calling back, "S'all right, mate—don't worry, we'll catch up with him, wherever he is."

CHAPTER 9

Billy gave the taxicab driver directions to follow the most likely route that Freddie would have taken from school, to home, to the Albert Embankment, just in case they saw him running along the pavement. Their first stop was the school, which was quiet, as all the children had gone home, though an army lorry was parked in a far section of the playground now designated military property for the duration of the war.

Billy called out to a soldier who was working on the lorry. "Oi, mate—over here." The soldier looked up from the engine. "Do you know if everyone at the school has gone home now?"

"The kids ran out of here a while ago—but there might be a teacher or two in there working late."

"Much obliged," shouted Billy, waving to the soldier.

The doors for the girls' and boys' separate entrances were already locked, but they were able to flag down the caretaker in front of the main double doors.

"Hold up, mate—anyone in there?" asked Billy.

The caretaker shook his head. "Nah, the bell went at a quarter to four, and you can't keep them in there once they've heard it. Miss Rice sometimes stays for a bit—she's the headmistress—and so does Miss Arnold, who teaches art. She has a lot to clear up after her last class, but she left not five minutes ago." He turned the key and then looked around at Billy and Maisie. "You looking for anyone in particular? Not many kids here anyway, only the ones brought back from evacuation or who never went in the first place—I know most of them by name."

"We were looking for a boy named Freddie Hackett," said Maisie.

"Oh, young Freddie. Nice boy, that one. Works hard. No, he's gone. Saw him tearing out of here—quick on his pins, is Freddie. Can't think where he got that from because his old man's a right one—he moves from the house to the pub and back again, and only one way at any speed. We know which way that is!"

"Thank you," said Maisie, turning back toward the waiting taxicab.

"Funny, everyone seems to be looking for Freddie—popular lad today."

"What do you mean?" said Maisie, bringing her attention back to the caretaker.

"A bloke came round not twenty-five minutes ago, asking for him."

"Had you seen the man before?" asked Maisie.

The caretaker shook his head. "Never laid eyes on him. I thought it might be someone Freddie worked for, or the lad had got himself into a bit of trouble. Even the good ones get up to something every now and again—specially now."

"What was the man like?" asked Billy.

"Big fella, dark, sort of Spanish looking. Nice dresser. Good suit on him."

"Did he have an accent?" asked Maisie.

"He never said enough for me to notice. Asked if he'd missed Freddie Hackett, and that was it. Sounded all right, but then I'm a bit hard of hearing anyway—and it was noisy, what with lorries coming and going over there on the army side. It's quieter now—though give it a chance and the bombers will start flying in for another go at us soon. We won't be able to hear ourselves think."

Returning to the taxicab, Maisie instructed the driver to go to the Hacketts' address.

"Wait here, please," said Maisie as they stepped from the cab.

"What, again?" said the driver.

"Don't worry, you'll be paid," Billy called out over his shoulder as he followed Maisie through the courtyard, past the lines of washing.

She knocked on the Hacketts' door. There was no answer, so she knocked again, then both Maisie and Billy stepped back and looked up to the first-floor window.

"Freddie! Freddie, if you're there, it's Miss Dobbs and Mr. Beale here," shouted Maisie.

"If you're up there, come down and let us in, son," Billy called out even louder. "There's only us here, Freddie."

Maisie thought she saw the ragged curtains twitch, then she heard footsteps on the stairs.

"Mr. Beale." The voice was strained. "Is that really you?"

"I'm here, Freddie—are you alone?"

"No, I'm with Iris. Mum's not here."

"Where is she, love?" asked Maisie.

"I don't know—she's usually home by now."

"Fred—open the door for us. There's no one else here," said Billy.

Hearing a bolt being drawn back, Maisie reached into her purse and pressed a few coins into Billy's hand. "Better give the cabbie something to keep him here."

Freddie opened the door just wide enough for him to check that only Maisie and Billy were on the other side.

Maisie heard Billy talking to the cabbie and then his footfall behind her.

"Come on, son," said Billy. "Open the door properly and let us through, then we can lock up again so no one else can get in."

"All right," said Freddie. He pulled back the door just wide enough for the visitors to enter, then slammed it shut, let the latch down and pulled a bolt across.

"Will your mum be able to get in when she returns?" asked Maisie.

"She'll call up to the window for me to go down and open the door."

"Let's go upstairs and you can tell us what's going on," said Maisie. "I'll make us a cup of tea. Is Iris all right?"

Freddie nodded. His eyes were bloodshot and his left cheek bruised. There was a cut across the bridge of his nose.

A younger child's voice squealed from the top of the landing. "Freddeeee. Freddee!"

"Coming, Iris. I'm coming, darlin'— I'm here, and I've got a couple of friends with me."

Freddie ran up the stairs and picked up a girl who looked to be about five years of age and too big to be carried by her brother. Maisie showed no surprise when she registered the child's clear blue almond-shaped eyes and pale skin, with freckles peppered across her flat nose. Instead she smiled and made sure her eye contact was true. "Hello— you must be Iris! I've heard all about you from Freddie."

The girl began to suck her thumb before hiding her face in the curve of her brother's neck.

"Come on, Rissy, let me put you down—you're a heavy girl now." Freddie looked up at Maisie. "There's two chairs in the kitchen."

A kettle was boiling hard on the gas ring. As Freddie grabbed a cloth from the line above the stove, folded it around his hand, and removed the kettle, Maisie fought the urge to move Iris clear of her brother—she was clinging onto the frayed edge of his pullover.

"Iris was crying because she's hungry, so I was making her some toast and a cup of tea. She has it milky, but not too hot because it makes her cry."

"Here, let me do that," said Maisie. "You sit down with Iris and Mr. Beale will get the cups for us. I know where your mum keeps the milk."

Soon Maisie had tea on the small kitchen table. She watched as Freddie placed his sister's hands on either side of the cup filled with milky, lukewarm tea Maisie had prepared and watched her drink. Both children were seated on wooden crates, which Freddie had pushed close together. Billy sat down opposite them after toasting a slice of bread on the gas ring and cutting it into small squares for Iris. There was no margarine or jam in the kitchen.

"There you are, lovey," said Billy.

"What happens to Iris when your mum is at work?" asked Maisie.

"The school won't have her, so she goes down to Mrs. Dunley, but Mum's worried because she thinks the old girl puts something in her tea to make her sleep. Sometimes she goes to another neighbor who has a girl a bit younger, so she's not at school yet. Mum pays her—and what I earn on the side helps. The doctor said Iris should go into a special home. He called it an 'institution,' but Mum said she didn't want her little girl ending up with a load of old lunatics. I don't like that word—institution." He looked down at his tea, stirring it idly with his spoon, before putting an arm around his sister's shoulder and pulling her to him. "She might be a . . . a mongol, but she's lovely. And people don't realize it, but she's very bright. Mum says it's just a different sort of bright, and it shines better than most because Iris has a good heart."

"She looks very bright to me, Freddie—and you can tell she loves her big brother." Maisie paused, ready to change the subject to what had happened at the school, and more to the point, how he had bruised his cheek, but Freddie began talking again.

"I reckon I saw a bloke at the school today—he reminded me of that man, Miss Dobbs. The bloke who killed that other one. The bell had gone, so I ran out of the classroom toward the door, but then I looked through the window and saw him talking to one of them bomb-squad soldiers, who was pointing toward Mr. Chambers, the caretaker. I wasn't going to let him see me, so I legged it to the other door at the back of the school, then I went through where the army keeps tools in the yard, and ran home that way. I knew I had to get here to see Mum and Iris before going off to the Albert Embankment, but I was scared he'd catch up with me. And now I can't leave Iris on her own because Mum's late. I hope I don't lose my job. My dad'll kill me and then take it out on Mum."

"What about Iris?"

The boy shook his head. "Oh, he don't see her if he can help it—we have to keep her out of the way. He says he wants her in an asylum, but Mum says no. If he's in a really bad temper, he takes that out on Mum too, that we've got Iris."

"Where's your father now, Freddie?"

The boy shrugged. "Probably waiting for the pubs to open—there's a few he goes to. Sometimes he comes home after closing, but other times, well, I don't know where he goes."

Maisie was about to ask another question when they heard a voice outside calling out. "Freddie—Fred! Let me in love. I'm late enough as it is."

"That's Mum," said Freddie, extricating himself from his sister and running down the stairs.

Mrs. Hackett's voice carried up from the courtyard. "Whatever have you locked the door for, or was it her downstairs again? Batty old thing, isn't she? They kept me on at work—big pile of ironing was put in front of me just as I was about to leave and no extra money for my trouble either. Now come on, help me with this bag. I managed to scrounge a pound of scrap vegetable ends from a coster for a penny, and bless him, he gave me some extra because he was finishing his round. I've got to get some soup going before your father gets home. Not that he'll be here soon, but I don't want him to come in and find there's nothing on the table. That's it, love—you're a good boy."

Iris squealed with joy when she saw her mother and ran into her arms, though Grace Hackett's smile faded upon seeing Maisie and Billy waiting to greet her.

"Hello, Mrs. Hackett—sorry to give you a bit of a shock. This is Mr. Beale, who works with me."

"Is Freddie in trouble?" She looked sideways at her son, drawing him to her while still holding on to Iris.

"Not at all. We'd heard he was late getting to his job, so we were coming out this way and thought we'd make sure he was all right. And here we are."

"You look worried, Miss Dobbs—is my boy in any danger?"

Maisie placed her hand on Grace Hackett's arm. "Usually, I would like more time to consider different . . . different solutions to what I believe is not a danger as such, but an intimidation; a deliberate presence designed to unsettle not only Freddie here, but you as well." She removed her hand, folded her arms and looked out of the dusty window as she continued, giving herself time to frame the right words; words that would inform and strike a tone of vigilance without terror. "I believe there's someone who ultimately wants to talk to Freddie to find out how much he saw when he witnessed what we believe to be a murder—which means we have to act with some haste." Iris had slipped from her mother's grasp and was sucking her thumb while leaning against Grace's knees. Grace kept her gaze on Maisie, as if bracing herself for what might come next.

"Right," said Maisie, taking care to offer a positive tone. "Here's what we will do. I have a flat in Pimlico, across the water, and I think it would be best if you all go there. It's empty at the moment—my secretary was living there for a while, but she's moved to the country with her husband and son. It's furnished and there are some sheets and so on in the linen cupboard, which means you won't need anything except a few personal bits and pieces. There's a cellar underneath the building, so you've somewhere to go when there's an air raid, and there's a shelter down the street. Now then, quickly gather whatever you'd like to take with you, and leave a note for your husband. Tell him you've gone to stay with relatives—make up something."

"He'll kill me for leaving him," said Grace, tears filling her eyes.

"Not on my watch, Mrs. Hackett," said Billy

"Billy's right—we'll make sure your safety isn't compromised. If you prefer, you can leave a note here with my name, our office address and telephone number for Mr. Hackett to get in touch. The fact is that I want Freddie away from here and I want to feel confident that you and Iris are out of harm's way—and I will be honest with you, as things stand with Freddie not working this evening, he won't be bringing home money, which means none of you are safe if you remain at home. We both know why."

"But—"

"Please, Mrs. Hackett—Grace—please do as I say."

"Come on, Mum," said Freddie. "Miss Dobbs is right—I've seen that man, and I'm scared. I saw him kill his mate. And I don't want another right-hander from Dad either."

"Oh, Fred, you shouldn't talk like that about your father, not in company," said Grace Hackett.

"This is a really good plan, Mrs. Hackett," said Billy. "And you're like Doreen, my wife—you're a lovely mum to your children, so you know what's the best thing to do for them. Look how you've kept little Iris from being put away."

At once Grace Hackett stood up and took a deep breath, as if drawing in strength. "Yes—we'll come. Freddie—you gather a few bits for yourself while I put what I can in a bag. It's not as if we have much, so it'll only take a few minutes. And I'll scribble a note for your father."

Ten minutes later three members of the Hackett family were safely ensconced in the taxicab, with Billy and Freddie sitting on the fold-down seats opposite Maisie, Grace and Iris. Maisie gave an address in Pimlico, then added that there would be another stop afterward.

"Billy, I want you to go to number sixty-four Baker Street and ask for MacFarlane—if he's there, tell him what we're doing and why. See the porter and let him know that Freddie is not at work because . . . because . . . well, make up something—he'll then get onto the other porter at Albert Embankment. Oh, and ask MacFarlane what to do about briefing Caldwell at the Yard. I don't want Caldwell to think we're going around him to MacFarlane about a murder investigation— that won't help us in the future, so do what's necessary, even if you have to go back down to see Caldwell. He seems to be in his office at all hours now, so he's hardly likely to be going home early."

"Right you are, miss."

As the taxicab drew up outside the flat, Maisie realized she had not seen it for over two years. When she had first applied to purchase the property, unbeknownst to her, Priscilla had arranged to be a guarantor on the loan so she could proceed with ownership—otherwise there would have been no means by which a woman of Maisie's background and standing could secure a loan. Maisie knew nothing about the gesture for a long time. Now she was using the home where she had always felt so sheltered to secure the safety of a boy she believed needed protection of his own.

"Here we are," said Maisie, reaching for the light switch—the Hackett family would soon get used to the advantages of electric lighting instead of gas lamps.

"Oh my, this is big," said Grace Hackett as Maisie ushered the family past the bedrooms and into the sitting room. "You could have a room to yourself, Freddie—and you deserve it, my boy."

Freddie blushed as he put down the two paper bags he was carrying, one holding half a loaf of bread and a few vegetables, the second a book and a clean pair of socks.

"The blinds can be a bit tricky, and the flat could do with a little dusting as no one's lived here for a while, but there's everything you need in the kitchen, and there's a linen cupboard through there in the hall where you'll find sheets, pillowcases, blankets and towels. There's not a lot of furniture, as you can see, but there's a settee and armchair here in the sitting room, and Freddie, that desk over there will be perfect for you to do your homework. We'll have to arrange for you to continue your education here—there's a school down the road, so not far to go once we've got you enrolled. And there are a few shops not very far away, so you can take your ration books down there, Grace. I'll vouch for you, and I can get in touch with the school to help you register Freddie. And I'll think of something for Iris, Mrs. Hackett, so you don't lose your job. You can catch a bus on the corner that will take you almost all the way to your work."

Maisie went on to show the new residents the kitchen and pantry, and demonstrated how to open the door to the fire escape, which was accessed via the kitchen.

Grace Hackett nodded. She seemed close to tears.

"Let me put the kettle on, and you can make a nice cup of tea while I see the caretaker so he knows you're here." Maisie turned on the kitchen tap, which spluttered and ran brown water for a few seconds, before it was clear enough for Maisie to fill the kettle. "You know, before the war, his wife used to take in children to look after while their mums were at work," she continued. "I'll ask if she can keep an eye on Iris—would that be all right?"

Hackett nodded, the faraway look in her eyes reminding Maisie of soldiers she'd treated in the last war, and later in the secure hospital where her patients were men who had experienced a fear so debilitating in the face of battle, it had left them shocked to the point of paralysis. Yet by the time Maisie departed the ground-floor flat in Pimlico, though Grace Hackett was still trembling, she was busying herself in her temporary home, setting to work and settling her demons with tasks to be completed before she and her children spent their first night in quarters they considered the height of luxury.

As Maisie walked along toward the Embankment to hail a taxicab, she reflected that luck had been on her side when she visited the caretaker; not only did he offer to call on the family to ensure that all was well, but his wife was delighted to be asked to care for Iris if needed, and seemed not at all fazed by her disability. "Oh, my niece has got one of them," she said. "Lovely little thing she is—no, that doesn't worry me at all. In fact, I think I'd rather have one—always smiling they are, though they do have tummy aches that the other children don't get, and my niece's little girl has a dicky heart too."

By the time she reached the office, her thoughts had drifted to reach a certain level of hope that one day another word would be found to describe children such as Iris Hackett, because being named after a tribe of people in far-flung Asia wasn't good enough. But as she searched her bag for her key, those thoughts were interrupted.

"Oi, you—you! Dobbs, or whatever you call yourself!"

Maisie looked around, drawing upon years of training and experience to remain calm, focused and direct.

"May I help you, sir?"

"You've taken my wife, so you'd better look lively and tell me where she is, or I'll—"

"You'll what, mate? What exactly will you do?" said Billy, emerging from the downstairs flat and joining Maisie on the step.

Hackett moved back a couple of paces. "Where have you taken them?"

"Your family are in a very safe place, so you've nothing to worry about, Mr. Hackett."

"They were safe enough where they were."

Maisie stepped toward Hackett, who had been slurring his words and was now swaying. Any patience she might have felt toward the drunken man began to slip away. "Were they, Mr. Hackett? Were they really safe? Funny, isn't it, that with them being so safe, both your son and wife have been bruised black and blue, and your son is not well— which means he doesn't have a penny to give you because he hasn't earned anything today."

"Well, that's bleedin' marvelous," said Hackett. "Lazy little . . . wait until I get my hands on him."

"And that's just it, Mr. Hackett—you won't be getting your hands on him, either today or any other day."

Hackett drew back his fist. "I'm telling you—"

"You want to tell someone something?" said Billy, standing in front of Freddie Hackett's father. "Then tell someone of your own size, mate. You tell me."

"I'll . . . I'll . . ." Hackett staggered again, and began to stumble away.

"Mr. Hackett!" Maisie ran to the man's side and caught him by the arm. "Mr. Hackett, you are in no fit state to go anywhere like that. We'll get you a taxicab home."

"Who said I was going home? Can't stand the place. Never could."

He flapped his hand as if dismissing all connection to his wife and children. "Only one home for a bloke like me. Now leave me alone."

Billy joined Maisie, and they watched Hackett weave from left to right toward the corner.

"He seemed to get worse as he came for you, didn't he, miss?" said Billy.

"Yes, he did." Maisie was thoughtful, watching the man as he wavered before turning right onto Warren Street.

"Probably had a few in the pub along the street, then came round here and before he knew it the drink hit him."

"Hmmm," said Maisie, then drew her attention to Billy. "Did you see MacFarlane?"

Billy nodded. "Gave him your message—he didn't say much, just thanked me. The porter got on to the other two to let them know they wouldn't be seeing Freddie tonight; made up a story about him being not well. And I telephoned Caldwell—told him you'd taken the family to your old flat for their safety, just in case." He studied Maisie, who was looking along the road into the distance again. "What're you thinking, miss?"

"Just thinking. Just thinking that it's all very sad, isn't it?"

"Bloke beating his wife and son all very sad? I dunno, miss—I think he's a you-know-what, and I hope he never goes near them again."

"Me too, Billy." She turned toward the door. "It's just that people don't become violent like that in a vacuum, do they? It all starts somewhere—that's the sad thing, that it has to start in the first place."

"It did with him, and yet look at Freddie—he's not going to turn out to be a brutal piece of work, mark my words. He's a lovely lad. Mind you, he gets it from his mum." Billy stopped speaking and looked at Maisie. "What is it, miss?"

Maisie sighed. "It's that scar, Billy. That scar on the side of his face." She shook her head. "It's just too much of a coincidence—and perhaps not a clue, or an indication of anything, except . . ." She closed her eyes as if to shut out all other images.

"Except what?"

"The imagination, Billy—the sort of imagination that arises like a plague from constant terror."

CHAPTER 10

Maisie was late leaving her flat on Tuesday morning. Following supper with Priscilla the night before, she had walked home and then stayed up at her desk working on case notes and indexing paperwork to take back to Sandra at her cottage in the village of Chelstone on Thursday. She sometimes felt as if she had gathered everyone she loved around her in rural Kent, ensuring their safety when the bombings began. First a cottage was found for Priscilla and Douglas and their boys, and later another was found in the area for Sandra, her husband, and their toddler son Martin. Sandra had expressed a wish to continue keeping invoices and accounts up-to-date, which was a godsend, as neither Maisie nor Billy relished getting to grips with administrative matters, and she also found work with Douglas, for whom she had once typed manuscripts. Then Billy decided that, with his sons both in the services, his wife and daughter would be much safer in the country, so it was not long before Maisie's father and stepmother were giving up their bungalow for the Beales to live in, while they moved full-time into the Dower House, becoming a constant in the life of their new granddaughter.

Yes, Maisie was happy to have drawn everyone she cared about around her. All the moves had seemed to slot into place—though danger was still ever-present. No one was safe, even amid the fields, forests, orchards and hop gardens of Kent. But life had to go on.

Now the late night had caught up with Maisie and the morning was escaping her. Scotland Yard was her first destination. She had received a postcard message from Caldwell yesterday, to the effect that he had tried to reach her by telephone, and that he wanted to talk to her. Sometimes it was better to see Caldwell in person; like MacFarlane, he had a tendency to end a telephone call with no warning, leaving her listening to the long tone of disconnection just as she was about to ask another question—and sometimes that question was the most important of her queries. Fortunately the desk sergeant recognized her as soon as she arrived at Scotland Yard, and waved her on with the words "He's in his office—you can go on up."

Maisie tapped on the open door. "One of these days I'll have to rescue you from underneath a pile of papers, Detective Chief Superintendent."

Caldwell looked up from a file from which papers fanned across the desk, and shook his head. "Afternoon, Miss Dobbs. It wouldn't be so bad if I had a bit more fresh air in here." He pointed to the visitor chair with the barrel of his fountain pen. "Shove those bits and pieces onto the floor and take a seat. I just want to sign off on this warrant here and—" The sentence was left unfinished as he returned to his task.

Maisie gathered the clutch of papers on the chair and placed them on the floor.

"There we go," continued Caldwell, closing a folder. "That's one job out of the way." He put his hand to the side of his mouth as if it were a loudhailer and called out, "Anyone out there? Someone come and get this warrant and—" He lowered his voice. "Oh, right, there you are, Collins. Run this over to the commissioner for me. Time being of the essence and all that."

"Right you are, sir," said the detective constable, taking the folder from Caldwell and leaving the office, banging his shoulder on an open filing cabinet drawer as he went.

"Did you want to see me about the Hacketts?" Maisie had known Caldwell since he was a detective sergeant, and though they did not get on well at first, over time they had each won the other's respect, a quality enhanced by being direct.

Caldwell sighed, shaking his head while looking for another file and pulling it toward him. "I'll get to them. It's about your French deep-river diver."

"Have you found out any more about him?"

"First of all, let's be fair—we don't actually know he's French, do we?" said Caldwell. "All right, the pathologist made a bit of a guess there and it looks likely, given everything you've said, but we don't really know. And I have plenty I *do* know about to be getting on with—but I was wondering if you had anything more you could push across my desk."

Maisie shook her head. "I would have been here before now, if I had. And if we're talking about who knows what, we also both know you wouldn't have called me unless there were more to discuss—and my guess is you have something important to tell me."

Caldwell leaned back and rubbed his eyes. Maisie could see the man was exhausted.

"It's at times like this, Miss Dobbs, I sometimes think I should have upped sticks long ago and taken myself, the wife and our nippers down to the country so I could be on a rural beat and only have to worry about the odd sheep snatcher or blokes nicking copper roofing from churches."

Maisie laughed. "We both know there's all manner of untoward goings-on at those big country houses, don't we? You would've been sniffing out murderers in dusty old drawing rooms."

"Ha! So the penny dreadfuls would have us believe, eh, Miss Dobbs?" He shook his head. "Anyway, here's what's bothering me. I made a few inquiries myself about this here conundrum we've found ourselves sinking into—I talked to a few people here and there, and what I'm really interested in is the witness to the crime."

"Freddie Hackett?" Maisie frowned, any hint of humor now draining from the conversation. "What's he done?"

Caldwell shook his head. "I don't think he's done anything, as such." His tone was uncharacteristically gentle. "But I was in the area, so I went over to the school and had a word with his teacher—nice woman, Miss . . . Miss . . ." He referred to his notes. "Sorry, seeing a lot of people lately—her name's Miss Pritchard. Also had a word with a Miss Arnold, the art teacher. Anyway, she said something that made me think. The father's a bit of a toe-rag, not a nice bloke at all, and I reckon we both know that. Seems he might have brought home more of the last war than he should have, and he kept it inside him—though he wouldn't be the first." He shook his head. "He's not quite all there—got a temper on him."

"But—"

"Let me finish. This is not to do with Hackett senior—well, not directly. What I found out was that every week in Freddie's class, they do composition, you know, telling a story. I remember having to do it when I was at school, and all I wrote about was dogs—I told you, I should have been a country copper, bicycle and all that."

Maisie detected a certain nervousness in Caldwell's demeanor. *He doesn't want to tell me what he's discovered*, she thought. She leaned forward.

"Well, Freddie's stories are all very vivid, according to the teacher, and amount to something horrible happening to a man with a scar on his face," said Caldwell, his words hurried, as if he were in a race, trying to outrun the truth in his pronouncement. "Not all the time, mind you, but it turns out he's quite the little storyteller and can weave a yarn about anything. The teacher usually gives the class the first sentence and then they write what they want. Apparently she started a story a couple of weeks ago, along the lines of 'You're walking along the road and a dog goes running by with a string of sausages in its mouth, and—' She said Freddie even turned that opening into a story about a man with a scar on his face chasing the dog, and he ends up nabbed and put away, and the dog's a hero!"

"So what you're telling me is that Freddie could have been spinning a tale about seeing a man murdered by another man with a scar on his face." Maisie sighed. "Which is all very well, but I have reason to believe there is sufficient evidence in hand to see at least some element of truth in Freddie's claims. Let me tell you why." Maisie went on to describe, again, the ground where Freddie had seen the murder take place, about finding the wallet and the end of a French cigarette.

"Anything else, Miss Dobbs?"

Maisie sighed. "Well, yes, there is. It's to do with the house where Freddie had to deliver the envelope—and as you might imagine, that is where I must zip my lips or have the full weight of the Official Secrets Act tied to my feet as I'm thrown from the ramparts of the Tower of London. Suffice it to say that there was enough there for me to have doubt."

Caldwell leaned back in his chair again. "I'll accept that." He sighed. "It's bloody scary out there for a lad like Freddie. Running the streets when bombs are falling. I don't hold with mollycoddling children, but there's the other extreme and that's expecting too much of them. My two have to pull their weight—as I tell them, they're big enough and ugly enough now and all grown up—but at night when it's raining bombs and god knows what else, I want them down the bloody shelter with their mum." Caldwell pushed back his chair and stood up, pressing his hands against the small of his back. "To be honest with you, I feel sorry for the lad—hard blimmin' life, if you ask me. But given what I've heard, I'm advising you to let this whole thing drop. That's what I'm doing. I've got to close the case."

"There's the question of a dead body and a boy who might be in danger because a killer knows he could likely identify him—and you're closing the case?"

"Miss Dobbs, what makes you think he's in danger?"

"Apparently a man was asking for him at the school—and the caretaker has corroborated the story."

"Probably the school board inspector, wondering why Freddie's absent so much."

"Caldwell—"

"All right, all right—I know you're worried about the lad, Miss Dobbs. But as far as I'm concerned, this case is as cold as ice and I don't have the manpower for it. You'd be advised to let it go too—it's not as if you're being paid by Freddie Hackett to prove he had all his faculties about him, and was not scared witless running messages just to keep his dad in drink."

"If it's all the same to you, I'm going to continue. I believe Freddie—and I don't like letting people down."

"Oh, I believe him, Miss Dobbs—I do believe he *thinks* he saw something, just like a man fearful he'll expire in the desert will see a blimmin' great pond in the distance. There's no accounting for what's going on in that boy's head."

"Fair warning, Detective Chief Superintendent." Maisie stood up, and though she was disappointed, she softened when she took account of Caldwell's gray, tired pallor, and the deep purple circles under his eyes. "Thank you for taking me into your confidence—and for at least going to the school. I know how stretched you are here, and rest assured I appreciate your looking into the case." Maisie stood up to leave. "I'll keep you apprised of anything I can find out."

"I'd be much obliged if you would, Miss Dobbs." Caldwell seemed subdued in his response. He put the file to one side and picked up another sheet of paper. "This might interest you too, while you're about your investigation."

"What is it?" Maisie reached for the paper.

"Information from the birth certificate of one Frederick Bartholomew Trantor."

"Trantor?"

"His mother's maiden name. I asked one of the new blokes to do a bit more digging on the matter—nice little job to see what he's made of, seeing as his flat feet kept him out of the army and he ended up moved from uniform over to my doorstep. It's surprising what he found out. Turns out Grace Trantor was a governess at one of those nice country homes—you know, the sort you were talking about, with dining rooms where they find a body or two. Well, at least they do in those cheap books people are taking down the shelters." He gave a half-laugh. "Anyway, you know the story—all very predictable, I suppose. There's a widower with two children who needs a nice young woman to care for the nippers because he's been left alone. Governess falls in love with widower, one thing leads to another . . . and he no more wants to marry the lowly governess when she gets into trouble than he wants to fly to the moon. He looks after her enough for her to have the baby well away from anyone who knows her, and then the next thing, she finds out he's upped and married a nice young lady more fitting to his station in life. Meanwhile, with the money he's 'settled' upon her running out fast, Freddie's mum passes herself off as a widow and marries the first man who comes along and sees she's got enough in her purse to treat him to a drink or two. But it's rough for her because he turns out to be a bit of a nutter. They have another child, and that child is . . . well, you've seen her, poor little mite. Hackett senior doesn't have a son of his own, but what he does have under his roof is two kids who are a reminder that he is a failure. And as we've already mentioned, he's quick with his temper and even faster with his hands."

"Oh, poor Grace."

"Poor all of them. But I've heard from your Mr. Beale that you've swept in to the rescue."

"I have the means and opportunity to lend a hand and I've an empty flat, so someone might as well use it."

Caldwell nodded. "Good for you, Miss Dobbs. I'll make sure our boys over at the local station walk past a bit more regular than usual when they're out on the beat. They could even pop in just to make sure."

"Thank you, I appreciate it."

"So, what will you do, Miss Dobbs?"

"Continue with my work, as I said. I believe Freddie. I believe that on this occasion he saw events unfold exactly as he described them to me."

"I don't doubt he saw them, Miss Dobbs. I just don't think they happened. It's all very delicate and that's why I wanted to have this here little chat, so I could tell you what we've done at this end, and what we found out. Now then, I haven't got all day. Must be getting on—which is what the missus says when she's been listening to the wireless and dinner's nowhere near the table."

Maisie extended her hand toward Caldwell, who nodded in her direction and shook her hand. No words were spoken; there was no need.

———

The conversation with Caldwell had thrown Maisie. Walking along the Embankment at a slow pace, she reconsidered everything that had happened since she received the call from Billy regarding Freddie Hackett. She held each image in her mind and aligned them like pieces from a jigsaw puzzle, yet even though she pressed hard on those she thought should fit, the whole picture failed to emerge. She saw the scene of the murder, the items found at the site, her visit to the house where Freddie delivered a message to a man he maintained had scars—or at least deep lines—on his face. She reflected upon her journey to Scotland, meeting the Frenchman, Major André Chaput, and then the second murder. Yes, the second murder. She had to find out more—and she had no reason to believe that MacFarlane would help her at this juncture.

Taking a seat on a bench, Maisie closed her eyes, feeling another weight—that of doubt settling inside her as it prepared to take up residence, ready to sap her energy, slow her mental reflexes and bring down her defenses against that most powerful of emotions: fear. And wasn't there enough fear in the air, despite the fighting talk of politicians and despite the cheery strength of Londoners who were doing their best to keep each other going every single day, surmounting it with humor, compassion, hard work, and an immersion in being busy? Fear, she thought, had a viscous quality to it, to the extent that you could even feel it in your feet as you were running to the shelter; a burden slowing you down, despite the fact that you were moving as fast as your legs could carry you. Fear was sticky, like flypaper, something to steer clear of as you went about your business, because if you were sucked into that long banner of worry, you would be like an insect with wings adhered and feet stuck, never to escape. Fear was the scariest of emotions and it nestled there, growing ever stronger and sprouting shoots, a seed in the fertile soil of doubt.

Once again she drew upon her early lessons, reaching back into the foundations of her work to answer the question of what lay before her. "Go back to the facts, Maisie. Return to the question of information," Maurice had counseled. "When the way forward is not clear, perhaps there is a need for discovery. Identify new sources, Maisie, and go toward them." She allowed her eyes to close, turning her head toward the sun's beams and for a moment banishing the acrid smell of smoke that hung in the air. Sounds of the city became fainter, and a light sleep enveloped her.

"Sorry to bother you, madam, but is this seat taken?"

Startled, Maisie gasped and began to apologize.

"Oh, it's me who should be apologizing." The man sat down at the other end of the bench as Maisie came to her feet. "And please do not leave on account of my arrival here. I won't disturb you; I have my reading matter." He held up a paperback book.

"No, no—sorry—it's not you. I just have to be on my way to see someone. Really, you did me a favor, waking me up."

She thanked the man and walked on, increasing her pace to a run. She knew exactly where she was going and what she would do when she arrived at her destination. She was returning to the task of gathering the facts, building a cache of information and while doing so, remaining alert to the possibility that she might encounter that nugget of illumination that would change everything.

Crossing the road in the direction of the nearest telephone kiosk, Maisie decided it would be best to place a call first, especially as Dr. Elsbeth Masters might be in the midst of another attempt at retirement. All previous efforts had come to naught, given not only her passion for her work—the psychiatric care of those who had suffered a profound, debilitating emotional and psychological shock—but the fact that an abundance of energy rendered her indefatigable also made her something of a nuisance for family, friends and neighbors during any extended period of relaxation. Stepping into a kiosk, Maisie drew an address book from her black bag, lifted the receiver and pushed the requisite number of coins into the slot, then waited for her call to be answered. Pressing button A directly she heard a voice on the line, Maisie made her request.

"Good afternoon—may I speak to Dr. Masters, please?"

"Right you are, caller, just one moment." A series of clicks followed as the hospital operator put through her call.

"Masters!" An exasperated sigh followed a greeting that reminded Maisie of MacFarlane.

"Hello, Dr. Masters—Elsbeth. It's Maisie Dobbs here."

"Maisie! Good lord! Breath of fresh air before I completely lose my mind—though I suppose I'm in the right place if I mislay my faculties. What can I do for you, Maisie? I'm sure this isn't a social call."

"If I could get over to your office within about half an hour, would you see me?"

"Drat! I've patients until this evening, and then I have to dash as soon as I've seen my last patient—a very difficult man—he gets what I call the sundowner seizures, though when I was a child in East Africa, a sundowner seizure was what my father appeared to experience when our house boy was late coming in with the gin and tonics!" Masters's throaty laugh echoed down the line. "Anyway, time is tight because my nephew is home on leave for only a couple of days, and I really must see him with his wife and the children while I can. I am so sorry—but look, I've a moment or two now. How can I help? Can I telephone you back? It sounds as if you're in a telephone box."

"Would you? Here's the number." Maisie gave the number, replaced the telephone receiver and picked it up again as soon as it began to ring.

Elspeth Masters's voice was filled with concern. "Right, what's troubling you, Maisie? I can hear urgency in your voice."

"It's about a child. I really would love your advice," said Maisie. She went on to describe Freddie Hackett witnessing a murder, and his home circumstances, together with the news she had learned earlier from Caldwell.

"Hmmm." Maisie imagined Masters twitching her lips from side to side, something she would do when considering a problem. "Hmmm. Well, you've come to the right place, but I don't know that my colleagues can do the right thing for your Freddie." She paused. Maisie waited, knowing Masters was considering all options and the best advice to offer. "Right, here's what I would suggest," said Masters. "As you know, one of our doctors—William Moodie—pioneered child psychiatry here, though you may remember Dr. Dawson, who started the children's clinic. Moodie went on to open the London Child Guidance Clinic—unfortunately, they had to move out to Oxford when war was declared. I've worked with both of those men, so I have some knowledge to impart. Now, the problem I see is that Freddie isn't suffering any of the symptoms our doctors are used to observing—he's not having seizures, he doesn't have obvious nervous tics, digestive problems or aberrant behaviors such as biting, hitting, screaming, hair-pulling, that sort of thing. And we don't want him to be weighed and measured before anyone even speaks to him—plus these stories of his are not troubling to the extent that the school has seen fit to refer him to the clinic. The schools are being vigilant at the moment, especially with some children returning quite upset from evacuation. So, no, we don't want to put him through that. We just require some indication of his level of what I would call 'psychological wounding.'"

"According to his mother, he is scratching his arms, sometimes until they bleed, so that's one thing. Otherwise, how do we do make an assessment regarding his psychological wounding?" asked Maisie. "What do you think? Will you see him?"

"Children are so different in their response to the world around them. Yes, I can identify certain traits—and when I bring out my collection of trinkets from Africa, that can always get the young mind off the fact that I'm a doctor. But I think you would be better served by someone really up on the latest research with regard to what goes on in a child's mind—and your Freddie is an interesting case."

"Why do you say that, Elsbeth?"

"Because he's had to take on the work of an adult—he's a little man, Maisie. A troubled little man, and I feel so desperately sorry for him."

Maisie thought she heard a catch in the psychiatrist's voice.

"Now then, I don't want that boy to be intimidated by being brought to a hospital, but I think it would be good to get an initial assessment, so I'm going to ask Alice Langley to get in touch with you."

"Is she a doctor?"

"No, but she's one of the best nurses I've ever worked with. Alice was a sister here in the child guidance clinic and she worked alongside Moodie and also Dr. Rosalie Lucas, and as you know, here at the Maudsley, nurses have been at the forefront of testing patients and drawing up psychiatric assessments. She's up on all the latest research, and is a wonder with children—no spring chicken, I might add, and for the past few months she's been at home with her daughter's two youngsters because they are now in her care. I daresay she will be back to work soon, even if it's only for one morning shift—we need her—but she wanted to get the children settled. The eldest has just started school and the neighbor will look after the younger one."

"What happened to her daughter?"

"She was killed in a daylight bombing raid, while the children were being looked after by the neighbor. Poor girl was just walking along the street, having waited in line for ages for a loaf of bread. Then barely two days later, Alice's son-in-law was killed when his ship was torpedoed, and as far as Alice knows he had not at that point received word of his wife's death, which I think is an absolute mercy. Alice's husband is an air raid warden, so she is on tenterhooks every night until he comes home. He wanted her to go to the country with the children, but she won't leave him at this point. I think she might go to Oxford though, as she is a gem and they could use her at the clinic. It's such a terrible position for the family to be in. You know, I once asked Alice how she manages, because she's remained this very gentle soul, not hardened by hatred or a desire for some sort of revenge. And you know what she said to me? 'Hatred, revenge—they're just as bad as trying to protect yourself from more hurt—they can make you brittle inside. And if you're brittle, you break. One way or another, you break.'"

Maisie was silent. The words were echoing in her mind.

"Anyway, I'll have a word with Alice," said Masters. "I think probably the best idea is for her to go to Freddie's home, or to meet the boy at a neutral place." Maisie could hear a tapping sound, and imagined Masters striking her pen on her wooden desk in rhythm as she spoke. "In the circumstances, I think Alice should see Freddie without the mother present, as it's obvious he envisions himself as a protector, so to get an accurate impression, we would want him to be in a place without even a loving influence at his shoulder. Expect Alice to be in touch with you first, but if you don't hear, do give her a telephone call—miraculously she has a telephone at the house, largely on account of her husband's work. Don't send a postcard though—the eldest grandchild is a precocious five-year-old and could probably read every word and understand it!"

Maisie took a pencil and notebook from her shoulder bag and noted the number as Masters recited it. "Was Alice's daughter a nurse too?" she asked as she replaced the pen and notebook in her bag.

"No, she was a doctor, actually. Only working part-time since the children came, but hospitals need all hands on deck, so she put on her white coat and went back in. I'd take on a qualified person for a couple of hours a day, if they can manage it." Maisie held the receiver away from her ear as Masters' throaty laugh filled the line. "So how about it, Maisie? You have the training!"

"Oh dear, I'm afraid not—another time I'll tell you about what happened to me last year when I was a volunteer ambulance driver—it means I'm probably not your best bet." Maisie was aware of the change in her voice as she framed her final question. "Elsbeth, what do you think about Freddie? Do you think he could have imagined seeing a man with a scar?"

The tapping of pen against wood began again. Maisie thought it sounded as if cogs were turning in the doctor's brain. "I think he might well have imagined seeing a man with a scar—but it doesn't mean he didn't see a murder, does it, Maisie?" Masters asked. "Now then, I've just looked at the time and I have a patient waiting. Do call me again, Maisie—better still, come over to have a natter when I'm not so fraught. And please let me know how it goes with the boy."

CHAPTER 11

M aisie, I cannot tell you how good it is to have company yet again. I feel as if I have received manna from heaven. Now, tell me what this visit is all about before I expire waiting." Gabriella Hunter gave Maisie a wide smile as they settled into the deep, shell-like chairs in her study. "And I'm glad you came—I don't get the good cakes every day, you know, despite appearances to the contrary."

There was a pause in conversation as Mrs. Towner brought in a tray with tea and cakes. As the housekeeper left the study, closing the door behind her without a sound, Maisie poured tea, and handed a cup to Hunter before sitting down with her own cup of tea. "The French in England, I suppose that's it," said Maisie. "And here's why." She explained that she wanted to know more about the Free French currently in London—any information would be helpful. "Gabriella, I haven't forgotten that you once worked with Maurice in Paris—that you were, let us say . . . let us say 'involved' in intelligence work during the last war. You may seem to most like a very accomplished expert on early French literature, but I know you have many skills up your sleeve."

"Ha! There are residents around this square, the sort with hand-shakes like wet fish in your fingers, who would be horrified to learn that I have killed the enemy with my bare hands." Hunter laughed.

"I should probably let them in on that little snippet of my history just before I present a paper when they're working themselves up to take down my theories along with my good name. It might give them second thoughts!" She became serious. "So, what is it exactly that you want to know? There's more at stake than a passing interest on your part?"

Maisie stood up and placed her now empty cup and saucer on the tray. "Character. Motivation. What drives people who have seen the enemy march into their country and along their city streets? People who have lost their homes, seen their neighbors dragged away. Many French citizens escaped across the Channel to England—and of course there's the man named de Gaulle in London too. They have sanctuary here, yet there is also animosity toward the British—they are working with us, and they seem to be working against us at the same time. It's to do with a case, so I want to know who they are—not specifically down to a name, though one or two of those would be handy—but who they are inside." She placed her hand on her chest, and took her seat again.

Hunter nodded. Maisie could feel a change in her demeanor, as if a cloud of melancholy had enveloped her.

"Strangely, the book I have just finished writing touches upon this very thing. Mind you, it's not going to leave me until I've read and reread my manuscript a thousand times—a nasty habit of mine that infuriates my publisher." She sighed, then continued. "Maisie, paramount, above everything, is this word: honor. Honor is in the heart and mind of every citizen of France, from the aristocracy to the most lowly man or woman. It is at the very center of Liberté, Egalité and Fraternité, our moral code—whether we stick to it or not. Honor is a word that strikes a chord with so many peoples, but it's different for the French." She glanced out of the window as she paused for a moment, then brought her attention back to Maisie. "So, that's the first thing—a thread that runs through the heart of every French man and woman."

"And what else?" Maisie was anxious for Hunter to continue.

"We can be defiant. Our defiance becomes very strong indeed when we are scared, when we are threatened, when the stakes are high and against us at every turn—and we take defeat very, very poorly." She became thoughtful once more. "Yes, I know the British are the same—and by god, there is resilience here in our country. But the French are a very interesting people—I am sure you know that British airmen would prefer to be shot down in occupied France rather than Vichy. I was told by a friend, one who knows about these things, that an airman will do his best to bring down his burning aircraft in the occupied area; he knows our people will help him because it's one in the eye for the Germans, who they hate. But in Vichy, Petain has shown a distinct paucity of integrity, a lack of respect for what France stands for; hence the Vichy authorities would hand over that same airman to the Nazis; a gift, if you will, to curry favor. Their dearth of fidelity to what France stands for means that Petain might as well be an out-and-out traitor—and if there is one thing the French hate, it's a traitor, though I concede he may be acting because he fears the Nazis and is intimidated by their power, but that's no excuse in my book."

Maisie said nothing for a few moments, allowing Hunter's words to settle inside her, words she would take out later and examine, along with the cache of information she had gathered since leaving her house this morning. There was a passion in the woman's summation of the situation in France, a passion that had escalated with every word as she responded to the question. However, Maisie had to know more. She came to her feet again and took the cup and saucer from Hunter's hands.

"Another cup?"

"Oh, yes please, dear—and I'm sorry. I rather went on, didn't I?"

"Not at all—your opinion is of great value to me, and if you don't mind, I've a few more questions." Maisie poured more tea and handed the cup and saucer back to Hunter before taking her seat once more. Even in her choice of china, Gabriella seemed avant-garde—the matching Clarice Cliff teapot, cups and saucers, sugar bowl and jug decorated in striking shades of orange, blue, red and green marked the woman as an individualist.

"It's extraordinary—that you remember exactly how I like my tea. First a little milk, then the tea, and then just a little hot water on top."

Maisie laughed. "Some things you never forget, Gabriella. You didn't have a housekeeper when Maurice first brought me here, so I always made tea while you two were catching up with your news, and then when I brought in the tray and poured for us all, you would discuss some subject or other and I was expected to contribute to the conversation."

"I know—cruel, weren't we? I always thought he expected too much of you."

Maisie shook her head. "Perhaps, but it never harmed me, and what he did was show me the road ahead and give me the tools to make the journey." She looked down at her hands, trying not to be swept back on a wave of nostalgia. Bringing her attention back to Hunter, Maisie continued her questioning. "Tell me about de Gaulle."

Hunter gave a slight shake of her head. "The man is in a difficult position. He is not in France, so it appears to the French that he has left them behind to become victims of the Nazis. Yet on the other hand, they know he is over here, and there are a good number who believe he is doing all he can to help France from a safe place. Think of his speech last year, on the eighteenth of June. Parts still ring in my ears—and there are words we will all remember, we who love France. Every aspect of his speech was calibrated for the moment, but his call to arms was spoken with passion. *'I call upon all Frenchmen who want to remain free to listen to my voice and follow me.'*"

There was another pause in the conversation before Hunter continued.

"I suppose I get quite taken with emotion at times, when I think of the war. The troubling element in all of this is a collective fear among the French that de Gaulle is collaborating with the British, that he is Churchill's poodle, a tool of Britain. And we in Britain look quite vulnerable to the French, don't we? They are convinced that Hitler will march in at any moment and fly the swastika over Buckingham Palace and the Houses of Parliament, so they anticipate that de Gaulle will then become Hitler's puppet. Thus de Gaulle has to step with care, demonstrating to his countrymen that he has the upper hand over Churchill. He therefore appears haughty, arrogant and dismissive, and at the same time he has to show an element of gratitude for his life and his ability to be a leader for France despite being in exile—when across the Channel there are citizens who speak of Petain's heroism during the last war and trust him implicitly. I must confess that I believe Petain has sold his soul to the devil who resides in Germany, and he's a man who should not be trusted by anyone, least of all Britain."

"What about the many men and women Britain is sending to France? I'm sure you know about our people who are risking their lives for the French."

"Indeed I do, but let's be clear—they are risking their lives to keep the Nazis in France and not over here. So from the perspective of the Free French, any resistance has to be seen to be French in origin and under French leadership. They want French heroes to be the driving force for the secret incursions into France by Britain's agents."

Maisie nodded, thoughtful. "And what if there was discord among the French agents here?"

Hunter put her cup and saucer onto the table at her side, balancing it upon a pile of books. "Unless that discord is rooted in petty arguments, Maisie, then you must attribute any discord to my first response—and that is honor. Personal or collective honor. Seek out the dishonorable, and you will find what you are looking for."

The women spoke a little longer before Maisie could see that Hunter seemed tired. She stood up to take her leave, kissed the older woman on both cheeks, and promised to visit again soon. It was as she reached the door that Gabriella Hunter called out to her.

"Maisie—one thing. A grudge can be held for a long time, can span generations, particularly for the French. And sadly, the desire to protect honor is not put aside in a time of war; indeed, the threat of death makes it only more urgent." She paused. "I believe you will require more from me sooner than you might think. I know I'm getting on, but once a spy, always a spy, and I still have contacts, you know."

As she reached the front door of her ground-floor flat, Maisie could hear the telephone ringing inside. Fumbling with the key in shaking hands, she unlocked the door and ran into the flat, slamming the door behind her and racing toward the telephone.

"Yes, hello—," she said, lifting the receiver to her ear, fearful she had missed the call she had not even realized she was waiting for until she heard the ringing from outside. "Yes, are you there?"

"Miss Maisie Dobbs?"

"Yes—" Maisie heard the sound of two operators talking.

"Connecting you now," said the British operator.

"Putting you through, caller," said an American voice, followed by a clicking sound.

"Mark?"

"Maisie?"

"Oh, I hoped it was you."

There was silence on the line.

"Mark—"

"Well, well, well—what happened to that stiff upper lip?" Mark Scott laughed. "That's a first—you sound pleased to hear my voice."

Maisie felt tears prick her eyes. *If you're brittle, you break.* "Mark— I've . . . I've missed you."

"I've missed you, too, Maisie. I've missed you, and I've missed Anna, and I've even missed Brenda giving me the evil eye every time she sees me. I miss the bombs, the weak tea—no, check that, I don't miss any tea—but I miss London. And I'll be home soon. I'll be leaving DC in a day or two, or maybe three, and coming back, so chill a bottle of wine for me. Better still, don't be shy about putting a beer in the icebox."

Maisie laughed, feeling lightheaded as the truth seeped into her. She was bending to the reality of her feelings for Mark Scott and in that moment could do nothing more than offer words that echoed her lover's. "Come home soon, Mark. Come home safe and soon."

"What is it, Maisie? What's going on? Something's wrong—I can hear it in your voice."

"I'm—I'm just a bit weary, I suppose. It's been a long day. I have a difficult case in progress and I feel as if I'm on a boat sailing into a headwind. Two steps forward, then I stumble back." She laughed. "And I'm not even getting paid for it!"

"You've faced the headwinds before."

"I know, but this time . . . this time there's a young boy involved and I fear it will be hard to get to the truth of the matter. He's not a . . . well, I suppose there's a shadow of doubt over him."

"Maisie, if there's one thing I know about you, it's that when you follow your best instincts, you're on the right track. So do that. The gusts coming at you are only you doubting yourself." He paused for a second. "See, I know you, Maisie Dobbs—contrary to what you might think."

Maisie nodded, as if Mark Scott were in the room with her and could see her every move. She wondered whether this might be the right time to acknowledge how unsettled they had been, at times snappy, so busy that they often failed to understand each other—or just didn't make the effort. It had crossed her mind several times that they wanted the same things in life, but not at the same time. She decided to say nothing, considering it best to keep the peace, and not burden either of them with her fears that their affair was sometimes like a heart beating out of rhythm, and therefore at risk of failing. "Yes, of course—you're right. Use my best instincts."

Their conversation moved on to other matters, as Maisie told Scott about Anna and her despair at losing her beloved Emma, that she had been so upset she did not want to ride in the gymkhana. Mark described Washington in October, and told Maisie that he never thought he would miss London, but there was much to do when he returned with new orders. They both accepted that he couldn't discuss his work at the embassy, any more than Maisie could reveal anything more about her cases.

"I've got to go now, Maisie. I waited until the small hours to call you and now it's time for this old bear to get some shut-eye before a meeting with the president tomorrow morning. It might be okay for him to have gray sacks under the eyes, but I have to look bright-eyed and bushy-tailed."

Maisie laughed. "Take care, Mark. And I'll see you soon."

"You can bet on it, Maisie Dobbs."

Maisie waited, wondering if there would be more before the line clicked and the conversation was terminated. The long, lonely tone of the disconnected call echoed in her ears and she at once felt bereft, for the spoken declaration she so wanted to hear had not come. And she had forgotten to thank him for the necklace.

Maisie returned the telephone receiver to its cradle and began to take off her light woolen jacket, touching the diamond with her fingertips as she removed her silk scarf. She ran her fingers through her hair as if to release the tight band of tension around her head. Throwing the jacket across the back of an armchair, she set her shoulder bag on the desk and made her way toward the kitchen. She filled the kettle and set it on the smallest gas ring, then lit the flame with a match from a box she kept on the shelf above the stove. While waiting for the water to boil, Maisie stepped back into the sitting room, then to the dining room and each of the two bedrooms, drawing blackout curtains as she moved through her home.

"I feel as if I'm shutting myself inside a cave," she said aloud. Opening the refrigerator—she was still getting used to the sound of what Mark Scott referred to as "the icebox," even though it had been installed over a year earlier—she saw two bottles of Guinness and a bottle of wine. She turned around, extinguished the gas flame underneath the kettle, removed the bottle of chilled white wine and opened it, pouring herself a glass. Once again she began to walk through her flat, taking note of a book set on the small table alongside the armchair that Scott favored. In her bedroom, she opened the wardrobe and ran her fingers along the sleeves of two crisp white shirts with labels indicating that they came from a shop in America called Brooks Brothers. A pair of Scott's polished black shoes had been left alongside the wall, the name inside the shoes revealing that they had been made by hand according to the customer's specifications. There was something about the shirts, their shape and the residue of Scott's cologne, that made her want to hold them close, as if to do so would ensure that something precious would never slip through her fingers. She often did the same thing in the smaller bedroom where she kept a change of clothes for Anna, for the rare occasion when Maisie brought her to London, a special treat she loved. When Anna had left again, usually with Frankie and Brenda, Maisie would sometimes return to the empty flat and bury her head in her child's clothing, and once she fell asleep clutching one of Anna's soft toys. How she ached to return to Chelstone each week, running for the train and counting the minutes before she could hold her daughter in her arms—just as she rushed back to the flat when she knew her lover would be there.

Returning to the kitchen, she realized that Mark Scott had taken up residence in her life and in her heart, and she wanted him to remain there.

The telephone began ringing again; instinct informed Maisie that it would be MacFarlane calling. It seemed that even the Bakelite telephone was under his orders and appeared to emit a more forceful ring when he was on the line, as if to say, "For heaven's sake answer this telephone right now because he's beating me." She picked up the receiver.

"Robbie—how are you?"

"I'm not even going to ask how you knew it was me."

"It's the way the telephone rings. I always know when it's you. Why are you calling? I'm starving and I've not had a bite to eat all day."

"I'll have something for you when you get here, lass," said Mac-Farlane.

"But—"

"Bright should be outside your door at any minute. Just get in the motor car and she'll have you here before you know it. Bring that glass of wine in your hand if you like."

"How did you know—"

"I can always hear a telltale sip—it's as far as my intuition stretches, but it works every time. Anything else I accomplish in a day is due to solid, old-fashioned detection—or perhaps you've forgotten what that is? Now then, get in the motor car, Maisie."

"Robbie—what's happened?"

"Can't say until you get here."

"Is it serious?"

"I don't drag my people out of the comfort of their own homes when they've been racing round London all day, their feet are sore and they miss their Yank—though heaven knows why—unless it's bloody well serious."

CHAPTER 12

Maisie's journey was through darkened streets, yet Corporal Bright maneuvered the vehicle with ease. Only searchlights beaming up across the sky offered any kind of direction, but the ATS driver made her way to Baker Street as if flaming torches marked the route. Maisie had grown used to Bright, and noticed that instead of her usual effervescent demeanor, the young woman was silent. *She knows,* thought Maisie. *She knows why I'm being summoned.*

"I think you might have an idea why I'm being called in to see Mr. MacFarlane," said Maisie. Almost as soon as she had uttered the words, she knew it was wrong of her to do so. "I'm sorry—I shouldn't have asked. Forget I inquired."

"It's all right, Miss Dobbs. I probably look as if I know something, but I don't—I'm too far down the ladder, just the driver." She was silent for a moment, then spoke again. "Mind you, if it's honesty you want, here's what I know about life. When my mum wasn't feeling well and her stomach kept going dickey, she went to the doctor. The doctor sent her for tests. Two days later she gets a postcard to go in straightaway. That's when we knew it was bad. We didn't have a telephone, so they had to send the postcard. Mind you, it came that afternoon. You know when something's urgent, don't you? So when people get telephone calls from the likes of Mr. MacFarlane and he drags me in just as I'm going off a shift I started at five in the morning and he tells me to pick

185

up someone important, I know I can't complain about the job, because it's obvious to me that they're not being brought in so MacFarlane can tell them they've got the all-clear, if you know what I mean."

Maisie sighed. "Thank you for your candor, Corporal Bright."

"You knew it was serious anyway, didn't you, Miss Dobbs?"

"Yes. I knew."

"And I know what goes on in that office. I'm not silly, and it doesn't take the brains of an archbishop, does it? I have to drive the men and women who are going over to France to their departure point. I take them to whichever house they're staying at while they wait for the weather or the moon or whatever it is, and then later if I'm the driver on duty, I take them to the airfield." She paused. "It's a wonder old Mac hasn't sent me over there—he will if they lose any more, I bet."

"You have to be fluent in French, Corporal Bright."

"I am. Mum was French—she died when I was sixteen. Stomach cancer—so no, she never got the all-clear when she was called back to the hospital. Dad met her in the last war, fell in love, and then after the Armistice he brought her over here. By which time, I might add, yours truly was a bun in the oven!"

Maisie laughed. "You're right—with that information, I'm surprised MacFarlane hasn't recruited you."

"He told me he would never forgive himself if anything happened to me and he had to break the news to my dad, and then he said"—she began to mimic MacFarlane's accent—"More to the point, Charlie Bright, you're a bit too quick with your wit. It's wits *about* you we need, not the kind of wit that's your stock-in-trade. You'd be a liability, lass. A liability if I sent you over there.'" Bright reverted to her own accent. "To be honest, I think he's right. And I wouldn't want to go anyway—I see quite enough from here, thank you very much!"

"Well, you've got MacFarlane down pat, Corporal."

Bright laughed. "Dad says I'm a parrot. Got me into a lot of plays at school—and a lot of trouble too!" She slowed the car and pulled into the curb. "Here we are, Miss Dobbs. Just a sec—I'll come round."

Corporal Bright opened the passenger door, allowing Maisie to step out of the motor car. "I daresay Mr. Mac will be coming out of that door any time now . . . and there he is, waiting for you."

"I don't like that look," whispered Maisie to herself, seeing Mac-Farlane outside the door, then louder, "Thank you, Corporal Bright. Excellent driving, as usual."

Bright saluted and closed the door at the same time as MacFarlane approached.

"Well done, Bright. You're off duty now. I'll get another driver to take Miss Dobbs home." He reached for Maisie's arm. "Come on, Maisie. Haven't got all night."

"What's going on?"

"In a minute."

MacFarlane escorted Maisie past the porter's desk toward a staircase she knew would take them into the bowels of the building. Opening a door into a small office, he held out his hand for Maisie to enter first, then followed, locking the door behind him. It was warm in the windowless room; she began to feel a hint of claustrophobia.

"Sit down, lass," said MacFarlane.

Maisie took a seat. MacFarlane eased into the chair on the opposite side of a desk with only one file on top—no other documents or papers were visible. It looked like a room that was only used in certain circumstances. She knew rooms like this. Anyone who had ever worked in a hospital knew this room. It was the room where death was announced.

"Is it Pascale?"

He shook his head while opening the folder. "Elinor Jones was captured by the Gestapo and is now believed to have been tortured before her death, which took place in France. As far as we know, she was not transferred to Ravensbrück—the concentration camp where the Nazis send women like Miss Jones. We know at least one other agent who was taken there, but in this case not Miss Jones. We hope to receive intelligence confirmation that, while she may have experienced some terror that I don't even want to think about, she had an opportunity to ingest her L-pill. At least we bloody well hope she did."

Maisie drew breath to speak.

"Let me finish first, Maisie," said MacFarlane, without looking up. She suspected he was not reading a report, nor was he referring to it, but kept his head down because he could not meet her eyes. He continued, "Um . . . right, where was I? Yes—fortunately, her partner, the lass who receives transmissions from Jones, recognized the fist change immediately a new message came in, so we knew she must have been captured. We believe it was a German radio operator who was using her equipment and trying to get his hands on information that would put a raft of agents in danger. You see, Miss Jones had the bright idea of teaching a few words of Welsh to her partner while they were training, so they used them at the beginning and end of each transmission. The Germans might know some of our colorful street vocabulary to fool us, but they don't know Welsh!" He pinched the bridge of his nose. "We've given her partner compassionate leave for a few days; she's in one of our safe houses."

Maisie could wait no longer, feeling as if she might scream at any moment. Only it would not be a scream, it would be an explosion from her heart and it would bring down the roof, pulverizing the walls and shattering glass windows on the way. "I shouldn't have let her go. I should have put my foot down."

"It wasn't up to you, Maisie. You interview these people for us, you give your qualified opinion of their state of mind before they leave, but do not for a moment think that you are the last word—because you're not. You are just a cog in a wheel. We're all just cogs in the wheels of war."

"So, who gives the last word, Robbie? Who does that? Who do I speak to about Elinor?"

"So you can do what?" Now his eyes met hers, shocking her with their clarity and resolve. "You made an assessment and you were bang on right about her. But she was not captured because she made a mistake. She was caught out because she didn't stand a chance. The Germans have ever more sophisticated detection equipment, and they are fast. We have boffins doing their best, and by golly they are good, what with the inventions they come up with, yet we still can't keep up with them. But the Germans—best engineers in the world when it comes to wireless transmission and signal detection. Those boys are born with antennae coming out of their ears and coils of wire running through their veins, Maisie." He paused. "Thank god our code-breakers are better than theirs. Anyway, I'm not finished."

Maisie felt chilled, as if any remaining air in the room had become colder. "Pascale! Where is she? What's happened to her, Robbie?"

"We know it was close—the whole unit was at risk from the start. As far as we know she's on the run. We hoped it would be toward the border—there are safe houses on the way. The other option would be for her to lay low and then we'll get her out on a Lysander as soon as she makes contact and it's safe. We're awaiting confirmation as to her whereabouts, who's keeping her under their wing, and then we'll know the best way to bring her home. That's where you come in—trying to predict what she would do."

Maisie did not pause to reflect. "She would make an attempt to go home."

"Well, that's a relief," said MacFarlane.

"No, it's not, Robbie. England is not her home." Once again she met his gaze. "Her home is her grandmother's chateau, and at the moment it is also home to senior Gestapo officers."

"God help us."

"It's in the notes, Robbie—or perhaps you were all so captivated by that clipped English accent and her perfect French, which as you know she speaks along with several other languages. It's a gift she has. And I'm sure you know that Chantal—her grandmother—has been running an escape line for RAF pilots from her cellar."

MacFarlane looked at his watch. "We're expecting to hear from one of our agents any minute now—which is why I wanted to get you in here sooner rather than later, so you can give us your opinion, and if there is contact with Miss Evernden, keep her on the straight and narrow. She's got a lot of her aunt in her."

"Robbie—" Maisie caught her breath. The news about Elinor seemed to have diminished her ability to draw air into her lungs. She had known Elinor since meeting her in Biarritz, when she was the young nanny to Priscilla's boys. "I'm sorry—just give me a second."

MacFarlane reached into his pocket and pulled out a thick white cotton handkerchief. "It's clean," he said, passing it to Maisie.

Maisie took the handkerchief, and wiped her eyes. She cleared her throat, composing herself. "Robbie, Pascale has all Priscilla's bravery, all her forthrightness, and she's a lot like her aunt, but she's also tempered. She's not quite so hotheaded. In fact, being too cool in a situation was something I commented upon in my notes—the middle ground can be a very safe place, whereas being brittle—and she can be brittle—renders you breakable."

MacFarlane nodded. Maisie had never known him not to have a quick retort. He glanced at his watch again, and pushed back his chair. "Come on, Maisie. Time to see what the radio operators are up to out there."

MacFarlane led Maisie along a corridor into another room, larger, with desks and radio equipment, and the tapping of Morse code coming from a unit in the corner, operated by a young woman with hair that had been drawn back into a smooth roll tracing the nape of her neck. Beads of perspiration had formed on her brow, and she was frowning as she leaned closer to the equipment. A man and a woman were standing behind her, peering over her shoulder. They both looked up as Maisie entered with MacFarlane, and nodded in their direction.

"Where are we?" asked Robert MacFarlane.

"She's alive," said the woman, her voice low. "But she believes she was shopped—someone gave away the radio operator's location and she was with her, having just disbanded with the rest of the group following a less than successful sabotage attempt on a train carrying men and ordnance. It's clear the Gestapo knew where to find them; it wasn't just the skills of a clever Nazi boy in a van with equipment locating her signal." She turned her head toward the operator, placing a hand on her shoulder as if to steady her. The young woman scribbled something on a piece of paper, which she handed to the man.

"Apparently our agent sustained a flesh wound, and she's been hiding out in the forest—well, we assume that's what it is," said the man.

"She said she's missed the big bad wolf and she's on her way to grandmother's house, whatever that means." He turned to the woman. "Did I miss something—is grandmother's house code for a safe house?"

"Oh dear—," said Maisie. All four people in the room now focused on her as she turned to MacFarlane. "It's as I feared, Robbie. Grandmother's house isn't a code—she's going to try to reach her grandmother's residence. It's in the country, a chateau. Very grand. But it's currently home to a few Gestapo officers, as I said. And she's well aware of that fact."

No one spoke, yet the young woman kept her attention on the signal coming through. She wrote more notes, and handed them to the man.

"The injury is manageable, as far as we know. She's been seen by a local midwife who cleaned the wound, so her arm has at least been bandaged. She's going alone on foot and will not be using safe houses—because nowhere is safe. And she's taken one of her pills."

"What pills?" asked Maisie.

"Benzedrine," said MacFarlane. "We can't have tired, injured agents making life-and-death decisions, so they're given a supply of Benzedrine to perk them up when they're exhausted. It wasn't necessary for you to know this." He turned to the young woman. "Who's operating the radio at the other end?"

"Jeanette, my partner," replied the young woman. "The agent located her, but she's signed off—we were on too long anyway, so they're on the move, then they'll split up and the agent will proceed alone." She removed her headset and set it down, before taking a handkerchief from her pocket and wiping her brow. Putting on her cap, she stood up. "Will there be anything else?"

"No—good work, Fredericks. Very good work," said the woman. "You can go now."

The man unlocked the door, allowing the woman to leave.

"Hold the door, we're leaving," said MacFarlane, then turned to the woman. "Do we have absolute confirmation that Jones is dead?"

The woman nodded. "Yes."

"Then we'll inform next of kin."

"Right you are. If we could meet when you're finished, Robbie?" said the woman.

MacFarlane nodded, and then led Maisie back to the small, cramped, airless office.

"What do you think she'll do?" he asked, reaching into a drawer. He drew out two glasses and a bottle of single-malt whisky. "Sometimes the moment calls for an eighteen-year-old single malt." He poured the amber liquid into the glasses, slid one toward Maisie and lifted his own glass to his lips. Emptying the glass in one swallow, he slammed it onto the table. "Bastards! Nazi bastards!" He poured again.

Maisie reached for her glass and took a mouthful, the burn at the back of her throat almost painful, but soothing all the same.

"What will she do, Maisie? When she gets there?"

Maisie took another sip, which seemed to counter the burn. "Benzedrine, Robbie?"

"Yes, Maisie—that's what we prescribe to keep them alive when they're half dead. The other one is to deliver them from the hell of Nazi torture. Now again, what will she do when she reaches Grannie's house?"

"I was at the chateau a long time ago, Robbie, but I know there are several secret routes to get into the house—they were used during the Revolution as a means of escape—and there are rooms that no one would ever find because they have disguised entrances. When she reaches the house, she'll lay low in the stables or a barn until the officers have left for the day, and then she'll use one of the tunnels—there's one that leads from the stables."

"And then? Will she use the escape line?"

Maisie considered the question for a moment. "There's also a very strong chance she'll remain with her grandmother—she worries about her, and she may be tempted to join the local resistance, right under the noses of the Gestapo."

"Until the Abwehr find out about her, and it will be fast. Any story she cooks up will not pass muster with the German intelligence service. We've got to get her back."

'She may be willful, Robbie—but she's usually measured with it, and she's nobody's fool."

"And neither am I. The 'usually' worries me. I'll give her a couple of days, and then she's on her own. And though I don't know the inner workings of the escape line, I don't want her putting our boys at risk. She should look at what happened to her mother in the last war—shot by the Germans. And her father gave his life for our country." He was silent.

Maisie finished her malt whisky. She knew what was coming next.

"Elinor Jones' next of kin." It was not a question posed by Mac-Farlane, but a statement, lobbed across the desk.

"Her next of kin amounts to Priscilla. Her parents are dead, and she listed Priscilla in her last will and testament. The Partridge home is her home, even though the boys are grown now."

"You'll deal with it?"

"Yes."

"And what will you say?"

"A tragic accident in a lorry at an army barracks in the west country. The burial has already taken place, with only her commanding officer and the chaplain present as well as the pallbearers. It was conducted at a military cemetery in accordance with the deceased's wishes, because she did not want her family to go through the burden of seeing the actual lowering of her coffin into the ground. However, a memorial service will be left in the hands of Priscilla and the family, again per the deceased's wishes."

"I knew I could leave it up to you."

"And I hate every bloody minute of it, Robbie." Maisie met Mac-Farlane's gaze and did not turn away, then she stood up to leave.

"Before you go—"

"Yes?"

"How's the boy runner?"

"Safe and well, as you know."

"Good—" It seemed for a second as if MacFarlane was going to add something about Freddie Hackett and her inquiry, but then he left the comment hanging in the air. "There's a driver waiting to take you back to the flat, Maisie—probably just as well Bright's off duty now, she can be a bit of a chatterbox, that one, and you'll want to go home in peace. I'll see you out." He pushed back his chair and stood up. "Sorry about supper. Couldn't lay my hands on anything here."

Maisie held her emotions in check all the way home to her flat, until she watched the young woman driver pull away from the curb and drive off into the dark night. It was not too cool outside, and earlier intermittent showers had abated, though it was late by the time she entered the house, claimed her glass of wine and walked into the walled garden of her ground-floor flat, making sure the blackout curtain fell back into place as she closed the French door behind her. Still with her coat on, Maisie slumped down into one of the wicker chairs. Setting her glass on the table, she leaned forward, rested her head in her hands, and wept. She wept for Elinor and for Pascale. She wept for Priscilla and her scars; she shed tears for Priscilla's sons and for her own daughter, Anna. And as she grieved, she realized that she had never trusted the world to keep herself or those she loved safe. From the moment of her mother's death, she had known that terror could be around the next corner at any moment. Had there ever been a time when she felt the clutch of fear in her gut loosen its grip, so that she could have faith in the future? Even now—even now that she had Mark Scott in her life, and a child she would move mountains to keep safe—she knew fate could fool you. Fate could play out the line and allow you to feel at ease, and then yank you back with anything from a sickening illness to an accident or a war and bombers in the skies above. Or a love lost. And now she had to try to deceive her best friend into thinking a young woman who had become part of her family had died behind the wheel of an army vehicle, instead of slipping a cyanide pill into her mouth so she would never reveal the names of her fellow agents and the means by which they intended to sabotage every move the enemy made.

And what of the enemy? As her sobs subsided, she wondered who was with her country and who was against it. Freddie Hackett knew who was against him, and he knew who he feared—yet in taking on his case, she had crossed paths with a powerful French agent, and she didn't know to what extent he represented a danger to the boy, or to herself. Maisie had to keep Freddie safe—and the only way to do that was to keep digging in her search for the truth.

The headquarters of the Free French was guarded and surrounded by sandbags and barbed wire—as were so many buildings across the city. However, she could stand and watch for a while from a short distance without anyone noticing as she took account of comings and goings before she made her move. On occasion a motor car would pull alongside the door and a man or woman would emerge and enter the building, or a vehicle would arrive and someone would be escorted out. She knew who she was looking for—a certain Major André Chaput.

Maisie had left the flat that morning determined to find out more about the man whose murder the Hackett boy had witnessed. Mac-Farlane might have considered him a nameless thug pulled out of the Thames, but he had an identity and he had a job. Was he an honorable man, an innocent victim? Or might his murder have been a violent settling of accounts? She was ready to poke the wasps' nest with a stick and watch them buzz around in a frenzy. Yes, she might get stung, but she was prepared to take the risk—to a point.

She had been keeping vigil for about half an hour when she saw a man in the distance to the right who appeared to have the same bearing, the same gait as the major. Hoping for an advantageous moment, she walked to the left, then crossed the road at what she believed was the optimum point, and began to make her way back in the direction of the French Free headquarters. She pulled a piece of paper from her bag and scribbled a few words, then folded it, holding on to the square note while she returned the pencil to her bag. Looking around as if searching for an address, she all but walked straight into Chaput.

"Oh my goodness, I am so sorry," said Maisie, looking up at Chaput. "I was not paying attention, sir, I—oh, my goodness, it's Major Chaput, isn't it?"

The Frenchman gave a short bow, and as he returned to his full height, Maisie's gaze was drawn to the ridges of skin extending from the outer corners of his high cheekbones and alongside his face.

"I'm sorry, madame—I do not believe we've met," he said.

"Yes, of course—you're right. I'm sorry—you looked familiar."

Chaput smiled. "I should correct myself—we are not supposed to have met, are we?"

"Again, you're right. Forgive me." She held up the piece of paper. "I was rather preoccupied. I'm on my way to an appointment nearby and was checking the address."

"May I help you?"

"No, not to worry—it would be rather embarrassing if a Frenchman had to direct a native Londoner, wouldn't it?"

"Indeed, madame. Now, if you would excuse me—" Chaput raised his hat and continued on his way.

Had she lost her chance? No—she was not ready to confront him— yet she had achieved one thing: confirmation in broad daylight that the man had those deep vertical ridges on either side of his face, and a paler patch of skin under the right eye.

She checked her watch. It was time to see Freddie Hackett again— this time at his new school.

Children were in the playground as Maisie came alongside the school. There were not many outside during the dinner break, but she spotted Freddie and another boy of about the same age taking it in turns to kick a ball back and forth against Victorian cast iron railings resembling a series of spears facing the sky. The boys seemed bored, kicking the ball in a desultory fashion, as if it were the only game they could think to play. She walked along until she reached the railings and called out to Freddie. He waved, said something to his friend, and kicked the ball back to him before joining Maisie.

" 'Lo, Miss Dobbs," said Hackett.

"Hello, Freddie. Everything all right? Are you liking your new school?"

"Well—it's still school, but it's all right." He shrugged, but then gave a wide smile. "But my mum, Iris and me, we really like the flat. I can't believe I've got my own room! Thank you very much, Miss Dobbs."

"I'm glad." Maisie glanced across to the teacher monitoring children in the playground and saw her consult her watch. "Look, we've only got a minute, but I wanted to ask you about the night you saw the two men fighting. How did you manage to see the lines on that man's face? Where was the light coming from? It's to help the police draw up their notes—you're not in any trouble."

"Have you got him, miss?"

"We're following him, Freddie. So don't you worry—you're perfectly safe."

"I can't remember about the light and any direction, miss. It was very bright everywhere, on account of the moon. There wasn't much in the way of clouds. And as I said before, I was close enough, but they couldn't see me. I saw them though. And I saw those lines, or whatever they were. I thought they were scars, like I told you before."

Maisie smiled. "That's all I needed, Freddie." She reached into her bag for her purse and took out a shilling. "There you are—every little bit helps, doesn't it? Are you working after school?"

Freddie took the shilling. "Thank you, Miss Dobbs." He put the coin in his pocket. "I've to go over to Baker Street, but I don't know if there's any messages for me to run with until I get there. They let me go home if I have to wait more than an hour."

"Use some of your money to get the bus over there, Freddie. It's a long way from here, so don't wear yourself out."

"Oh, I like running, miss. I like how my legs feel. All sort of tingly. Running's what I'm good at. Everyone says so. When the war's over, I'm going to the Olympics. Then when I'm too old to run, I'm going to teach other boys how to do it. My old PT teacher said I could be anything I wanted to be." The boy looked down and kicked his foot against the wall. "He was training me, but then he went off with the evacuees."

Maisie looked through the railings as if she were peering at Freddie through prison bars—though any railings were rare now, so many had been ripped out to send to the factories making war's hardware: aircraft, tanks and munitions. "You know, Freddie—I think you stand every chance of going to the Olympics."

CHAPTER 13

Maisie knew that as soon as she arrived at Chelstone railway station, her first task would be to go to Priscilla's cottage so she could get the conversation she dreaded over and done with. Only then could she set her mind to anything else. She would be unable to give any other matter her full attention until she had broken news of Elinor's death to the family who loved her.

Experience had taught Maisie that drawing back from the work of facing up to tragedy could cripple a person from within. She knew only too well that any reticence to look grief in the eye might cause emotions to atrophy, as if the heart had been drained of an ability to feel even the most searing pain. Hadn't she done the same thing, years ago, when she could not face the truth of what had happened to her first love, Simon, during the last war? The casualty clearing station where they were working came under attack, wounding them both, though Simon had sustained an injury to the brain from which he would never recover. Maisie had put off seeing him time and again, until months of fearful avoidance had become years and she was unable to take the first step in the direction of a man so changed by war. No, she was determined to see Priscilla as soon as possible, or she would drag her feet and too many days would elapse, and then MacFarlane would take up the task.

It was fortuitous that Douglas, Priscilla's husband, was working at the cottage for a few days. He would anchor his family as news of Elinor's death brought a dark cloud down upon them. Douglas, like his son, Tim, had lost an arm in the midst of conflict. It was an affliction that had become a joke in the family, after Tim recovered from his amputation. Yet Douglas had proven time and again that he had the ability to hold his family tight and close, that the act of encircling them during a time of deep sorrow had everything to do with inner and not physical strength.

"Maisie! My goodness, I thought I wouldn't see you until Saturday—you usually go straight home from the train and bury yourself away with Anna! Come on, let's have a . . . let's have a cup of tea." Priscilla chattered on, almost as if she had an innate awareness of something terrible closing in, and only constant conversation on her part would stave off the monster. "You almost caught me there—I was going to say, 'Let's have a gin and tonic,' and then I looked at the time—far too early for a drink. Mind you, I always maintain that the sun must be over the yardarm somewhere in the world, eh? Now then—"

"Pris—Pris, we must talk. Come along—let's go into the sitting room. Is Douglas here?"

"Is it Tom? Is that why you've got that look on your face? What is it? I've got Tim and Tarquin accounted for, and Douglas has popped along the road to post a letter, but I don't know about Tom."

"No, it's not Tom—all I know about Tom is that he's training new pilots somewhere in Northumberland, and he's in love with a flame-haired air force meteorologist."

"Thank god for that—though I have my doubts about the meteorologist, and—"

"Pris—sit down."

"Well, it can't be that bad if my toads are all alive and well." Priscilla took a seat on the small sofa and reached for her cigarettes and lighter. "Go on then, Maisie—fire away!"

Maisie took a deep breath, as if fortifying herself before plunging into a freezing cold lake. "Because we're friends—like sisters . . ." She felt her throat become tighter. "Because we're as good as family, I have been requested to inform you that Elinor has been tragically killed in a freak accident while driving a lorry between two military establishments. I don't know the specifics, though I was assured that her passing would have been instantaneous. She would have felt no pain, no prolonged suffering." Maisie looked at Priscilla to check her reaction; she was staring straight at Maisie, a single unlit cigarette drooping between two fingers.

"You're lying."

"No, Priscilla, I am not lying. I am telling the truth. I am really so very sorry." Maisie stopped to take another breath, feeling as if a weighted cloak had wrapped itself around her. She wanted to reach out and hold on to Priscilla, but could not move. She sought words to continue, trying to remember the script she had crafted in her mind over and over again during a sleepless night. "Given the nature of the accident and the location, Elinor has already been buried with full honors, though we can go to the cemetery together, if you wish—it's down in the west country, which I think she would have liked. Her commanding officer will render all assistance with the planning of a memorial service, again, only if you wish, but as Elinor listed you as her next of kin, it's—"

"Stop it! Stop it, stop it, stop it now!" Priscilla closed her eyes and broke down, falling forward as she wept. Maisie went to her, kneeling on the floor and holding her friend so close she could feel her heartbeat. "Oh my God, Elinor. Elinor! Oh Maisie—I owed her so much." Priscilla gulped back tears. "I was clueless when I had Tom. I had this squealing little red thing, and though I wanted to do everything my-self and I tried for months on end, I finally asked my aunt to find me a doughty English nanny—and she sent me this very young Welsh girl who saved us. Tom would have died before he was a year old if it hadn't been for Elinor." Priscilla pulled a handkerchief from her sleeve and wiped her eyes. "And she saved me too—she taught me how to be a mother, how to love my child, and for heaven's sake, it was as if she were a mother to me, too, and she was barely out of school. She just knew how to do everything. And with each boy, she just got on with it. If it hadn't been for Elinor, they would have grown wild, but she taught me how to make men of them, how they could be good boys and still be themselves, each one of them. And now this . . ."

"What's going on? What is it?"

Maisie turned to face Douglas Partridge, who had come into the room, followed by Tarquin.

Maisie broke the news again. Douglas reached for his wife, and pulled her to him.

"Darling—oh my darling."

Tarquin stood speechless, his eyes wide. Maisie put an arm around her godson's shoulders.

"Tante Maisie," said the boy, almost choking on his words as he turned to Maisie. "I'd better let my brothers know. I should get mes-sages to them, so they know to telephone us."

Maisie nodded and released Priscilla's youngest, a boy-man almost as tall as his father. She watched as he walked away toward the tele-phone, his shoulders shaking as he gave in to tears.

"I'll go now," said Maisie, as Douglas turned to face her. "I'm so sorry to be the bearer of this news, but I was asked to do so because of our personal connection. Elinor was loved by us all—the accident was a terrible, terrible tragedy."

"Thank you, Maisie—thank you for being the one to come, though I cannot imagine how this must have tormented you."

"Please let me know if there is anything more I can do. Elinor listed Priscilla as her next of kin, but I am sure she has relatives in Wales; I can help you find them if you don't already know their addresses."

"Driving a bloody lorry," said Priscilla, her face tear-streamed and red. "Serving your country by driving a lorry, and she gets killed. It's not bloody well fair."

"No, it's not fair, Pris. Nothing in war is ever fair. We both know that only too well. But I saw her not long ago, and she was happy. She was proud to be doing her bit—that's what she told me. That she was proud to be doing anything to stop Hitler marching into Britain."

"Well, that was Elinor," said Priscilla. "Even when she was mixed up with that most unsuitable Basque man while we were in France, she put us all first, before everything. We loved her, Maisie. We all loved her so much—she was family."

"I know—"

"And heaven only knows how she thought she was going to stop Hitler with a lorry."

Maisie turned to leave, but lingered when Priscilla called out to her.

"Maisie, darling, I think you might know how to contact my niece. She should be told. Pascale and Elinor became quite friendly, you know. She'll be very upset."

Maisie nodded. "I'll find out the name of someone who could relay a message to her. So yes, you can rest assured she'll be informed."

"Mummy, Mummy, Mummy!"

Anna rushed into Maisie's arms outside the school.

"Mummy—you're crushing me!"

"Oh, I'm sorry, darling—I just have so many cuddles inside me, I suppose they all came out at once," said Maisie. "Come along, let's go home for a cup of tea and you can tell us all about school today."

This was one of the most cherished parts of Maisie's week—coming home. Each Wednesday or Thursday afternoon, when she returned to the Dower House at Chelstone Manor following several days in London, she ached for half past three in the afternoon, when it was time to begin her walk to the village primary school. She would wait by the cast iron gates to hear the bell signifying that lessons had finished, then watch as children streamed from the Victorian building, some looking for their mothers, others setting off home because their mothers were working, perhaps on one of the local farms. Maisie would open her arms wide as soon as she saw the little girl with olive skin run toward her, her satchel half open and sometimes spilling a book and her pencils. Two almost jet-black braids would be bouncing off her shoulders, though it was not unusual for the ribbon to have been lost from one plait and then replaced with a rubber band supplied by the teacher. Anna would launch herself at Maisie, clinging to her with arms around her neck and legs around her hips.

As Maisie and her daughter walked home along the lane, Anna maintained a constant dialogue. "I wrote about Emma today in composition. The teacher asked us all to write a story about something we'd lost. Everyone else wrote about losing toys or their hats and gloves in winter, but I wrote about Emma. She's not lost really—I know where she is—but it's like losing something, and I miss her."

Maisie nodded, holding Anna's hand. "I know, darling. But remember how sad Grandad was when Jook died, and—"

"He cried," said Anna, a frown forming across her forehead. "I was supposed to be asleep, but I heard him talking to Grandma in the kitchen, so I came downstairs and looked in, and I saw him crying about

Jook. I went back to bed again and cried for Jook and Grandad, and I said my prayers for them." She sighed. "Grandad isn't as sad now, is he?"

"No, my love—that's because time helps, as it passes. Time puts a little cushion around our hearts."

"I've still got a big hurt here, where Emma lives," said Anna, placing her hand on her chest. "It's different from when my first nanny died, before you became my mummy."

"Shall we do this?" Maisie stopped and faced her daughter. She lifted her hands, and placed first her left hand against her chest, and then her right hand on top of her left. "Follow me—see what I've done with my hands? You can close your eyes and cradle your heart, then before you know it the pain starts to go away."

Anna faced her mother and followed her lead. Resting her small hands against the buttons on her school blazer, she closed her eyes.

"I can feel it, Mummy. The hurt is starting to go."

"We can do it again before bedtime—in fact, any time you feel the hurt about Emma. It's like giving your heart a lovely soft cuddle."

Emma opened her eyes, dropped her hands and began skipping along. "When's Uncle Mark coming again? I miss him."

"Oh, I'm not sure, darling. Perhaps in a week or so."

"That's good—we've run out of chocolate!"

Brenda met Maisie and Anna at the kitchen door.

"A woman just telephoned for you, Maisie. I told her you'd be back in a little while, so she said she'd try again. Said it was about someone called Hackett. She couldn't leave a number because she was in a telephone box."

"Oh, I know who that is. Thank you, Brenda."

"I see someone has lost more ribbons!" said Brenda, hands on hips as she looked down at Anna. "Come on—time to get out of that uniform so it's nice for tomorrow."

"There's the telephone again now," said Maisie. "I'll just be a few minutes."

Once inside the library, she closed the door behind her and reached for the receiver.

"Hello."

"Miss Dobbs?"

"Yes, speaking."

"Good afternoon. My name is Mrs. Alice Langley. Dr. Masters asked me to go to see a boy named Freddie Hackett, so I went to his school today and then found out that he was at home, so I took the liberty of going to see him there. I've not long left the flat, which is why I'm in a telephone box. I knew you would want to hear from me straightaway."

"Oh dear—I hadn't had a chance to talk to his mother."

"That's all right—I'm used to dealing with parents and children, though it's hard to think of some of the boys and girls of Freddie's age as children anymore. They've already seen more of life and death than we might have at that age. Anyway, I explained myself to the mother, who understood the reason for my visit. She was agreeable to my speaking with Freddie—first with her present, and then she went off ostensibly to make tea, but she gave us time to talk alone."

"And?"

"I'll put this all in a written report for you, but the boy is clearly under a cloud, and of course you can't miss that scratching on the arms, though it looked as if it had been healing a bit and then he started again. He is terrified of his father and he remained at home because his mother was not at work today and he was afraid his father would come to the flat and kill her."

"He was clear about killing her?"

"Oh yes. He indicated that the father had threatened as much on many occasions, and though the man might not mean to go so far, a child is not to know that. Freddie has probably heard threats of this nature since early childhood, and though he has grown and matured, in some ways he is still a small boy, fearful of the future."

Maisie drew breath to ask another question, but the woman continued.

"Regarding the event that Freddie Hackett is supposed to have witnessed, I would say he definitely saw something that scared him very much. Whilst I am not a detective, I would suggest that if further evidence were found to indicate someone had been murdered or there was some sort of attack in the place where Freddie maintains he saw a fight, then we should assume that he did not witness an apparition, but instead saw something untoward taking place."

"I see, and—"

"Freddie isn't sleeping well, and that will have an effect on his account of the event he saw unfold. And I don't mean he's suffering from a little bit of childhood wakefulness. The boy is becoming profoundly deprived of a good night's rest. I know you could say the same thing about half the population at the present time, but children have had a remarkable resilience to the bombings and have managed to sleep through the worst of times—of course the psychological pressure can do that too, as I am sure you understand. But Freddie Hackett is at risk of a deeper illness of the mind if he does not experience some lifting of the weight upon his shoulders. As a first step, he should not be running those messages all over London. It has to stop—but he is very scared that his mother and Iris will go without, and they will be on the streets and vulnerable. I also believe the running is not simply due to his love of sport or his obvious natural talent—it has a psychological connection to running from the things that frighten him, chiefly his father coming after him or his mother. Children can be as protective of their mothers as the other way around."

"Is there anything else I should know?"

As soon as she'd put forward the question, Maisie heard clicks on the line, and knew the caller had heard the pips indicating that more coins must be placed in the telephone box or the call would be disconnected. She held her breath.

"Sorry about that—one of my pennies dropped right through and I had to push it in again." The woman gave a frustrated sigh.

"Shall I call you back?" offered Maisie.

"Not to worry—I've put in enough money to finish. Now, where was I? Oh yes—suffice it to say that by the time I left, I was convinced that Freddie had indeed witnessed some sort of terrifying event, but I have to weigh it up against the experiences of other children I've met who have seen something equally troubling, and there's something different about Freddie. Children use all sorts of means to make the unthinkable normal, so they can deal with it and carry on. Freddie doesn't seem to have done that."

"And what would you suggest, Mrs. Langley?"

"I think it would help if we saw more of each other. I'm a believer in not just sitting in a drawing room talking, or in any place where there are chairs and a desk between two people having a conversation, so I could have a word with him during a stroll. I think the main thing is to ease his burden – after all, the old saying rings true, that a problem shared is a problem halved. Freddie needs it halved, halved again and then halved again, until he is a proper young boy with no more worries than anyone has at a time like this."

"Thank you, Mrs. Langley," said Maisie. "I know seeing Freddie has taken time away from your grandchildren. I was so sorry to hear of your daughter's death in a bombing."

"Yes, it's a terrible thing to lose a daughter—and she was so beautiful and clever. She was a doctor, you know. But we have to carry on for the sake of her children." The woman seemed to catch her breath before continuing. "But one more thing about Freddie. He is a sensitive soul— almost too sensitive. And in my experience, children of that kind do two things: they constantly imagine the future and see everything at its worst, and they try to stop the bad happening before it's even threat- ened to take place. They also become overly protective of those they love—to the extent that they would do anything in their power to en- sure their safety. Freddie Hackett is too young to have all that on his shoulders, and he is deeply aware of the volatility in his life."

Maisie's understanding of the situation was immediate. "Are you saying he is close to a breakdown?"

"Yes. That's exactly what I'm saying. The family feel safe in their new flat—which I understand you helped them obtain. But I don't think it's secure enough for Freddie—not yet anyway. That's the plight of a lot of people, but in the Hacketts' case it would be hard to place them as evacuees outside London, given the situation with the lit- tle girl. People can be picky about who they have under their roof, which we know is a terrible thing, but some people find any disorder unsettling—it's a reminder that it could have easily happened to them. There's no accounting for what might scare people. By the way—I met little Iris and she appears to function very well. Her disability doesn't hold her back as much as I might have expected—testament to her mother's care—though we both know there are those who would dis- criminate against her. I wish we could pull some strings . . ."

The nurse's words seemed to taper off, and Maisie wondered if it were by design, or if there was no more to say, though the call did not come to a close until Maisie had made sure she knew how much to pay the nurse and where to send the remittance.

Before returning to the kitchen, where she would linger with her stepmother and daughter, to laugh and joke, to listen to Anna's stories and Brenda's habit of telling Anna what school was like in her day, Maisie sat for some time with her hands on her chest, one on top of the other, as she tried to cradle away the pain in her heart.

Maisie's thoughts seemed to ricochet between Freddie Hackett, Elinor Jones, Pascale Evernden and Priscilla, and her concerns remained ever present as she worked in the Dower House library, played with her daughter or took long, solitary walks across the countryside. Priscilla, Douglas and Tarquin had returned to London, where they would grieve together with the two older boys, who were on their way to the Holland Park mansion.

It was late on Sunday afternoon when Maisie picked up the telephone receiver and dialed a number she knew by heart, but rarely used.

"MacFarlane!" The greeting was almost curt.

"Robbie—it's Maisie here. I'm sorry to call you on a Sunday."

"And at home. I could have been away at evensong."

"No, you couldn't Robbie—I know that much about you."

"Does your pal know about Jones?"

"Yes. I broke the news to the family as soon as I arrived in Chelstone. Is there word from Pascale?"

"You were right—she's making her way across to Granny's house. I just hope she's bloody careful." Maisie heard MacFarlane pause to take a sip of whatever drink he was holding in his hand. "But the good news is that she's going there because she can use an escape line to get back to Blighty. Our connections indicate she could be here within about a week, all being well."

"I'll breathe more easily when she's in London."

"Maisie, unless there are indications to the contrary, she'll only be here for debriefing to see if she's got the will and spine enough to go back there, and after some more training, that's where she'll be. We can't invest in qualified agents and not use them."

"I was afraid you'd say that."

"Hmmm. Anyway, you didn't call me to blether on about agents in France, and not on a Sunday when good people are singing hymns in a blacked-out church."

"I want your help, Robbie. I'd like a photograph of Major Chaput—I'm sure you have one in a file somewhere. I need it. And I want to know if he's been taken to see the body pulled from the Thames, on the off chance that he could identify the deceased."

"What the hell are you thinking, Maisie? Are you still trying to help that daydreaming boy? Who, I might add, has failed to turn up to run a few messages for us."

There were times when Maisie wanted to scream at Robbie Mac-Farlane, and those moments became more urgent—and therefore more volatile for Maisie—when MacFarlane seemed at his most obtuse.

"Here's what's been troubling me, Robbie. First of all, yes, this is conjecture, but I have a boy who seems to have witnessed a murder—and don't interrupt me; I'm coming back to that. Then he delivers a message, and there's a good chance it went to our Major Chaput, who was nowhere in the abandoned building when I proceeded to the same address. As you know the house was empty—of everything. Now, the message came from the department, and if it was you, it was therefore all above board, because you are liaising with a Free French intelligence officer. Fine. But Freddie believes he saw our Major Chaput kill another human being. The deceased vanishes in short order, and the next thing we know a body is being pulled from the Thames.

It would never have been found had it not been for the retrieval of a Spitfire from the river."

"That body could have been anyone's. And according to pathology reports, there were signs that a goodly amount of alcohol had been consumed."

"The pathologist believes he was French, and I think I'd go with his observation. So, I am formally requesting that you take steps to ensure Chaput is instructed to view the body. I'd like to know if he can identify the man—and I want the facts. Not just your idea of the truth." Maisie felt herself becoming terse.

"Maisie," said MacFarlane, his voice softer than usual. "I know you care for the safety of that boy and his family, but I must point out that it's not for you to give me orders, lass. Look, you've had a rough few days—breaking the news of a death is difficult, and god knows I've done it enough times. But you've got to drop this whole rigmarole with young Hackett. And it's not as if anyone is paying you for this one. Even though you've got a few bob tucked away, you should be taking on cases that bring in a bit of revenue, not ones that wear you down for nothing in return."

"I'll worry about the money, Robbie—and that's a fine red herring to throw around. In the meantime, Freddie Hackett is close to a breakdown, so if I have anything to do with it, he's not going to be running messages for anyone. But I really must have that photograph—surely you can at least do that for me, if only to dispense with this case once and for all so I can tell Freddie and his mother that I believe him but we don't know who he saw on that night. I must do this for Freddie. And I want to know, if at all possible, the identity of the man dragged up from the Thames. There may be a link to that dead man in Scotland—or did you think I'd forgotten about him?"

"That has nothing to do with you."

"Is that why you brought me in on the postmortem and then whisked me away? I believe you know very well that they could be connected, Robbie, and if so, you have a murderer in your midst. How can we keep the Free French even remotely settled here, balanced between hating us and joining us in our quest to fight the Nazis, if they're killing each other on our soil? I know I've signed a good deal of my working life over to you for the duration, but I can find a way out."

"I think you've been looking for a way out since that wee girl came into your life, haven't you, Maisie? You want to be with your child, but you can't give up your work, and there you are, falling over yourself to hold it all in your arms."

Maisie felt herself bristle. MacFarlane had a way of needling her, of seeing a situation in black and white—or pretending to. "My personal life is none of your business, Robbie, though I'll admit you always seem to know too much about it. Now, will you help me out? A photograph of Chaput?"

"Yes. My office, tomorrow afternoon. Two o'clock be all right for you?"

"Thank you. And what about finding out if Chaput can identify the man from the river?"

There was silence on the line, followed by a sigh.

"Robbie?"

"He's already done it. The dead man is one Charles d'Anjou, though seeing as it sounds more like a cheap wine, it's probably not his real name. But whoever he is, Chaput confirmed that he had been one of his men, and that he was also a drinker and a liability."

"Don't tell me he killed him for being a drinker?"

"Bit sarcastic for you, Maisie." MacFarlane gave a half laugh. "An alcoholic is always a liability, but it'll get you kicked off a job, not knifed by your boss. Chaput didn't kill him."

215

"So he says." Even to Maisie, her reply sounded childish.

"I believe him. Someone murdered the man, and Chaput has admitted that he wasn't sorry to see him gone."

"And the man in Scotland?"

"My bailiwick, Maisie—not yours."

"What if they're tied together in some way?"

"They're not."

Maisie sighed. "Robbie—"

"Look, Maisie, here's what you should do—and far be it from me to give advice to someone like yourself, plus I am sick to death of repeating myself on this one, but why don't you look after young Freddie and his family as much as you want, but drop this investigation. As far as your brain is concerned, I need you here as often as your expertise is required. In the meantime, you can leave all the other investigations to your Mr. Beale."

"That's what I was trying to do."

"Ah, but that's the rub, isn't it—you can't let go of the more interesting ones. You don't want to find out who's gone off with the family jewels, or even someone else's wife, but you do like it when a real puzzle comes along to pique your interest, and if you think you can save a life along the way."

Maisie sighed. "I'll see you tomorrow, Robbie—I'll collect the photograph when we meet."

"And you've three assessments lined up, just so you know."

Maisie paused for a few seconds. "I'll be there, Robbie. Until then—" She replaced the receiver before MacFarlane had a chance to hang up first. She was fed up with listening to the continuous tone of the disconnected call at the end of every telephone conversation with Robbie MacFarlane. This time it was her turn.

CHAPTER 14

ere you are, Maisie—you can feast your eyes on the dashing Major all you like now." MacFarlane pulled a photograph from an envelope and pushed it across the desk as Maisie entered his office on Monday afternoon. "There's your Major Chaput, looking all very debonair—and with a bit of luck those natural folds in his skin won't scare the boy."

"Thank you, Robbie. I appreciate it."

"Friends again, are we? Anyway, sit down, Maisie. I want to talk to you."

Maisie smoothed her narrow navy blue skirt with kick pleats just below the knee, and took the seat opposite MacFarlane. As always, the air was close in the small room, so she unbuttoned the matching navy jacket to reveal a cream silk blouse underneath. "What is it—have you news of Pascale?"

"No, not yet. But I have some other news. Freddie Hackett's father received a strong police warning on Saturday evening—I only found out this morning. It seems he discovered where his family are living and went over there. Luckily there's that locked outer door, and though he tried to lob a brick through the glass, no damage was caused, or he would have been behind some very strong bars by now. The caretaker telephoned through to the local police station and they sent a couple of young coppers around to have a word with him. He eventually went on his way, albeit with a promise to come back with a stick of dynamite."

Maisie rubbed her forehead. "I thought it would take a bit longer for him to find them. I wonder—"

"Don't wonder anything. He's probably all talk, that one. All mouth and trousers, as the saying goes. And I've checked the local constabulary to make sure they're following Caldwell's orders and keeping an eye on the family—another voice for good measure."

"What about keeping an eye on Hackett senior?" asked Maisie.

"That wandering waste of time? He wanders about looking for work until the pubs open, so he wanders in and that's it for another day until he wanders home. He'll soon be kicked out of his lodgings because Grace and Freddie aren't bringing him every scrap of money they make."

"I'd better go round to see them," said Maisie.

"Not just yet, Maisie." MacFarlane leaned back in his chair. He wore no jacket in the office; he had loosened his tie and slipped his trouser braces off his shoulders. "There's never any bloody air in these small rooms." He leaned forward again, resting his elbows on the desk before him.

"But Freddie—"

"Stop talking about Freddie blimmin' Hackett for just a minute, would you? Now then—how did Mrs. Partridge take the news?" MacFarlane had not missed a beat between subjects.

"The whole family is devastated. They're at their house in Holland Park—Tom managed to get a twenty-four-hour leave, and Tim came down from university. Elinor—Miss Jones—was as much a part of the family as if she had been born the boys' big sister."

"And you told them there had been an accident."

"All according to your instructions."

"Good. Good."

"Is there something you're not telling me, Robbie?"

MacFarlane shook his head. "No—not at all. I'm just thinking." There was a second's hiatus before he spoke again. "Now then—your orders for the week. Here you are." He passed a sheet of typewritten paper to Maisie. "The personnel files pertaining to the men and women you'll be interviewing will be available for you to read through as soon as you get here tomorrow, and then your meetings will commence one after the other. They've all passed through the tests up in Scotland, and of course the radio operators have gone through training. This is the final assessment before they go over."

Maisie took the sheet of paper.

"You're off to see the Hacketts?"

"Yes."

MacFarlane nodded. "Tomorrow, then."

"Right you are, Robbie. See you tomorrow. Ten sharp."

Maisie walked at a slow pace to the underground station. It was a fine day, a day when she might consider ambling through Regent's Park, if only to gather her thoughts.

Sometimes she imagined her work as akin to creating a patchwork quilt. Each square of fabric represented another piece of information, of intelligence or a consideration that had come to mind based upon previous experience—what MacFarlane would call a feeling in his gut. If different colors were assigned to that which was known fact, or conjecture, or elements of the case based upon a depth of feeling inspired by her training, she would hope to see the quilt formed of pale colors on the outer edges, and as she gathered more intelligence, the colors would become darker toward the center, as the heart of the case became clear. The colors of Freddie Hackett's quilt were coming together in a haphazard form, adhering to no clear pattern. However, she had a folded sheet with more information in her bag, and she knew who she would go to for help in determining whether the intelligence was light or bold. But first she wanted to see Grace, Freddie and Iris Hackett.

Grace Hackett appeared to have only just arrived home from work when Maisie rang the bell—she had retained a key to the outer door, so did not need to summon Freddie's mother to the street to let her into the entrance hall. Freddie was not at home, though it seemed that Iris had just been dropped off by the caretaker's wife.

"Lovely to see you, Miss Dobbs. Come in—I've just put the kettle on. Would you like a cup of tea?"

"I'd love a cup, thank you, Mrs. Hackett," said Maisie. "And where's Freddie?"

"Just nipped down to the shop for a pint of milk."

"Mrs. Hackett, I heard your husband came to the house and was troublesome. Do you feel safe enough? Are you all right here?"

"There's two doors between him and us, so yes, once I'm inside the flat I feel safe, Miss Dobbs. But not so much when I'm out."

"Is that why Freddie isn't at school? Is he going to your place of work to make sure his father doesn't come near you?"

Grace Hackett pressed her lips together as she fought tears. "Yes, he does. I've told him I want him to go to school, but he walks with me to the bus stop and then to the house, and after that he gives me a hand—he just won't leave my side in case his father comes after me. He worries that he's watching us."

"And do you think he is?"

"I suppose I worry, but I also know what he does with his day—he looks for work until the pubs open, then he hangs around hoping someone else will buy him a drink. Sometimes he picks up a job here and there, but not every day. And as for finding the right mark to buy him that drink—it's not as difficult as you might think."

"What do you mean?"

"My husband is a bit of a con man, Miss Dobbs, but of course you know that. He can chat to people quite easily when he likes—he's got that gift of the gab. Draws them in, and before long, they're buying the rounds. People who drink in pubs generally like a bit of company while they're downing the pints, and my husband can always see that need for companionship in people."

Maisie wondered if Hackett had seen the need in Grace, had identified a mark and drawn her in with his patter. The money settled upon her after Freddie's birth was not a fortune, but attractive to a man who had little. Maisie was about to ask another question when Iris—who was sitting at the table, turning the pages of a picture book back and forth—looked up at Maisie and gave her a broad, toothy grin. The little girl then held up her arms, opening and closing her fingers as if she wanted something.

"Would you like to sit on my lap, Iris?" said Maisie, pulling out a chair next to the child. "Come on, let's look at your book."

"I'll make the tea," said Grace Hackett, smiling as Iris clambered onto Maisie's lap.

Freddie returned with a bottle of milk just as Grace went into the kitchen and Maisie began reading to Iris, who clapped her hands and called out "Freddeee" when her brother came into the sitting room.

"Miss Dobbs!" Freddie seemed to pale when he saw Maisie.

"I thought I'd drop in and say hello—see how you're all getting along here, Freddie. And I wanted to have a quick word with you."

"I've just got to take this to Mum." Freddie lifted the bottle, and walked at speed past Maisie into the kitchen.

Maisie turned back to Iris, who had watched her brother and began to suck her thumb, and as Maisie continued reading to the little girl, she could hear raised voices in the kitchen.

"But I don't want to go to school, even if she is here to make me go," said Freddie.

"I promise you, Fred—I will be safe."

"How do you know that? He's a nutter."

Maisie began pointing to characters on the page, asking Iris to say each word after her, while at the same time trying to follow the conversation unfolding in the kitchen.

"Don't speak to your mother like that," said Grace.

"I'm fed up with school anyway. It's all really easy stuff. I'm not learning anything I couldn't learn from a book in the library. And I'm a man now. I've got to look after you—it's not as if he ever did, is it?"

"Freddie—he's your father!"

There was silence in the kitchen. Maisie stopped reading, and Iris looked behind her toward the kitchen door.

"I don't care, because he isn't my real father, is he? And we both know he's bad."

Maisie started as she heard the sharp slap of hand on face, and Grace gasping.

"Mum!"

"I'm sorry, Fred—I'm sorry. Look, love, let's talk about this later—we've to take in tea for Miss Dobbs. She wants to have a word with you. And you show her some gratitude, because if it weren't for her, we'd still be back there with him."

Maisie heard the rattling of crockery, and Freddie appeared, holding a tray with teacups and saucers, his mother following with the teapot and milk jug.

"Miss Dobbs, every time I make tea or put the dinner on, I'm so grateful to you for offering us this flat." Grace set down the tray and pulled out a chair. As soon as she was seated, Iris jumped down and went to her mother. "It's very nice here, and really it's too good for the likes of us." She began to pour tea.

"No—it's perfect for you for as long as you need it, and it would otherwise be standing empty, so I'm the one who's grateful, because any home should be lived in," said Maisie. "I understand you were once a governess, Mrs. Hackett."

Grace Hackett looked at Maisie for several seconds before handing a cup of tea to her. "Yes, I actually trained to be a teacher, so I can do more than clean, you know."

"Oh, thank you," said Maisie. "I've had a busy morning and not stopped for even a glass of water." She took a sip of tea and set her cup in the saucer. "You could still teach, if you wanted to," she continued. "You seem to be doing well with Iris. There are a number of children coming back into London, and I think some additional teachers are needed because so many have remained with their classes while they're evacuated. I know they're a bit short at my daughter's school, and that's in the country."

Grace shook her head. "No, I couldn't. Not now. It was a long time ago, and I've been cleaning houses to make ends meet for years. Even if I was called for an interview, I'd just be the woman who scrubs floors, dusts, does the laundry and polishes the silver."

"You've done well with your children, Mrs. Hackett. I understand that Freddie is coming along at school"—Maisie turned her attention to Freddie—"when he goes."

Freddie, still standing, looked down at his shoes.

"I know it's a new school, Freddie—but I think you should attend," said Maisie. "You're not that long from getting your school leaving certificate, and that will make all the difference to your future."

"I'll end up in the army anyway, what with this war," said Freddie.

"I believe it will be over by the time you're of enlistment age. But I want you to go to school, Freddie—and I can make sure your mum is safe."

Freddie shrugged, still sullen.

"Anyway, the reason I came here today is that I wanted to see you, Freddie." Maisie reached into her bag and brought out the photograph of Major Chaput. She passed it to Freddie. "Have you ever seen this man before?"

Freddie studied the photograph. "He looks posher in this photo, what with him wearing a uniform. And younger. But he's the one I saw when I delivered the envelope to that house, on the night I saw the murder."

Maisie stared at Freddie. "And you told Mr. Beale and myself that he was the same man who committed murder."

Freddie paused, looking again at the photograph. "Yes. Yes, he was. He's the same man." He passed the photograph back to Maisie. "And he's got them funny lines on his face, big folding lines like an old bloke, but he doesn't look old." He avoided Maisie's eyes. "I s'pose they look like scars, and there's that bit under his eye, like he got splashed with bleach."

Maisie nodded. "You're sure it was the man to whom you delivered the envelope?"

Freddie nodded. "Mmmm, yes, I'm sure. And he looks like the same man who came to the school. How did you find him, Miss Dobbs?"

"It was a bit of luck, actually. I met this man a few days after you came to the office to speak to us. Because he fitted your description, I thought it would be unusual to come across a person similar in looks so soon after having a picture in my mind of a man who looked like him, based upon your recollection. I paid attention, and I was therefore in a position to make inquiries. That's what I do."

"Mr. Beale said you make lucky guesses about things."

Maisie laughed, picked up her cup and took another sip of the cooling tea. "I suppose it might look like that—but as I said, it's about paying attention." She replaced the cup in the saucer and set it on the tray, and this time stared Freddie in the eye for more time than he might have found comfortable. "Yes, I watch and listen, Freddie. To everything people say and do. I also listen carefully to the things they don't say and do."

She put away the photograph, and came to her feet. "Mrs. Hackett, thank you so much for the tea. I should be on my way. Do not worry about your journey to and from work—you will be safe. You are secure in this flat, and it is being monitored by the local police—a favor to me from people I know." She turned to Freddie. "Which means you can return to school. If you like, I can speak to your teacher. You will be perfectly secure there, Freddie—and you don't have to worry about your mum. You are all so much better off than you were living with . . . living at your previous address."

"What about the other man, Miss Dobbs—the one who was knifed? Have they found him yet?"

Maisie's reply was direct. "Yes, they have. He has been identified, though I cannot tell you more than that."

"Will that man go to prison and be hung, the one who killed him?"

"Why do you ask?"

"Because he's important. I could see that in the picture. He's in a French uniform, and he's got a lot of medals. He must be important."

"No one is too important to get away with a crime, Freddie."

Maisie regarded Freddie Hackett and saw him draw into himself, as if he were already sprinting away in his mind, his legs carrying him from the room as a fear-stoked engine drove his energy forward.

O h how lovely to see you, Your Ladyship. I am sure Miss Hunter will be delighted you've called again. She's in her study, working on something she's penning for a journal." Gabriella Hunter's house-keeper stood back to allow Maisie to enter the hallway. "Mind you, I don't know when it will be published—it's all they can do to get enough paper for the dailies, isn't it? Everything's running short—except Mr. Hitler's bombs!"

Maisie agreed—it seemed that everyone had an opinion these days, whether it was about the shortage of sugar, of bread, or whether that beef in the shop was really horse meat and the butcher was pulling the wool over his customers' eyes.

"Maisie, my dear, I can't say I'm surprised to see you again so soon. You're so like Maurice at times—give you a little something to chew on, and then you come back to ask for more. Sit down and tell me." Gabriella tucked her bobbed hair behind one ear, as if ready to hear what Maisie had to say. "Something exciting?"

"It might be exciting to some," said Maisie as she took a seat.

"Go on." She put her notebook and pen onto a side table and faced Maisie, her hands in her lap. Maisie thought she looked like a school-girl.

"I am here to ask for more help. You still have some contacts in France, though you may not even have to go that far to find out what I need to know." She passed Gabriella the photograph of Chaput, along with a piece of paper on which was written his name and that of Charles d'Anjou.

Gabriella Hunter studied the photograph. "Quite dishy—if you're a Frenchwoman. This type doesn't appeal to the average British girl."

"Really?" said Maisie, smiling. "I've been told that he reminds people of Victor Mature."

"Good lord, no. Mature is . . . well, he's more of a heartthrob, if you ask me. This one is a bit too swarthy, a bit too . . . folded in the face. But I know just the person to ask."

"Gabriella, I have a feeling that there is a troubling past history connecting these men and perhaps another—and I believe it goes back a long way." Maisie began to rub her hands, at once unsure of her ground. "It's hard to explain, but there was something in your comments about honor that has been like a pebble in my shoe, nagging me a bit. I suppose because I was working on this case at the time, I couldn't help but wonder if honor might have some bearing on the investigation—whether it was a thread I should pull on."

"If there is something to know, I can find it—but I would like a few days. Fortunately, not all of my contacts are in France."

"They're in London?"

Gabriella Hunter tapped the side of her nose. "My contacts, my business, Maisie. I protect my sources."

Maisie nodded, smiling. "As you should, Gabriella. As you should."

"Where can I reach you?"

"If it's later this week, the best bet is Chelstone, the Dower House."

"Still Maurice's old number?"

"Yes, that's right."

"I loved the Dower House, you know. And the rose garden tended by the man who lived in the Groom's Cottage—is he still there? A dear man, he seemed to be able to make roses bloom from spring until autumn."

"Gabriella—that groom was my father, and yes, he still loves his roses, though he's living with me at the Dower House, along with my stepmother and my daughter. We're all together. Perhaps you'd like to come down to visit us? You remember Lady Rowan, I'm sure—she would love to have you to stay at the manor."

"Oh yes, before the last war she had some sparkling suppers—lots of arguments across the table. Julian always managed to prevent anarchy though. Such a distinguished man—I take it he's still with us."

"Both of them are at the manor house. A bit less mobile, yet very busy, always very busy, plus they have Canadian officers billeted there, which they love. They adore my daughter, and when I'm not at home she will often go to have tea with Lady Rowan after school."

"Yes, they would cherish her. It was such a tragedy when they lost their own daughter, and then to lose James years later . . . oh, Maisie, you were married for such a short time."

"It's been a few years now."

"Do you think— No, it's not for me to ask. I'm sorry, forget I said anything."

Maisie smiled. "You were going to ask about my gentleman friend again, weren't you?"

"Remember I'm half French, Maisie—I love romance, so you can't blame me for asking, can you?" Gabriella laughed, then grew pensive. "There are many ways of being at odds with a person you love, Maisie, and they're not always as serious as you think."

Maisie rubbed the back of her hand where the burns had been most deep. "Mark has to return to America every so often, which is of course a dangerous journey by aeroplane, usually via Ireland and Lisbon—it frightens me, to tell you the truth. I miss him very much when he's away, and I look forward to his homecoming—it's wonderful when he's here and of course Anna adores him, which warms my heart. But my concern is that Britain is not his home, and though he professes to love it here and has even said that he could see himself retiring to the life of a gentleman farmer in Kent, I'm never sure if he's serious, because so much of what he says is lighthearted banter. Of course, we both know that no one can plan during wartime—the future is so unsettled—but the truth is that I cannot leave England. I have responsibilities here. And I don't feel confident that he would stay, not only due to his work, but—well, this is not his home." She shook her head and rubbed her fingers against the scar again. "It all means the leap might be too far for both of us, and I sometimes think the little tensions that then become bigger are down to the fact that we veer away from any talk of the future, because we're afraid of where it might lead. It might be a relief for both of us if we part, but we veer away from that decision too."

Hunter nodded. "I think I understand, my dear. I was your age when I had an intense affair of the heart—certainly not my first, by any means. But it was important and I loved the man very much indeed. I look back and wish we had both been a little more, well, I suppose 'malleable' might be a better word. You see, with age we become somewhat less flexible in many ways, don't we? Even someone like you, who is trained to see the gray between black and white." She fingered the loose strap of her watch and whispered, so that Maisie could barely hear her, "And even the man who trained you." She looked up and smiled. "We also become rather reticent when it comes to taking the leap into love, which I think can be such a tragedy because love is always worth the leap."

The older woman held up the photo and sheet of paper with the two names. "Anyway, this is the second time I've lectured you on the subject of love, so I'll get on with this, Maisie. Expect to hear from me soon."

Maisie stood up, thanked Gabriella and leaned down to kiss her on both cheeks before turning to leave. As she reached the door, Gabriella called to her.

"Maisie—if you love your American, do say yes if he asks you to marry him. I said no too many times because I was afraid of losing myself and . . . well, what with my work, you know. But now the years have passed, I confess I harbor some regrets—I think I deprived myself of much happiness. Anyway, I'll be in touch, Maisie."

Consulting her watch, Maisie realized that, once again, it was time to make her way back to the flat in Holland Park, though on this evening she would not disturb the privacy of Priscilla and her family. She enjoyed the proximity to the house owned by Priscilla and Douglas. It was not unusual for Priscilla to telephone Maisie almost as soon as she knew she had arrived home from the office, asking her to come round and join her for a "quick G and T." The trouble was, Priscilla's G and Ts were neither quick nor to Maisie's taste, though she loved her friend's company.

When Gabriella mentioned Lord Julian in their earlier meeting, it had given Maisie an idea—one she admonished herself for not acting upon earlier. Having arrived home and checked her blackout curtains, she went to the telephone and dialed the number for Chelstone Manor. She felt a sense of encroaching loss when it took Lord Julian longer than usual to come to the telephone after being summoned by the butler—so much would change with his passing.

"Maisie—how are you? Our delightful Anna was here this afternoon, and she was quite enchanting. We had a long discussion about the next gymkhana, and I think she is up for it." Lord Julian's enthusiastic tone was encouraging.

"She's been very upset about losing Emma," said Maisie.

"Massive dog, wasn't she? Went a long time, that one. The larger breeds don't always have a good lifespan. Anyway, my dear, I do believe you've telephoned to ask me a question. Fire away!"

Maisie smiled, her dark thoughts now completely banished by the elderly man's hearty response. She knew he welcomed being asked to assist her with his contacts.

"There's something I'm curious about, and I think you might be able to help with it—you still have quite a name at the War Office."

"And a number of those so-called contacts who know that name are hanging on and haven't yet met their makers. I should warn you, though—in case you didn't hear—the records are in a terrible state, because the office where they were kept was bombed. But give me the details, Maisie, just in case I can find out anything. My pen is at the ready."

"I already know about the records office, but I'm just sniffing around for anything else. The name is Hackett." She spelled out Arthur Hackett's surname. "According to information I have already, he was in the East Surrey Regiment. It would be useful to know if there was a neurasthenia report—any comments from commanding officers regarding temperament." She paused. "And any special skills for which he was noted."

"Special skills?"

"Oh, you know—was he an excellent shot, or was he trained in hand-to-hand combat? That sort of thing. Or perhaps he had an ability in languages. Any details about his background, that's what I'm looking for—and pension arrangements."

"Right you are. Probably take a couple of days—so I suppose you can rest until then." Julian laughed.

"Too busy—as you well know!" Maisie had an easy relationship with her former father-in-law, though she had once found him intimidating. "Before I go—do you remember Maurice's friend Gabriella Hunter?"

"Gabriella—once met, never forgotten. Fiercely intelligent woman. Brave and opinionated. Rowan loved her, though they were known to lock horns—and come out laughing. She and Maurice were . . . were very good friends, I suppose you could say."

"Yes, so I understand. I've seen her a few times lately, and I think she'd very much like to see Chelstone again. As you know, the Dower House is full, but I wondered . . . perhaps you and Lady Rowan might invite her at some point. I think she could do with a Friday to Monday." Maisie ran the telephone cord through her fingers, a habit formed by nervousness on the first occasion she had ever used a telephone. "Julian, I think she's rather lonely now."

"I'll have a word with Rowan, and she'll give her a ring—excellent idea to get her down here, and it would do Rowan the power of good to see her. And when will you be home again?"

"By Thursday, I hope—I only came up to town today."

"All righty, I should have something for you regarding this Hackett in a day or so, I would imagine. Always interesting to be one of your worker bees! Until then, Maisie."

Worker bees. Maisie considered the comment. Yes, she had her worker bees, valuable contacts who would seek whatever information she needed, buzzing around their gardens of endeavor until they found the pockets of intelligence she had requested. But the riches they brought to her were never sweet; indeed, the plethora of detail gathered during a murder inquiry tended to have a stark bitterness to it.

CHAPTER 15

The interviews with F-section agents who would be leaving for France within the week took up Maisie's entire day. In addition, she was tasked with reviewing files on new recruits. For those who had endured the rigorous training, once again Maisie would be compiling reports on each man or woman, attesting to their state of mind prior to departure. It would have been unusual for one of the cohort to be plucked out and sent home at this final stage, but it had happened in the past.

It was late in the afternoon, following a final interview, when a young woman in the uniform of the First Aid Nursing Yeomanry entered the interview room. Female recruits to the Special Operations Executive were ostensibly members of FANY.

"Mr. MacFarlane requests your presence, ma'am. Please follow me."

Maisie was glad to leave the small room, which had only a skylight to provide natural illumination. She was escorted down a flight of stairs to a room where MacFarlane was seated alone at a desk. The young woman pulled out the only other chair for Maisie, who began to feel a little claustrophobic in the windowless office.

"Thank you, Lawson," said MacFarlane, without looking up at the young woman. "That will be all."

"Is it Pascale?" asked Maisie.

MacFarlane nodded. "The next forty-eight hours will be crucial.

We've heard via our sources that she managed to reach her grandmother's house and is in hiding. The shoulder wound was caused by a bullet, though as far as we know it's not too bad, but not entirely superficial—and she has lost some blood. The grandmother wants her to recover, but Granny is also nobody's fool. She knows Pascale is effectively hiding in plain sight and must be on the move again soon. Seems both the old lady and Pascale have a way with canines, otherwise both would have been torn to shreds by the German guard dogs. I'd pay good money to see how the women calm them down—I could use their technique with my sister's Jack Russell. Little piranha that he is. If it were a Saturday-morning comedy at the picture house, this would be a funny situation—how that grandmother is working right under the noses of the Gestapo."

"How will Pascale get out?"

"Same way she got in—as you suggested, the place is full of hiding places and escape tunnels used by the aristocracy during the Revolution. She's been seen by a local doctor—ostensibly called to attend to Chantal, who as we know is as strong as an ox. She'll leave tonight, alone, then meet her courier on the road. All being well and with the gods in attendance, she'll make it into Spain and then to Gibraltar. We'll have someone ready to meet her as soon as she reaches British territory. At that point she'll be as good as home and dry."

Maisie rubbed her forehead.

"Gibraltar bringing back memories, lass?"

Maisie nodded. "It's the thought of her getting through France before reaching Spain that worries me—and she could be at risk in Spain. It might be a neutral country, but we both know the police there have been handing over known escapees from Belgium and France to the German authorities."

"We have confidence that she will get by in Spain because she speaks the language as fluently as if she were a native. Amazing, being able to slip from one language to the other like that, and then into English as if she were born to the upper classes. Anyway, if a navigator from Stepney named Dennis Kemp, who bailed out of a Wellington over France ten days ago, can get home and be in his mum's kitchen having a cup of tea this afternoon, then she can make it to England in one piece too."

"The shoulder wound—that's a giveaway, surely."

"Any German soldiers might try to flirt with her if they see her in a town, Maisie, but I don't think they're going to rip off her jacket." He shuffled his notes.

"But you're worried, I can tell—they know who she is, don't they? The Gestapo must be looking for her."

"Maisie—she'll get home. She's been trained for this—she's laying low and will be moving with care under cover of darkness for the most part, and she won't take any chances—she knows the risks."

There was an hiatus in the conversation. An image flashed in Maisie's mind's eye: thirteen-year-old Pascale galloping toward her on a high-spirited stallion, laughing as she directed the horse toward the gate and clearing it by a foot before executing a perfect landing and cantering in a circle around Maisie.

"There's the problem, Robbie—and I'm on the record drawing attention to it in my report. Pascale might know the risks, but it never stopped her taking them, even if she isn't as hotheaded as Priscilla." She looked down at her hands, then at MacFarlane. "You say she's coming home via Gibraltar?"

MacFarlane appeared to consider the question for a moment. "No. I'm ahead of you, Maisie, even before you float the suggestion toward me. The answer is a very firm 'No.' I'm shocked you'd even think about it."

"I was just thinking that—"

"We will have someone meet her—someone else who knows her and knows Gibraltar and that part of Spain just across the border—but it won't be you. You have other things to attend to, and other responsibilities. One of them is named Anna."

"Yes, of course. You're right. Sorry—it should never have crossed my mind. Am I free to leave now?"

"It's gone five o'clock in the afternoon, so yes, you're dismissed, Miss Dobbs. But before you go—a couple more files to take a gander at. Early days. Nothing doing yet—just possibilities. Bit of homework for you—but be careful with it. I'll telephone in the morning."

An ATS driver took Maisie back to her flat, where she once again checked the blackout curtains, then flopped down into the armchair next to the fireplace. She had not bothered to remove her jacket, though she unpinned her hat and threw it to one side, where it landed on the sideboard. She kicked off her shoes.

"Five minutes, and I'll make a cup of tea," she said aloud.

"Just what the doctor ordered—a nice cup of tea!"

Maisie started and jumped up from her chair. "Mark!"

Mark Scott walked from his hiding place in the dining room and took her in his arms, pressing his lips to hers before speaking.

"Missed you, Maisie."

"I missed you too." She looked up at him, the instant honesty of her comment rendering her heady. "I really missed you."

"How about my specialty? Spaghetti, a nice bottle of wine and a great guy on the opposite side of the table?"

Maisie smiled. "Perfect! Though where will we find the guy?"

"I fell into that one, didn't I?" Scott held her close. "I'm afraid I must leave after supper. I've a late briefing at the ambassador's residence."

"Oh—"

"But I can come over here every evening for dinner this week until you leave, and then down to Chelstone on Saturday morning until Sunday, or even Monday morning—if you like."

"I'd like that very much, Mark. So would Anna. She'll be so excited—she has been despondent since Emma died."

"I'll cheer her up. And I'm sure Brenda will be overjoyed to see me!"

Maisie laughed. "Oh, it's good to have you home, Mark Scott." She blushed again as she spoke the words.

Scott lifted her chin and looked into her eyes. "We've come a long way, haven't we, Maisie?" He kissed her again.

Maisie must have dozed in the armchair for a while after Scott left the flat, but she was nudged awake by the rumble of bombers passing overhead. She knew she should go to the cellar and shelter until the all-clear sirens sounded, but as she glanced at the clock, it occurred to her that there was just enough time to read through the additional files that MacFarlane had passed across his desk before she left Baker Street—her "homework." The first candidate was a young man named Giles Mason, who had been awarded honors in French literature from Cambridge and was fluent in the language. She ran her finger down his list of accomplishments, along with notes from the scout who had spotted Mason in a bookshop in London and struck up a conversation with the young man, who was at the time in the process of purchasing a novel in the original French.

"Clever lad, aren't you, Giles?" said Maisie, as she closed the file and put it to one side.

She opened the second file and studied the name.

Charlotte Bright.

Maisie held her breath, and felt herself tense.

"Oh no you don't, Robbie," she said aloud. "I've had enough of your bloody tests, and this one won't fly. Why are you doing this to me?"

She took a thick red crayon from a pocket in her document case and scrawled "Rejected" in large letters across the front of the file.

"If you don't like it, Robbie—I know where the door is. I don't care which of your official bloody papers I've signed either."

She returned the files to her document case, switched off the lights and went to bed, where she lay awake for hours, listening to the bombers overhead, and the *crump-crump-crump* in the distance as they dropped their lethal loads.

B een a few days since we were both here in the office together, eh, miss?" Billy handed Maisie a mug of steaming tea, then joined her at the long table situated perpendicular to her desk. Several files were already laid out for attention, along with a rolled-up case map.

"It has indeed," agreed Maisie. "Let's go through every case and see where we are with them."

Over the next ten minutes, they discussed cases in progress, all of which, bar one, Billy was dealing with. Maisie studied her assistant as he responded to each of her questions, and remembered the man who'd introduced himself to her when she moved into the shabby office around the corner some twelve years earlier. He was the caretaker then, yet he had recognized her straightaway: she had assisted the surgeon when Billy was brought into the casualty clearing station during the Battle of Messines, in 1917. Having helped with her first case following Maurice's retirement, Billy became her assistant, and though others thought her mad to take on a man untrained in investigation, he had proven himself through diligent, if sometimes slow work on one case after another. Perhaps it was time . . .

"Let's talk about Freddie Hackett," said Maisie, reaching for the case map, which she passed to Billy.

As Billy pushed the closed files to one side and pinned the case map out on the table, Maisie took a jar of colored wax crayons from the top of a filing cabinet. She began adding lines to the map, and notes—all leading to the center of the case map, which, as always, was created on the reverse side of an offcut of wallpaper.

"Sounds like a bottle of cheap wine, that one," said Billy, pointing to the name Maisie had added after striking out a question mark above the words "Deceased from River."

"MacFarlane made the same observation." Maisie did not look up as she added a name here, a note there.

Billy looked at the map and rubbed his chin. "I can see what you're thinking, miss, and it's all very well—but how did the body get moved, and so fast?"

"Two possibilities," said Maisie. "Well, more may emerge, but I've two so far. Number one is that this was indeed a planned assassination, though I don't yet know what our d'Anjou might have done to deserve that sort of extreme attention. If it was, then the killer would likely have made arrangements to dispose of the body."

"Charming bloke," said Billy.

"Indeed. The other possibility is that he was being followed anyway, and when he was murdered, perhaps by a common criminal for his money—remember the wallet was empty of cash—the people on his tail made sure the body was removed."

"Why would they do that?"

"If—and it's always an 'if' at this point—his movements were being monitored by the people he worked for, or even an enemy, I would imagine that when he was killed, the officials might well have wanted his body removed for security reasons so there would be no more questions asked." She looked up at her assistant. "Billy, he was working on the periphery of the Free French and he wasn't quite up to snuff—rather a drinker, apparently—so we have to consider the variables."

"Hmmm—not exactly what you might call cut-and-dried, is it?" Billy furrowed his brow. "All right, let's say he was assassinated. What would he have to do to get himself topped by a professional killer, aside from being a drinker and a security risk?"

"I paid a visit to a woman named Gabriella Hunter—she knew Maurice and is also half French. Anyway, she had a lot to say about the French sense of honor, so I thought it would be worth keeping it in mind. It sounds as if it could also be a weakness, dependent upon the circumstance, and it made me wonder if the man Freddie saw murdered lacked honor—or perhaps he just upset someone."

"That'd get your throat cut in the East End, never mind France."

"Be that as it may, Billy—I think 'honor' is going to be part of the answer here. The fact that the victim couldn't hold his drink could have led to him being unable to keep a secret, which could be fatal for a good many souls if he was mouthy and the wrong people were listening." She tapped a corner of the paper with the red crayon. "We have to take into account that enemy agents are likely operating in London and other places."

"Well, look at that bloke who had the flat downstairs, right under our office here."

"I know."

"I thought he was a nice chap, then all of a sudden he's been copped by the authorities and is in the Tower of London!" He looked at Maisie. "Wonder what happened to him."

"He's probably dead, Billy."

"Dead?"

"Yes. In a time of war, that's what happens to a traitor of whatever stripe."

Billy turned his attention back to the case map. "So . . . so this man could have been a traitor?"

Maisie was thoughtful. "It's a possibility—something for us to bear in mind, because he could have been."

"Only in his case, someone couldn't wait for him to meet the hangman."

"Or the guillotine."

"Blimey."

Maisie sighed, took one more look at the case map and stood up. "Let's put the case map away, Billy."

"Where are we going? You've got the look that's telling me to get my cap on."

"We're off to see Freddie Hackett's father—before he's had a few."

There was no answer when Maisie knocked on the door of the squalid house where Arthur Hackett now lived alone.

"Let's have a look in the Coach and Horses, just down the street," she suggested.

Walking together along the street, they parted to avoid a large pile of rubble. "Funny how you get used to it, isn't it?" said Billy. "You sort of look down and expect to see a bit of brick or sand here and there, or a house half demolished. It's not a shock anymore."

"When I first saw a street after a bombing, I thought it looked like a row of dolls' houses with the sides ripped off. The curtains were hanging down and you'd see a bed half in and half out of the room, or the pictures still hanging on the wall."

"I tell you, miss, I thought I'd seen the worst in the last war—and what I saw was about as terrible as you could imagine. Soldiers torn to pieces or blown up so nothing's left of them. But we were men in uniform. Now we're seeing ordinary people lying there with no limbs, or dead, or with terrible wounds—it'll stay with every one of us, what we've seen."

They walked the rest of the way in silence, stopping outside the pub.

"Hang on, miss—let me go in and have a quick look. This is what I'd call a drinking pub, a bit 'spit and sawdust' if you ask me—it's not one ladies would generally frequent, even in the snug."

As he opened the pub door, Maisie caught a strong waft of smoke and beer fumes.

"He's not in there," said Billy, returning within a minute. "But the landlord said he'd been in, and when he saw him, he was a bit more flush than usual; bought his own drinks for a change."

"I wonder whether he went home and we missed him—could he have taken a different route, do you think?"

"There's another pub up the road, a bit closer to the water." He pointed along the street. "It's not far to walk—and in fact, miss, it's closer to where Freddie thought he saw that man knife the other bloke. You know, we could kill two birds with one stone—while we're there we could have another gander at the scene of the crime, as our mate Caldwell would say."

Maisie was about to agree, when a man stumbling along the pavement in the distance caught her eye. "I think that's Hackett. Come on."

"Blimey, I reckon you're right, miss."

"Mr. Hackett!" Maisie called out. "Mr. Hackett—are you all right?"

Hackett squinted as they approached, then held up a fist and shook it at Maisie. "You! You're the interfering cow who took away my wife and children. You—"

"Steady, mate." Billy stepped forward, a barrier between Hackett and Maisie. "The lady was only trying to be of assistance. Now then, wind your neck in."

"And what will you do, you bleedin' long tall drink of water?"

"Come on, mate—we'll see you home."

Hackett seemed to waver on the street, but allowed Billy to take his upper arm and lead him toward the decaying back-to-back houses.

"If I wasn't ill, I'd give you a right-hander and you'd be gone," slurred Hackett, his eyes almost closed. "This is what she's done to me, that woman there."

"I reckon you've done it to yourself, sir." Billy continued to steer the drunken man along the road. "Now then, pick up your feet or you'll never get home."

Maisie remained on Hackett's other side, occasionally reaching out to help him keep his balance by supporting his elbow. They soon arrived back at the house, whereupon Hackett pushed his hand through the letterbox to draw out a length of string with a key on the end. "See what I've had to do? No one at home when I get there anymore, so now I'm like a nipper coming home from school early, and have to get in this way."

"You could keep the key on you," said Billy.

Inside, Hackett began to calm down. "No need to come up. Much obliged to you, sir." He turned to Maisie. "Even if your wife took my family away—nasty piece of work she is."

"I'm not Mr. Beale's wife, Mr. Hackett." She paused. "How are you feeling?"

"I'd be better if you two would bugger off now."

"We'll come upstairs and make sure you're settled," said Maisie. Without waiting for an answer, she nodded to Billy, and they walked up the stairs behind Hackett. She watched his every step.

She also watched the way he opened the door at the top of the landing and how he made his way into the kitchen. It was as he reached the kitchen table that she grabbed Billy by the sleeve of his jacket and pulled him back. In a flash Hackett had grabbed a carving knife from the table and was lashing out at Billy.

"All right—we're leaving," said Maisie. "But if you move with that thing, you will be sorry—and you'll also be behind bars for a very, very long time."

Hackett laughed as he stumbled against the table, then shouted, "Sod off—both of you."

Outside the flat they caught their breath before Billy spoke.

"Bit close for comfort, wasn't it, miss?"

Maisie held her hand against her chest. "Did you see the way he took the key from the letterbox and then opened the door?"

"Oh, a lot of people do that, miss—keep a key on a bit of string inside the letterbox. My old mum used to do it before she came to live with us, you know, before she passed away. It meant that when I went round there I didn't have to knock, I could just unlock the door and let myself in."

"That's not what I meant. Did you watch him work the key?"

"What d'you mean, miss?"

"Billy, we saw him stumbling along the road, apparently drunk as a lord. We helped him along, and when we arrived at the house it was with a certain dexterity that he pulled out the key, slipped it into the lock and turned it. Most drunks would have spent a good while trying to focus on the lock and trying to get the key into the slot. He went upstairs without missing a step. Yes, he knows his place, but those stairs are not solid. Then the knife."

"He was quick, I'll give you that," said Billy.

"He was no more drunk than I am," said Maisie.

"Oh, I don't know about that, miss."

"Well, perhaps he'd had one or two, but he was not as drunk as he pretended to be."

"What do you think he's up to?" Billy began to pat his pockets.

"That's exactly what you should do, make sure you've still got your wallet!" Maisie stepped around a pothole in the pavement. "I think he has a few tricks up his sleeve, Billy—that's why I wanted to follow him upstairs, to observe him. He can pretend to be drunk, just enough to gain some sympathy perhaps—look at us, we tried to help him."

"Yeah, but we also wanted to have a word with him."

"Granted. I bet he pulls that one every day and some poor soul loses a wallet or a watch or something. According to Grace it's his specialty. He finds a mark, a solitary customer in a local pub, perhaps a soldier from another part of the country who's new to London. He'll engage them in conversation, and the next thing you know, they're buying drinks and he's keeping relatively sober—not what you'd call 'sober as a judge' but enough to retain his balance and, more importantly, his reflexes. And then he's slipped another wallet into his own pocket."

"I wonder where the money goes, if he's that good."

"Probably on the real drinking, the habit he has when he's on his own—that's why he's a danger to his family and probably himself. I wouldn't mind betting he's got a bottle or two of the hard stuff stashed at home, where he drinks and drinks and has days when he cannot get out of those paltry rooms at all."

"Nasty piece of work."

Maisie stopped walking.

"Miss?"

"I was just thinking—it's such a tragedy. When people drink like that, it's the demons they're trying to dull that make me wonder what on earth happened to them." She looked at Billy. "You know what I'm talking about, don't you?"

Billy nodded and looked away. Her assistant's once-blond hair was now almost gray under his flat cap, the lines across his forehead deeper. "The white stuff? Yeah, I suppose I do. But I never lifted a hand to my family—they're too precious to me, miss, and you know it. I just didn't know what to do with the pictures in my mind or the pain in my legs. It's well behind me now, though if truth be told, them pictures have never gone away."

"I know, Billy." She began walking again, Billy falling into step beside her. "We just have to do our best to let them fade into the shadows, then build a wall of new things in front of them."

"Easier said than done, what with all this bombing—and my boys enlisted."

Maisie realized she hadn't asked about Billy's sons lately. His eldest had survived Dunkirk; now it was the younger son, an apprentice aircraft engineer with the RAF, who was the cause of most concern.

"How's Bobby? Doing well at the college?"

"Still looking to be a navigator on the bombers. He told me they've got a new one in the works, and he's in line for training on it." He shook his head. "They've already sent him up to Manchester so he can see what it's all about. Of course, he said he can't tell us much, but he made my head spin, going on about Merlin engines made by Rolls-Royce and that sort of thing. I tell you, that boy leaves me behind when he tells me about his work—and remember, I was in the Engineers in the last war, so I can generally keep up with that sort of talk. Not with Bobby though."

"I'm sure it's a feather in his cap, being chosen to learn something new." Maisie tried to appear positive, though she knew why Billy wasn't smiling.

"Not to me, miss. New bomber means more bombings and with bigger bombs. Then he'll be going over there every night to bomb Germany, won't he? And look how many of them bomber crews come back—not many, eh? That would definitely drive me to drink, if I lost one of my boys. At least our Billy is having it jammy, out there in Singapore. I bet it's all sun and getting in rounds of fancy drinks, with just a bit of square bashing in between. Mind you, good on the boy. He deserves it, after Dunkirk."

Maisie and Billy walked on in silence until they reached the bus stop, where they would catch a bus to take them back to the West End. Both were lost in their thoughts. There seemed nothing left to say, as if they knew any words would only take them back into the terrors of the last war, memories that could rise up from the dark shadows if they paid them too much attention.

CHAPTER 16

S andra, what are you doing here? Why aren't you at home?"

Maisie's secretary looked up from her desk, her smile broad as Maisie and Billy entered the office. "Hello, Miss Dobbs. I've been doing the books at my house and keeping the files, and it's all very nice being down in Kent—don't get me wrong, I'm really grateful to you for finding us that cottage—but as I said to Lawrence, 'I'd like to get up to London,' and he said, 'Why don't you go up there on the train, and I'll look after Martin. I'll take him fishing.' He's still a bit young for that, but I'm sure they'll do something together. Anyway, I'm here—and if you don't mind my saying, it's just as well."

"Are you suggesting Miss Dobbs and me are not very good at filing, Sandra?" After their meeting with the volatile Arthur Hackett, Maisie thought Billy's laughter was a relief. As she joined in, the anxiety she had been holding in her body began to ebb away. Billy could always be depended upon to bring humor to the proceedings at just the right time.

"I think that's exactly what Sandra is alluding to, Billy. And probably with good reason. We've let things go a bit."

"And I'm sorting it all out. Almost done. I'll put the kettle on." Sandra picked up the tea tray, adding, "Oh, and a Mrs. Towner called—she asked for Lady Margaret at first, but I told her you use your maiden name for your work, so it's Miss Dobbs. Just as well I was here—you never know how many telephone calls you might have missed, what with me not being in the office very often. Could you telephone her back, miss? She said it's important."

"Thank you, Sandra—and we would love a cup of tea. I'll telephone her now." Maisie watched the young woman leave the room, and thought how she had become less strained since becoming a mother—still competent, but with more ease in the way she met the world. Though Sandra had known tragedy in her life, she appeared to take everything in her stride, the days of sadness well behind her.

Billy stepped across to his desk, where Sandra had left a series of notes, each one with a question. "It's nice having Sandra back, but she is the only person I know who can nag on paper."

Maisie laughed. "Put your head down and get on with it, Billy—it'll only get worse if you don't answer her questions."

Once in her office, Maisie dialed Gabriella Hunter's number. No one picked up. As the ringing continued, Maisie felt a knot in her stomach.

When at last the housekeeper answered, Maisie was alert to the crack in her voice as she recited the number.

"Hello—it's Maisie Dobbs here. Are you all right? Hello!"

"Oh, Miss Dobbs. Miss Dobbs—I mean, Lady Margaret—oh dear—"

"What is it? What's happened?"

Maisie heard the housekeeper's gulps, as if she were being deprived of air.

"It's Miss Hunter. She's been rushed to University College Hospital. I was only meant to be out for a little while, running some errands and getting a few groceries. But you have to queue for such a long time, so I wasn't back when I said I would be. And when I got here, the lock was broken." She gulped again.

"Breathe slowly through your nose," said Maisie, her voice slow, calm. "Do you have a paper bag? Perhaps one the grocer put something in?"

"Right at my feet—"

Maisie could hear more rasping as the housekeeper fought for air. "Good. Take a bag now—never mind what drops out onto the floor— take the bag and put the opening over your nose and mouth and breathe as calmly as you can."

She could hear the sound of rustling paper and the woman's breathing, fast and shallow at first, then becoming steady.

"Are you still there?" asked Maisie.

Paper crackled again before the housekeeper replied. "Yes, I'm feeling better."

"Good—do that whenever you feel the panic coming on. Now, what's happened?"

Maisie heard the woman breathing into the paper bag again.

"Hello . . ."

"Sorry, Miss Dobbs." She coughed once more, then went on. "What happened was that I came home and the door was closed, but I could see the lock had been tampered with. I rushed in, dropped my groceries, and went straight to the study, where Miss Hunter was lying on the floor. Blood all over her face. Someone had hit her and left her for dead. Her papers were all over the place. Drawers open, books strewn around."

Maisie placed her hand on the buckle at her waist.

"I knelt down, listened to her heart," continued Towner. "Then I got a hand mirror and put it in front of her mouth—I knew she was alive, so I telephoned for the police and an ambulance straightaway."

"You've been remarkable, Mrs. Towner."

"I just tried to do the right thing."

"Can you remember the name of the policeman who came to the house?"

There was the sound of crinkling paper on the line and the housekeeper breathing into the bag.

"Hello?"

"Sorry—it was a Mr. Caldwell. Yes, that's it—in fact, no, sorry, he was a Detective Chief something-or-other."

"That's all right—I know who you mean."

"He said . . . he said . . ."

"Mrs. Towner?"

"He said it was attempted murder and he made me tell him everything."

"Yes, that's his job."

"He wanted to know everyone who had been to the house over the past few weeks."

"That's perfectly normal—that's what he has to do."

"I gave him your name."

"As I would expect you to, Mrs. Towner. Now then, I'm going to go straight to the hospital, and then I'll come to see you. Is the lock mended?"

"No. The door won't shut. I'm scared."

"Right you are. I'm sending someone round right now." Maisie looked at Billy, who, along with Sandra, was standing at the open doors into Maisie's office and had been following the conversation. "In fact, I'm sending two people." She turned to Sandra, who nodded. "They're my assistants. Mr. Beale is a tall man, grayish blond hair, and he'll be wearing a cap. Mrs. Sandra Pickering is about my height, dark hair, and she's wearing a pale blue day dress and a navy jacket." Sandra reached to one side, picked up her hat from her desk, and held it up for

Maisie to see. "And a navy blue hat with a pale blue band. They'll be with you in about fifteen minutes and will look after you."

"Thank you, Miss Dobbs."

"And Caldwell didn't leave a policeman with you?"

"He said he would normally do that, but he's short-staffed."

"Yes, that's right. Anyway, Billy and Sandra will be with you very soon." Maisie replaced the receiver. "Right—you heard all that—you know what to do." She scribbled the Mecklenburgh Square address on a scrap of paper, passing it to Sandra. "And have a look around to see if you can find anything else the police might have missed." She was already at the door, Billy and Sandra behind her.

"Why do you think someone picked on Miss Hunter, miss?" said Billy, as they hurried down the stairs.

Maisie opened the front door, turning to Billy and Sandra. "Gabriella Hunter is no ordinary lady. She was an agent during and immediately after the last war, and she knows much, much more than anyone might imagine. More to the point, she was finding out a few things for me, getting in touch with some very well-informed old contacts—and of course, she has her own experience to draw upon." She looked at her watch. "I'll see you at Miss Hunter's house as soon as I've finished at the hospital. And Sandra, you must catch your train home directly poor Mrs. Towner is settled and safe. In the meantime, I'll leave it to you two to decide if she should go to an hotel."

At Tottenham Court Road, Billy hailed a taxicab.

"You two go first, Billy," said Maisie. "I'll get the next one along."

Billy opened the door for Sandra to climb aboard, but just before he stepped into the taxicab, he looked back at Maisie. "Grayish blond?"

Billy had just slammed the door behind him and Maisie was raising her hand to hail the next taxicab on Tottenham Court Road when a black Invicta motor car pulled up alongside her. The back window wound down.

"Miss Dobbs—I was just coming to pay you a visit. And I bet I know where you're going. Come on—I'll run you over there."

It was clear from Caldwell's tone that even if she had wanted to decline, this was an order. The passenger door was barely closed before the Invicta pulled away from the curb, alarm bells ringing as the driver negotiated busy streets at speed toward the hospital.

"Right then." Caldwell gave Maisie a pointed look. "We've got about five minutes. How about telling me what's going on."

Maisie looked out of the window, then back at Caldwell. "I can tell you some things, but I will have to leave gaps."

"Hush-hush work and all that, Miss Dobbs?" Caldwell gave a half-laugh. "Always the way these days, isn't it?"

Maisie nodded.

"Right then, just tell me what you can. By the time we get over to the hospital, this could be a murder case anyway."

Maisie felt the air leave her lungs, so she placed both hands against her chest and began to tell Caldwell the story of Gabriella Hunter, but with those details that might be of most interest to him edited with care.

'm afraid she's very poorly, though she has regained consciousness. At her age . . ." The registrar—the most senior doctor on duty in the ward—consulted his notes as he briefed Caldwell and Maisie outside Gabriella Hunter's private room. "Sixty-one—she seems fit other than a nasty hip, which I must say flummoxes me as it appears to have been caused by a bullet wound a number of years ago, and she has another similar wound on her upper arm." He looked up. "Any ideas how she might have sustained those two?"

Caldwell looked at Maisie and raised an eyebrow. "Miss Dobbs?"

"She was in France during the last war," said Maisie.

The doctor looked from Maisie to Caldwell and back to Maisie again, then smiled as if he had at once seen the funny side of a joke. "Oh, right then. Anyway, she has suffered a serious concussion. Even though she's come round, she won't be 'all there' when you go in—and I must insist upon no longer than five minutes."

"Her other injuries?" asked Maisie.

"Bruising to the cheeks, and there was an attempt to take her life with a blade, but it seems not to have penetrated too far, given that she was wearing some sort of protective shield under her blouse. Her housekeeper apparently told the ambulance men that it was a special corset for her back." He stopped as if to gauge Maisie's reaction to his revelation. "Perhaps she had to watch her back too, do you think?"

"It's entirely possible," said Maisie, acknowledging the inference. "But it seems there was clearly an attempt to kill her, not just frighten her."

"That's for you people to decide, but yes, I'd say someone wanted to finish her off. You will see we've had to shave her head to stitch up a nasty cut where she was hit with something sharp."

"Can she see visitors now?" asked Caldwell, who had taken on a distinct pallor.

"Five minutes. Sister will be in to collar you if you are a second over. A word of caution, though—do not try to test your authority with our ward sister, otherwise you might find yourself being trepanned."

Caldwell did not follow as Maisie opened the door to the hospital room, explaining that he had a few more questions for the doctor.

She walked straight to the side of the bed and reached for Gabriella Hunter's hand.

"Gabriella. Gabriella, it's me—Maisie."

She watched as the closed eyelids flickered; Hunter was trying to open her eyes.

"Squeeze my hand if you can hear me," said Maisie, feeling the pressure as Hunter increased an otherwise loose grip.

"Do you know who did this to you?"

Hunter moved her head in a shallow nod.

"Was it the man with a scar?"

A slight frown formed across Hunter's forehead.

"Or long lines down the cheeks?"

Hunter made the barest movement of her head from side to side. No.

"Gabriella, what were they looking for?"

A smile crossed the woman's face, and she tried to speak. Maisie leaned in so her ear was close to Hunter's mouth.

"M . . . m . . . Maurice."

Maisie looked up. "Maurice?"

Hunter spoke again, this time with some force. "Book."

"Which book, Gabriella—you have so many books!"

"Mmmmm."

"Gabriella?"

"Mine. Mmmmm." With tremendous effort she finished the sentence. "My book."

Maisie turned as she heard the door open.

"I think that's enough now." The sister in charge was not yet frowning, but Maisie thought it would not take much to get on her wrong side. "Time to leave, madam. The patient needs rest."

"Indeed, thank you, Sister. I was just leaving." She turned to Hunter, who had opened her eyes. "I'll come again soon, Gabriella. Now, do as the sister says—rest." She leaned down and kissed the older woman on the cheek, squeezing her hand as she whispered, "Nice work with the corset."

As Maisie stood up, Gabriella Hunter managed a wink.

"You can come again tomorrow," said the ward sister. "But not before two, and only for another five minutes. Patient might be a little more with it by then."

"Don't underestimate her, Sister," said Maisie as she passed the senior nurse. "Miss Hunter is more with it than you might imagine."

'Allo, miss." Billy smiled as he opened the front door of Gabriella Hunter's house. "Come in." He stood back to allow Maisie to enter, and pointed to the lock. "Got that mended straightaway—mate of mine is a locksmith and came out quick as a flash. Right then, follow me—she's in the dining room, with Sandra."

Sandra was sitting next to Mrs. Towner at the table, a tea tray in front of them and an empty plate in front of the housekeeper. As Sandra greeted Maisie she stood up, stepping aside to allow her employer to take a seat alongside Mrs. Towner.

"Cup of tea, Miss Dobbs?" said Sandra. "I'm making more for Mrs. Towner."

"Oh lovely, thank you," said Maisie. "I'm gasping for a cup. Then you must get along to the station, Sandra."

"Right you are, Miss Dobbs. I won't be a minute."

Maisie turned to Mrs. Towner. "It looks like Sandra managed to get you to eat. I'm glad—you need your strength."

"Made me a nice Welsh rarebit, she did. Lovely girl, that one. She's been telling me about her little boy—sounds like quite a scamp, but he's at that age." Mrs. Towner reached for her teacup. Maisie noticed her hand was shaking. Towner put down the cup without raising it to her lips.

"This has all been a terrible shock for you, Mrs. Towner—but I must ask you some questions while the event is still somewhat fresh in your mind."

"That's what the detective said, when he asked me his questions."

"Yes, it's when the memories are still most raw, though some things might come back to you later, after you've had a good night's sleep. Some of my questions will doubtless be the same." Maisie allowed a pause. "Mrs. Towner, did you actually see anyone leaving the house as you returned—perhaps someone on the street who you're not used to seeing? Or getting into a taxi?"

Towner shook her head. "Nothing. I've racked my brains. I remember being in the shop, and when I'd got everything we needed, I walked back. I didn't really see anyone, except the street sweeper, and then I walked up to the house and, well, you know the story from there. That's when I saw the door had been prised open, so I ran in to find Miss Hunter on the floor, her head lacerated and her face covered in blood." She pulled a handkerchief from her cardigan sleeve and dabbed her eyes, then pushed the handkerchief back into the sleeve and pulled the unbuttoned cardigan around her, shivering.

Maisie looked around, but Billy had already stepped forward, holding a blanket. "I put this around her when we got here—she was in shock, but it comes and goes."

"Thank you, Billy—shock is like that."

Sandra returned with the tray and poured two cups of tea, removing the cup from in front of Mrs. Towner. "I'll just wash this and get on my way."

"Lovely—thank you, Sandra. Would you telephone me at the flat when you get home, just so I know you've arrived safely?"

Sandra smiled and nodded, turning to Mrs. Towner. "Miss Dobbs likes to keep tabs on us, you know."

"Thank you, my dear—you've been most kind," said Towner, smiling at Sandra.

Billy accompanied Sandra to the door; Maisie heard voices in the distance as they bid each other good-bye. Yes, she was lucky with her little band; they worked well together.

"The street sweeper—do you know him, Mrs. Towner?"

"Mr. Jeeps? Yes, everyone knows him—very friendly, very nicely mannered, though he can get a bit familiar. You know, with his betters. Some people think he's a bit too friendly."

Maisie suppressed a smile as she moved on to her next question. "Do you think Mr. Jeeps might have seen anything untoward?"

Towner sipped her tea, becoming visibly calmer. "He might well have. I know he works from a depot not far from here."

"I'll get Mr. Beale to look into it." She looked up as Billy returned to the room.

"Got that, miss—I'll find the depot as soon as we leave here."

"Thank you, Billy—would you just sit with Mrs. Towner for a while? I'd like to have a look at the study." She pressed Mrs. Towner's hand, and as she left the room, she heard Towner asking Billy where in London he was from, and whether his people were in trade.

Gabriella Hunter's study-cum-library had indeed been turned over, though as Maisie looked around the room she had a feeling that the invader had gone through the drawers and shelves in a systematic manner and only later made the incursion seem more chaotic to give the impression of a random burglary. Had the assailant wished to kill Hunter? Maisie wondered if he or she might have intended only to cause injury, or not expected to encounter her at all. She walked to the window and, reminding herself of the view across the square from that vantage point, considered the possibilities. The assailant could have looked out and seen Mrs. Towner entering the square with her shopping bag, so he knew his time was limited. After breaking in and attacking Hunter, he had not found what he was looking for, and he had assumed he'd killed Hunter—according to Towner's statement, Hunter's breathing was so shallow, she had required a mirror to assess whether she was alive. Yes, he meant to take Gabriella Hunter's life, but was it for what she knew, or because he was startled by her entering the study while he was going through her papers? One thing was clear to Maisie: the interloper had assumed or had been briefed to the effect that because she was a writer, the information he wanted was written down somewhere. If only she knew what it was.

Stepping over the small table alongside Hunter's Art Deco armchair, Maisie proceeded to the desk. Papers were strewn messily across the top; others were on the floor. Maisie replaced the papers into a neat stack, studying each page quickly before adding it to the pile. She moved on to the bookcase, her attention drawn first to a series of books bearing Hunter's name on the spine. Maisie opened every book, ran her finger along the binding and checked the endpapers, and then turned every single page, scanning for a letter, a document, an underlined paragraph, anything that might offer a motivation for the attack.

She was becoming frustrated with the task when Billy entered the study.

"Miss—poor Mrs. Towner is looking awfully tired. I've thought about her going to an hotel, but I don't think it's a good idea. She definitely shouldn't be alone, and we know that at night the hotels just make everyone go down to the cellars as soon as the air raid siren goes off, and she could do without that worry. I reckon she should go to someone who knows her and she knows them."

"Of course, yes, you're right. I want to have another word with her, and then let's see if we can make some alternative arrangements."

Returning to the dining room, Maisie once again took a seat alongside the housekeeper at the table.

"I should get on and clean up that mess in Miss Hunter's study, Miss Dobbs." Mrs. Towner began to push back her chair. "I don't want her coming home to see her beloved books in that terrible state."

"No, please don't worry about that," said Maisie. "Miss Hunter will be in hospital for a little while, so you've plenty of time. First of all, do you have someone—a relative, perhaps—with whom you might be able to stay for a few nights? I think it would be a good idea if you weren't here at the house. You've suffered a terrible shock, and it's best if you recuperate in another location."

Mrs. Towner looked down at her hands. "I can't say that I get on very well with my family. I've a sister in Peckham, but . . . well, she was never the right sort, if you know what I mean. My nephew comes around—he lives in Bromley with his wife. It's a bit far, I would think." She looked up at Billy. "He's not been called up because he's in a reserved profession—an engineer doing quite important war work." Her tone was almost apologetic.

"We're not checking up on him, so you don't have to worry about that," said Billy. "And it's not too far, because my house is in Eltham, though my wife and daughter are in the country now, but I was planning to go over there later to keep an eye on the place. I'll escort you to Bromley first. If your nephew has a telephone number, I'll get on the blower to him."

Mrs. Towner reached into her handbag, which had remained on her lap throughout as if for security, and brought out an address book. She opened it and passed it to Billy, pointing to an entry.

"I'll give him a bell now," said Billy.

As Billy left the room, Maisie drew her attention back to Towner. "When I saw Miss Hunter at the hospital, she mentioned a book to me. She specified that it was one she had written herself, and the way she said it, I thought she was trying to tell me something, that there was a clue in the book—some indication of what was at the heart of the attack. I've checked each one and I can't find anything in her books; no notes or a letter." She paused as tears filled Towner's eyes again. "Do you have any idea what she might have been referring to?"

Towner retrieved the handkerchief from her sleeve once more and dabbed her eyes. She nodded. "I think it must have been her new book. It's not published yet. On literature following the Great War— it's all about books and essays published in the immediate aftermath and of course the Peace Conference, and she told me she's put in some autobiographical notes too. Her words, not mine. She's normally very difficult about getting a manuscript to her publisher—she prevaricates, reads it over and again and makes changes and she types all the corrections herself. Miss Hunter will type a whole page again if a comma is out of place. Usually the publisher has to send his assistant around to the house every single day when the book is due, and Miss Hunter can get very annoyed about it. They have to drag it out of her."

"And where is that manuscript now?" asked Maisie.

"That's the funny thing. She only finished her third draft a couple of weeks ago, and because I knew the deadline was coming up, I thought, 'Here we go again—I've got to watch that poor girl leave the house with tears in her eyes every day for a month before Miss Hunter relinquishes the manuscript.' But instead she telephoned her publisher first thing this morning and told him to send the girl to pick up the manuscript because it was finished. It was so early he came over here himself, and she just gave it to him in brown paper tied with string and said she had to get back to work. Sent him packing at eight in the morning. Didn't even give me time to offer him a cup of tea, and usually she'll sit there for ages chatting with him, discussing books and all those sort of literary things she likes to talk about."

"What's her publisher's name? Where can I find him?"

"John Hillman. Of Hillman and Sons, only it's his daughter who works for him now, because his son died in the last war. It's his niece he sends over here to collect the manuscripts, as a rule. It's a true family business. They're over in Bedford Square, just on the corner with Gower Street."

"Billy—"

"S'all right, miss," said Billy entering the room again. "I've spoken to Mrs. Towner's nephew—got him at work—and he'll meet us at Bromley Station, then I'll come straight back and find the street sweeper. Consider it all as good as done—I can go over and have a look at my house another day; make sure no one's been looting it!"

"Thank you, Billy." Maisie turned to Towner and took her hands in her own. "Don't worry, Mr. Beale will look after you. And I'm sure you'll be able to see Miss Hunter in a couple of days. I think she's much stronger than people give her credit for."

Towner nodded. "I'll just go and put a few things into my case."

Billy accompanied Maisie to the door. "Here you are, miss—spare key to the new lock. Just in case you want to come back for another gander."

"Good thinking, Billy," said Maisie, placing the key in her bag. "The day is escaping us, and I'm off to see Miss Hunter's publisher, so please telephone this evening to let me know what you find out."

"Right, miss. Good luck with the publisher."

It was as she went on her way at a brisk clip—it was easier to walk than to wait for a taxicab—that Maisie's thoughts turned to Maurice. What had Maurice to do with the manuscript? Or was it a case of a wounded woman speaking the name of a man she had loved so long ago, hoping he would come to her aid, if only in spirit?

CHAPTER 17

Maisie kept up such a pace that she was breathless when she arrived at the Bedford Square offices of Hillman and Sons. A receptionist seated at a desk in the entrance hall was studying a thick manuscript and making notations in red ink across the pages; she was so engrossed in her work that she failed to look up even when Maisie was standing in front of her desk.

"Good afternoon," said Maisie.

The young woman started. "Oh my goodness—you made me jump!"

"I'm sorry," said Maisie. "My name is Maisie Dobbs, and I'd like to see Mr. John Hillman, if I may. It's a matter of some urgency in connection with the author Gabriella Hunter." She passed her professional calling card to the woman.

The receptionist studied the card, then looked up at Maisie. "Miss Hunter? Is she all right?"

"Well, not exactly, and I'd like to speak to Mr. Hillman about it if I may. And as I said, the situation is quite urgent."

"Just one moment."

The receptionist placed an open book across the manuscript and rushed from the entrance hall, card in hand. Casting her gaze upward, Maisie followed the young woman's progress as she ascended the broad winding staircase to the second floor. A door opened and closed, then opened and closed again a minute later as the receptionist ran back down the stairs.

"You can go up. Second floor, door to the right," said the receptionist, catching her breath.

Maisie took the stairs at the same speed as the receptionist, then knocked on the door to John Hillman's office, which was slightly ajar.

"Miss Dobbs, do come in," said John Hillman, as he came from behind a wide oak desk laden with papers and books. "My niece managed to make the door almost bounce off its hinges as she left." He gestured toward a chair placed in front of the desk, and waited for Maisie to be settled before taking his own seat again. He clasped his hands together. "Now then, what can I do for you? Miss Hunter is one of our most esteemed authors, and the manuscript I collected this morning promises to be an important book—I think it could find a readership well beyond the academic domain."

Maisie described her relationship to Hunter, explaining that she had known her since girlhood. "I'm afraid Miss Hunter was the victim of a vicious attack mid-morning. She is in University College Hospital, where her condition is serious but stable." She paused, taking care to frame her words despite the urgency of the situation. "Suffice it to say that Miss Hunter has been assisting me in an important investigation. She knew the information she had gathered—whatever it was—would put her life at risk, and I believe it is hidden within the manuscript she submitted this morning. I would very much like to see it, if I may."

Hillman came to his feet again, pushed back his chair and stood before the window that looked out across Bedford Square. As he clasped his hands behind his back and appeared to be pondering whether to assist her, Maisie felt her patience ebb.

"Mr. Hillman—"

"Miss Dobbs." Hillman turned around to face Maisie. "I find myself in a difficult position, as do you. I don't know what you might know about Gabriella's background, and you don't know what I know, so we have to tiptoe, and—"

"Did she ever introduce you to Dr. Maurice Blanche?"

"Why, yes—indeed she did. Now, there's a collection of papers I'd like to get my hands on. That would indeed be a publishing coup."

"Mr. Hillman, Dr. Blanche was my longtime mentor, and he was also my dear friend. That's how I met Gabriella." She paused for a second to allow her words to sink in. "Now, I cannot express the extent to which this is an urgent matter—one of life and death."

"Right you are." Hillman marched to his desk, picked up the telephone and placed a call. "Joan—Daddy here—" *Pause.* "Yes, I know you know it's me, but just listen for a change, would you? Now then, Miss Hunter's manuscript—has it arrived? The messenger should have delivered it several hours ago." *Pause.* "Oh, you're already working on it. Well, stop. Stop now. Wrap up the manuscript again, secure it with the string and keep the whole thing safe until a Miss Dobbs comes to collect the parcel." *Pause.* "Joan, I'm sure she knows where Tunbridge bloody Wells is, so would you simply do as I say?" *Pause.* "Joan, I don't have the time to discuss anything else at the present time, but please just indulge me and do as I ask without argument." *Pause.* "As a matter of fact, it *is* a matter of life and bloody death, so just get on with wrapping the manuscript and stop questioning my every instruction!" Slamming the telephone receiver onto its cradle, he picked up a pen and scribbled on a sheet of paper, which he handed to Maisie with a pained expression. "Miss Dobbs, my daughter is a first-class editor, but as you may have gathered, she's at her home in Tunbridge Wells today. You can have a good look at the manuscript when you meet. All right?"

Maisie stood up and took the sheet of paper with an address in

Tunbridge Wells, folded it and put it in her shoulder bag. She extended her hand. "Thank you very much, Mr. Hillman. I'm sorry if I've caused family discord, but this is very serious."

"I'm sure it is. And please don't worry, Joan and I snip at each other all the time—actually we all get on famously, considering this is a family business. Do take care of the manuscript though."

"Of course—you have my word." Maisie smiled and walked toward the door, turning back to Hillman as she reached for the handle. "By the way, Mr. Hillman—about Dr. Maurice Blanche's papers. I thought you might like to know that he bequeathed them to me, so I have them. All of them. Every last page."

Maisie left a message at her office for Billy, to let him know that she was going directly to Tunbridge Wells and might spend the night at the Dower House. Given that it was so close and a short journey on the local branch line, if she were late it would make sense to remain in Kent, rather than return to London.

There was another reason. Throughout the visit to Hunter's Mecklenburgh Square home, she had felt watched. It was a familiar feeling when working on a case and one that Maurice had described during her apprenticeship. "Remember, Maisie, that in identifying and focusing on the evidence we collect, we are also putting everything we know under the microscope to shed light on our inquiry, and without realizing it we also put ourselves under the same microscope. All that vigilance can make us feel as if we, too, are being watched—yet it is ourselves who are doing the watching when the task of looking inward becomes rote. You must be ever conscious of the landscape surrounding you, as well as that which is inside you."

Might Hunter's attacker have not left the environs surrounding her home following his incursion, but instead hidden in plain sight? And might he have followed Maisie to Bedford Square, taken note of the office she had entered and then concluded the reason for her call? Could he now be waiting for her? If that were so, then she would have to take utmost care in planning her journey to Tunbridge Wells.

By the time Maisie reached her destination, it was getting late. She had traveled by motor coach to Sevenoaks and from there caught a train to Tunbridge Wells, before the final leg of her journey in a taxi. She had studied every passenger on the coach and found nothing to concern her among the motley assortment of travelers. By the time she arrived in Tunbridge Wells, she was sure she had not been followed.

"You must be Miss Dobbs," said Joan Hillman, as she answered the door of her Georgian house situated on a street close to The Pantiles. She was an interesting study, slender verging on thin, wearing a pair of wide-legged trousers with pleats at a wide waistband. A collarless white shirt made for a man was tucked into the waistband, giving a blouson effect, and she wore her blond hair drawn up in a hurried topknot secured with a pencil, completing her ensemble with a floral folded silk scarf pulled around from nape of neck to crown and tied in a bow. On her feet she wore ballet slippers that were just visible under the trouser cuffs. She held a cigarette between two fingers as she answered the door.

"Yes, that's me," said Maisie.

"Come on in then. My study is at the back of the house."

Joan Hillman continued speaking as she walked ahead along the hallway, stubbing out the cigarette in an ashtray on a side table as she went. "I was going to come to the door with the manuscript, but

I thought I'd better not in case someone was there waiting to have a go at me with a cosh—after all, my father made it sound all very cloak and dagger." She opened the door to an orangery filled with all manner of exotic plants growing in large terra-cotta pots around the perimeter of the brick and glass room. A circular patterned carpet was positioned in the center of the flagstone floor, with a desk situated in the center as if it were the bull's-eye on a target. A single log smoldered in a small cast iron firebox at one end of the room, and a pair of armchairs upholstered in a deep burgundy heavy-duty linen flanked either side of the heat source. A calico cat was asleep on a blanket thrown across the seat of one chair. A walnut drinks cabinet was set to the left of the double doors that led back into the house, and a matching walnut filing cabinet stood on the other.

"Is it really that bad?" said Hillman, turning to Maisie.

"It's fairly serious. Miss Hunter is now in hospital, having suffered a grievous attack in her home."

Hillman looked at Maisie. "Come on, sit down and take the weight off your feet. I'll get the manuscript for you."

Maisie was grateful to sit back in the armchair, while Joan Hillman unlocked the filing cabinet and removed a thick buff-colored envelope.

"Do you have any idea what's in this book?" asked Hillman.

"I only know that there's something in there for me—something Gabriella might have left there for me to find because she knew others might want to intercept the information."

"I've not managed to get very far with it, as I had another job to finish first. In fact, I hadn't expected her manuscript for at least another month. Gabriella has a history of being a tyrant when it comes to getting her work in on time. Just terrible."

"May I?" said Maisie, holding out her hand.

"Sorry—here you go." Hillman passed the envelope to Maisie.

"Would you like a drink? And I mean a drink, not a soppy cup of tea. Hate the stuff."

"Just a small one. Cream sherry, if you have it."

Hillman nodded, stood up and went to the drinks cabinet. Maisie opened the envelope and began to turn each page of Gabriella Hunter's manuscript.

"It's an interesting book," said Hillman, handing Maisie a glass of sherry. She brushed aside the cat, threw the blanket on the floor and settled into the chair opposite Maisie. "Quite different from anything she's ever written before." She sipped her drink—Maisie detected the aroma of anise. "Usually her work is firmly directed toward the student of European literature, whether that student has just come up to university or is a few years on and working on a doctorate," continued Hillman. "But this is different. Yes, it is a sort of review of literature in the immediate period following the last war, right up until the present, but there's more than that—it's woven in with her memories." She gave a half-laugh. "Mind you, I doubt she'll go right into that realm of her past, after all, it's all rather murky—isn't it, Miss Dobbs?" She looked at Maisie, giving her a knowing wry smile.

"I'm anxious to go through the manuscript. I believe that what I am looking for might not be part of the document itself, but something specifically for me."

"Look—would you like to read it here?"

"But the blackout—I should be on my way."

"I think you're a bit late for that, Miss Dobbs—it was almost as dark as pitch outside by the time you arrived. I have guest quarters at the top of the house with everything you might need, right down to a new toothbrush. And you can look at the manuscript, find what you're searching for and leave it with me to continue my work tomorrow morning. I think this plan could suit both of us very well—and I'm clearly making the offer for selfish reasons, as I want to get on with my first read and the task of editing Gabriella's book so I can send it back to her immediately she's discharged from hospital. It might be the first of her books that we manage to get out according to the actual publishing schedule."

Maisie consulted her watch and realized that Joan Hillman was right—it was the best plan in the circumstances. "I'm sorry—I hadn't realized it was so late." She sighed. "Sometimes there are never enough hours at my disposal. Thank you very much for the offer, Miss Hillman—I'll take you up on it, and I assure you I will be away from here and out of your hair on the early train. I think the peace and quiet of your top-floor room might be just what I need."

"Good, that's settled. I'll throw together something for us to eat— how about a salad, cheese, some bread and a glass of wine? We can tuck in and call it supper."

Maisie laughed. "That sounds like my staple diet when I'm in London."

"Cheese is getting harder to come by, but fortunately my cleaning lady makes her own bread. I don't ask how she comes by the ingredients. Oh, and if we're to open a bottle of wine to share, you must call me Joan—so enough of all this 'Miss Hillman' lark. That's for the staff and even my father when we're both in the office. All very proper. We're 'Mr. Hillman' and 'Miss Hillman,' though I sometimes think my father would like to be 'Saint John Hillman, patron saint of the publishing world.' "

"Thank you, Joan—and please drop the 'Miss Dobbs.' It's 'Maisie.' "

"Good," said Hillman as she reached for a packet of cigarettes, shook one out and tapped it on the packet before picking up a lighter. As she ignited the flame she nodded toward the doors leading back into the house. "If you wander down the hall to the library—second door on the left—there's a telephone in there. Nice and private for any calls you need to make. Then I'll show you to your quarters. In the meantime, I'll make sure all the blackout blinds are in place, otherwise we'll be sharing our wine with Mr. Shilling, our local Air Raid Precautions man."

As Maisie made her way along to the library, she reflected on Hillman's earlier confession of selfishness; the esteemed editor had yet to ask how Gabriella Hunter had fared following the attack, or whether she might visit her at some point. But for now, Hunter's relationship with her editor was not of great import. Maisie wanted to telephone her father and Brenda at the Dower House and to speak to Anna, who she ached to see. She also wanted to contact Billy at the office—there was an extension line to the downstairs flat now, so if he had locked up the office, she hoped to locate him there.

" 'Allo, miss—I wondered what had happened to you."

"I've been chasing the not-yet-published book written by Gabriella Hunter." She went on to explain the circumstances, looking around to ensure her privacy. Though she trusted Hillman not to be the slightest bit interested in her work and personal life, it was a habit to confirm there was no one listening while she discussed a case.

"So have you read it yet?"

"I'll do it later this evening. I should be a good guest and not vanish to my room too quickly, though I doubt Joan Hillman will care much—she looks as if she'd rather have her nose in a book anyway. How about you?"

"The first thing I've got to tell you is that Mr. Scott has been on the blower time and again, looking for you. He thought you were going to be at your flat, and had dinner on the go and everything, and now he's a bit, you know, upset about it."

"Oh dear, I completely forgot."

"I'd say you're in a bit of a pickle there, miss. You've blotted your copybook, and it's not as if you can buy a bunch of flowers to say sorry to a bloke, is it? Anyway, I told him I was bound to hear from you this evening, and I'd get you to telephone him at your flat, which is where he's going to wait. And he said, 'Lucky you, knowing you'd get a call.' "

"I'll telephone him as soon as I've spoken to Anna." Maisie rubbed her forehead. "Anyway, that aside, have you made progress today?"

"I'm seeing my mate tomorrow morning, the one who knows a bit more about the Free French, and he said he's got something on Freddie's dad too. It took a while, what with one thing and another. He was in a telephone box and didn't have enough money; said he had to get going. Drives me mad, that sort of thing, because I wanted him to tell me what he had there and then. Anyway, I'll be seeing him in a caff just off Fleet Street."

"Frustrating. Very frustrating. I'll meet you in the office after you've seen him. All right?"

"Before you go, miss—I've got one more thing for you."

"Yes—what is it, Billy?"

"The street sweeper, Mr. Jeeps. Nice bloke, though he's a bit of a talker—probably down to spending all that time alone cleaning the streets, because he likes to have a chat. Anyway, he didn't see anyone coming or going from Miss Hunter's house, and the only other person he saw in the square asked him the way to the tube station. Young bloke, twenty-five-ish, looked like a student, had one of them scarves with the long stripes that students wear. Had a book or two under his arm, wore spectacles. That was all Jeeps could tell me."

Maisie sighed. "I'd put money on that being the attacker, and sticking around after the event."

"Me too."

"Thanks, Billy. I'll see you in the office—about half past ten, do you think?"

"Yes, miss. I'll be there. And don't forget to telephone that Yank. He's like a blimmin' terrier with a bone, I'll give him that."

Maisie, before you do anything else, you must ring your flat, because if I have to run to the library telephone one more time this evening, only to find it's Clark Gable looking for you, I think I will just let him have a piece of my mind and with both barrels."

"Oh, Brenda, I am sorry—I forgot he was coming over and I've been caught up. Caught out, more like, because I won't be returning to the flat this evening."

"Well, where are you then?"

"I'm safe and with a client—a lady who's connected to another client. It became late and she offered me her guest room, which meant I didn't have to find my way home through the blackout."

"Hmmph—perhaps Mr. Scott has good reason to get a bit upset then."

"Brenda—can you put Anna on, please?"

"Look, Maisie, sorry if I was a bit sharp, but I've said it before, that when you're in the midst of a case, you do remind me of Dr. Blanche at times. I'm now starting to feel a bit sorry for Mr. Scott. He's a very nice man, after all."

Maisie raised her eyebrows. "You've changed your tune."

"No, I always thought he was nice and he's good to you and Anna. I'd just like to see a bit more, you know—"

"I'll telephone him as soon as I've spoken to Anna."

Maisie?"

"Yes, it's me, Mark—I am so terribly sorry, I have been incredibly—"

"Incredibly what? I'm the one who's been incredibly worried, Maisie. You could have been dead under a bombed-out building somewhere, and how would I ever know? How would anyone get in touch with me if you were in a hospital somewhere, fighting for your life?"

"Mark, this is not like you. We are both working on sensitive . . . sensitive remits, and I always thought we accepted it as it is."

"Well, I don't know about that anymore. Maybe the sensitive thing around here is me, because I've been doing a lot of thinking about it all, and I reckon it's time some big decisions were made. We can't go on like this, Maisie."

Maisie placed her hand on her chest, feeling her heart begin to beat faster. So, this was it. She should have known it was all too good to be true. She should have realized that she would lose this man who she believed had loved her, who seemed to adore her daughter and re-spected her parents, even putting up with ways that must have seemed so strange to him. Now she had to accept that they'd had a good run, and though she loved him, it had come to this. He wouldn't be the first man who'd had trouble with the nature of her work.

"Yes, I think you're right, Mark. We can't go on like this." She paused. "Look, I'll be back in London tomorrow morning. Perhaps we can have one last dinner together—but I have to go now, and—"

"A last dinner? Maisie? I know you're listening, but I'm not sure you're hearing me."

"All right, if you don't want to, again, I understand. Perhaps it really is too much to ask of you. Anyway, I'll be at the flat tomorrow evening. Good night."

Maisie quickly replaced the receiver before Mark Scott could say more, but remained standing by the telephone until there was a knock on the door.

"Everything all right, Maisie?" Joan Hillman cracked the door just enough to see her guest. "There's supper and a nice glass of chilled sauternes on the table." She stopped speaking, studied Maisie and then continued. "I know that expression—only a man could cause a woman to look like that. Come on, let's get stuck into the whole bloody bottle. Women of our vintage should not be enduring even one shred of angst about a man."

It was an hour and a half later, having listened to Joan Hillman's entire romantic history involving three engagements, cold feet on the morning of her wedding—the expected culmination of engagement number three—and a series of wild affairs with "utterly the wrong sort," that Maisie climbed the stairs to her room at the top of the house. She was grateful for Hillman's nonstop monologue, for she had not felt obliged to offer a shred of information regarding her own personal affairs, beyond the fact that she was a widow with a child. Now she craved some peace and quiet, a time when she would sequester all thoughts of Mark Scott in a separate corner of her mind and heart, leaving room to apply her full concentration to the task at hand. She lay back on the bed, took up Gabriella Hunter's manuscript and turned the first page, then the second and the third, feeling her breath become faster as she began the hunt for the former agent's hidden message—a communiqué left in secret because she feared for her life.

CHAPTER 18

"According to my mate," said Billy, "he doesn't know a lot about the Free French, other than de Gaulle meeting with Churchill and speculation about what they think of each other. But he does know that Major André Chaput is quite a high-up bloke. Apparently he was decorated in the last war—awarded the Croix de Guerre for bravery in battle."

Billy flicked open his notebook. "Mick—my mate, known him since the war—poked around a bit and found out that after the war, Chaput was sent to the Levant, to Syria, because—and I've got to get this bit right . . ." He looked at his notes again. "Because of what went on between the British and the French out there. All right, I don't want to get into all the details—mainly because I didn't really want him to get into all the guff about it, but he said that the Arabs, who'd been our allies in the war, had all come together and planned a new sort of agreement, based upon peace with all the countries there—Syria, Lebanon, Palestine, Mesopotamia. It looked very promising; we, the British, were supporting them—that's his words—because they'd been our allies, but then we sort of did the dirty on them and handed it all over to the French, who wanted to get in there." Billy looked up at Maisie. "Bit rough, when you think the Arabs were on our side, eh? Anyway, Mick said the Arabs got angry—and of course, they're all different, from the different countries—because they were afraid of being pushed around because they knew exactly what they were doing and especially considering the hard work a bloke called Faisal had done. It was their land, after all, not anyone else's. French soldiers were sent into Syria, and Chaput was put in charge of a band who were trained in a different sort of fighting. This was more like skirmishing, fighting with knives and pistols as well as grenades, and they'd been trained to kill with their bare hands. They fought dirty, and it was all done in secret. Not exactly a very nice way to treat your allies."

"The pathologist who conducted the postmortem on the man dragged from the Thames thought he had been killed by an assassin, and could well have been one himself."

"Looks like we might be able to make a guess about where they learned how to do that, eh?"

"We might." Maisie picked up her own notebook, and looked up at Billy. "Last night, as I was reading through Gabriella Hunter's manuscript, I came across information that corroborates your friend's report. Now, it's not clear to me why Gabriella was in the Levant in 1920, but she was, and after I went to see her to ask if she had any information that might help me with the Hackett case, I think she was able to dig up a few things over and above what she already suspected. Sadly, I believe it was the digging that led to her being attacked."

Maisie studied her notebook, scanning pages she had filled the night before in the small guest room at Joan Hillman's house, a cozy bedroom with electric lighting that enabled her to read Gabriella Hunter's manuscript from the first page to the last, and where she found a folded sheet of paper between pages 50 and 51, with "Lady Margaret Compton" printed in bold lettering. Having refreshed her memory regarding certain details in that letter, she reached for her bag and put away her notebook.

"Billy, about the dead man, the one Freddie Hackett saw murdered—

we know he was a member of the Free French intelligence services, but he was also with Chaput in Damascus and another place called Aleppo—they were part of one of those units your friend told you about. There were a number of other men in this special strike group. I understand one of those men, named Claude Payot, was something of a . . . well, I suppose you could call him a troublemaker. Miss Hunter wrote that Payot and Charles d'Anjou—the dead man pulled from the Thames—are one and the same man. While in this unit, Payot constantly made fun of Chaput's features—certainly he could pass for a Levantine—intimating to the other soldiers that Chaput might be more loyal to the Arabs than France. Payot was ambitious, according to Gabriella's notes, and wanted to undermine Chaput. The cohesiveness of the unit was crucial because their orders were fraught with danger. Payot put the whole operation in peril. However, it is also true that Chaput might have been having doubts about the orders, not so much based upon the fact that he indeed has Arab blood in him—a Lebanese grandmother, I believe—but because he had begun to wonder if what he was doing was right, something he had never experienced before, according to Gabriella. The moral ambiguity of what he had been asked to do weighed upon him. The upshot of the discord between Payot and Chaput, together with Chaput's personal doubts, was that the group walked right into an ambush. Chaput, Payot and one other man survived. Apparently in his report Chaput took responsibility for the deaths, though he also reported Payot for insubordination in a time of war—which is tantamount to mutiny."

"So you could say your friend Miss Hunter was right about honor."

"Yes, I suppose you could " She checked the time. "Billy, there's a pub called the Waterman just this side of Vauxhall Bridge—I want to go over there to speak to the landlord, and it should be open by the time we get there. I'll tell you more in the taxicab on the way."

As Maisie took out her key to lock the office door, the telephone began to ring.

"You go and flag down a taxicab, Billy, while I answer this call." Maisie picked up the receiver.

"Maisie, Julian here. Look, I hate to disappoint you, but I've had one hell of a job finding out about your man. However, I do have a couple of pieces of information for you."

"Good of you to telephone me, Julian."

"I'm glad to say a bit of digging revealed something rather nasty about the chap—I wouldn't like to come back to you empty-handed, so to speak." He cleared his throat. "One of my old colleagues put me in touch with Hackett's commanding officer. He knew who I was asking about immediately, and said the man had a temper on him— apparently he would start a fight with anyone over anything. Had rather a violent streak—and as we know, war is already a stage set for violence, but he was in another league altogether. Very questionable individual. It seemed as if being a soldier gave him leave to indulge his love of violence. The most extraordinary thing is that it appears he might have saved the life of a French officer during the war—a fight in an estaminet that turned very nasty indeed."

Maisie recounted details of the incident involving Chaput that Gabriella had described in her letter.

"Pretty much the same, Maisie." Lord Julian paused, and cleared his throat again before continuing. "If that is the case, then do take care, won't you? I don't like the sound of this man—not only does Arthur Hackett hold a grudge, but from his commanding officer's account, he is one to want recompense for his favors too."

"Please don't worry, Julian. I'll be in touch."

Maisie left the office and made her way along Grafton Street toward Tottenham Court Road, where Billy was waiting alongside a taxicab. As soon as they were on their way, he ensured that the glass partition between the driver and his passengers was closed, and turned to Maisie.

"All right, miss?"

"It was Lord Julian, confirming some of what we already know—but good to have the information. He gave me some additional intelligence too."

"So what do you think is going on, miss?"

Maisie took a deep breath. "First of all, we know the dead man who was drawn from the river was Claude Payot, and not d'Anjou."

"Right, he was a Frenchman, and he's the one who caused trouble for Chaput."

Maisie shook her head. "I learned more from Gabriella's letter, and her manuscript. Payot was actually French Canadian by birth, and he fought in the last war as a young man. He came over to France from Quebec. However, instead of joining a Canadian regiment as part of the British Empire forces, he enlisted with the French."

"And then he went to Syria with Chaput?"

"Indeed—though as far as Chaput was concerned, he would never see him again after the disaster in Syria. But when he turned up again in London and presented himself to the Free French, once more offering his services for the love of France, it was something of a reunion between him and Major Chaput."

"Oh, blimey."

"Blimey, indeed. Chaput believed that when they were in Syria, Payot had in effect caused the unit to walk into an ambush resulting in the deaths of all but two of the men. In addition, while in the unit, Payot had the support of one of the men, who egged him on and became another thorn in Chaput's side—Payot's French cousin, whom he met as a boy when his family sailed from Canada to France to see their people—and not surprisingly, he had a reunion with the cousin when he landed in France to join the French army. The cousin came from a village somewhere in the Lot region, but again, not so important, though it seems that at the time he was a naive country boy, easily led by his more worldly cousin. Yet in a way Payot was also naive, chasing the dream of being a hero for the old country—but morally corrupt in the manner he chose to exercise his so-called heroism."

Billy was thoughtful. "I can see all that, miss—but what I still don't get is why Miss Hunter was attacked."

"To stop me finding out what had happened and to stall the investigation." She turned to look at Billy and pointed to the driver. "I cannot say any more at this moment—I don't want to take the risk. But I'll fill in the gaps for you later."

"Looks like we're here anyway, miss. The Waterman. Not one I'm that familiar with—and it's not far from where—"

"I know, Billy. Come on. According to Gabriella's letter, a man named Sharpe is the landlord."

W̲hat can I do for you, sir, madam?"

"Half a pint of light ale for me and a cream sherry for the lady, if you please," said Billy. He looked at Maisie and nodded.

"Right you are," said the publican as he lifted a half-pint glass, put it under the tap and drew a half-pint of light ale, filling the glass slowly and leaving a perfect one-inch head on the beer. He placed the ale in front of Billy before taking up a sherry schooner.

"Oh, just a small one, if you please, Mr. Sharpe," said Maisie. "If I drink a whole schooner of sherry, I might never leave."

Sharpe raised an eyebrow, smiled, and exchanged the schooner for a smaller glass. He uncorked a bottle of cream sherry and poured the reddish brown liquid into the glass until it was almost at the brim, then placed the drink on a mat in front of Maisie. "Now then, are you two going to tell me how you know my name, and yet you've never even set foot in here before?" said Sharpe. "Are you from the authorities or something? I'm telling you—I pour according to regulations in here, and I keep my hours tidy. Everything's above board."

"Not to worry, Mr. Sharpe, I know you do—and we're not from the ministry." Maisie took out a card identifying her as an associate of Scotland Yard, a leftover from a previous case when she had worked for MacFarlane. She handed it to Sharpe, who raised an eyebrow and returned it to her.

"Follow me—there's no one in the snug, so we can have a private conversation in there." He turned toward a young woman serving men in overalls and flat caps in the public bar. "Rosie, hold the fort at both ends for a bit, love."

"All right, boss. I've got everyone here sorted out."

There was laughter and joshing among the men as Sharpe lifted a flap on the bar and came through, leading the way to a secluded area at the end of the bar, set off by a wooden partition with a sign identifying it as "The Snug." They each took a seat at the round table tucked away in the corner.

"You'd better tell me what this is all about," said Sharpe.

"First of all, my apologies if my approach seemed a bit cryptic. However, I think you have some information that would be of use to us. We're investigating a murder, and we believe the victim was a man who was something of a regular here."

"Name?"

"We think he went by the name Charles d'Anjou—he was French Canadian, so his accent would have been quite distinctive. His English might have been very stilted too."

"There's one bloke, not been in for a while. He sounded French. Could drink a lot, but I don't think his name was Charles. Something like 'Clod.' And when I say he could drink a lot, I had to keep an eye on him. I sometimes wondered if he'd had a few at home and then came in for the company, or to pick a fight with someone." He nodded toward the public bar. "But our lot are working men, they don't want trouble—mind you, if trouble finds them, I wouldn't want to mess around with any of them. Strong lads. Know how to take care of themselves."

"I was born and bred in Lambeth. I understand." Maisie took a sip from her glass. "Did he ever meet anyone here, as far as you can remember? Or did he strike up a conversation with another man?"

The publican looked thoughtful, rubbing his chin. He turned around and called out to the barmaid. "Oi, Rosie—Rosie, just a minute, love. Over here."

"Yes, boss?" The barmaid was wiping her hands on a cloth as she entered the snug.

"Remember that bloke who used to come in a fair bit; a French fella? Tall, mustache. Dark hair. Name of Clod."

"Knocked back brandy and was always asking if we had Armagnac. Him?"

The publican nodded. "That's right. Ever see him with anyone?"

"I reckon I saw him with a bloke once or twice," said the barmaid. "That fella from over the water, the one who always manages to get someone else to stand him a drink."

"Did you ever see him with anyone else?" inquired Maisie

Rosie frowned. "There was one. Tall, dark, had deep lines on his face, and when he smiled it was a funny old smile. You know, sort of put on. He spoke really good English, but I didn't think he was from here. Well, he came in once on his own—" She paused, looking at her hands as she wound the cloth around them. "In fact, it was just a few days before the last time I saw the other Frenchman, the drinker. You were off that night, boss. It wasn't that busy, so I remember—that fella who was always broke was having a word with him. Then I saw the bloke with no money again outside, the last time I ever saw that Clod." She frowned. "Funny, that, because he was drinking an awful lot that night and the man who never put his hand in his pocket was with him. At first I thought he seemed as if he'd had a few himself, though I'd not poured anything for him." She shrugged. "P'raps they were drinking somewhere else beforehand, but I remember thinking I should keep an eye on them—you've always said to draw the line if I think someone's had enough, and those two had definitely had enough."

Sharpe nodded. "Thanks, Rosie. You'd better get back in there, that lot are just leaving and another couple are just coming in."

"On my way, boss." Rosie the barmaid cast a smile and nodded toward Maisie and Billy before hurrying back to the public bar.

"What can you tell us about the man who managed to get everyone else to buy a drink for him?" asked Maisie. "I believe his name is Hackett."

"Can't tell you much at all—except he's the sort you have to keep an eye on, like Rosie said." He folded his arms and leaned back in his chair. "Nothing comes as a surprise in this job, even two bods with identification from Scotland Yard that may or may not be genuine." He waited for a comment from either Maisie or Billy; neither said a word. Sharpe leaned forward. "It works like this—a bloke with not a penny to his name comes in and eyes up the fella who looks like he's drinking not to feel lonely. The next thing you know, the only one putting his hand in his pocket is Mr. Lonely. But the next morning he finds that his wallet is either gone or it's lighter by a few quid. Probably the latter—because the first fella knows it will be a while before the mark has him sussed, so he can do it all over again. I reckon that first bloke—this 'Hackett'—bought himself a bottle on the way home or went into another pub with the money, because in truth he's a serious drinker, and that sort usually likes to drink alone."

"Why didn't you stop Hackett coming in, if you thought he was fleecing your customers?" asked Maisie.

"If he'd been tapping up my regulars, I'd have had him by the scruff of the neck and tossed him out on the pavement. And it's not as if he came in all the time—only a few appearances, so I reckon he did most of his business elsewhere. No, I reckon he was working some sort of racket with that other bloke, the one Rosie talked about who looked like that actor—oh gawd, what is his name?" Sharpe scratched his head.

"Victor Mature?" asked Billy.

"That's the one. I suppose you know about him then."

Maisie nodded. "Yes, we know him." She glanced at Billy, who shook his head. "I think I have enough information for now, Mr. Sharpe— and thank you for your time. I know you run a busy establishment here, so I'm much obliged to you."

They pushed back their chairs, and as they left the snug, Sharpe turned to Maisie. "There was another bloke who came in once with the one who looked like Victor Mature, a Scottish fella. You could see he enjoyed his malt whisky, I'll give him that."

Maisie felt Billy looking at her, waiting for her to say something. Touching Sharpe on the arm, she stopped him as he moved to lift the flap and return to his place behind the bar. "What Scottish fellow?"

"Big chap. Going bald. Didn't say much, but went outside with old Victor. Started to take his drink with him, but I had to tell him drinks inside only. He was all right, said sorry, put down his glass—and he only had one sip, but it was a big one—then off they went."

"Was this before Hackett arrived? And the other Frenchman?"

Sharpe nodded. "I reckon so. The Scots bloke didn't stay long."

"And was this on a Friday, about two weeks ago?"

"Friday, yeah." He scratched his head. "I should know, shouldn't I? Friday can be a bit noisy in here—but that's probably why I remember, because people who don't want to be remembered like to get lost in a crowd, don't they? And people like me notice them."

Maisie thanked the publican again and Billy shook his hand as they left.

"Let's walk across the bridge, Billy," said Maisie, as they stood outside the Waterman public house.

They walked at a slow pace for some moments, Billy understanding that his employer wanted to think, to slot pieces into the puzzle as a picture formed of what had come to pass on the night Freddie Hackett witnessed a murder.

At last, Billy could wait no longer. "What do you reckon, miss? Right spanner in the works back there, him talking about a Scottish bloke coming in."

"Indeed it is, but it makes sense too—though not in a way I might have hoped for. It renders things very tricky for us."

"Yeah, you can say that again."

Maisie stopped and turned, looking into the distance as if following the Thames as it made its way toward Greenwich, then onward to the place where it would become one with the open sea. She sighed. "In a short while we will have completed our investigation, and we will be able to tell Freddie that he really did witness a murder, but when he asks who did it, we won't be able to confirm anything for him, though I have every confidence that I will be able to ensure his safety."

"Who did it, miss?"

Maisie closed her eyes. "A system did it, Billy. War did it. Terror did it, and so did people living in fear." She sighed. "But that doesn't mean I'm not going to confront the man at the heart of this killing, and I'm going to make sure those concerned understand exactly what I know."

Maisie felt a wave of fatigue beginning to claim her. At once she wanted to be at Chelstone, waiting to collect her daughter from school. She wanted to be at the flat, counting the minutes until Mark Scott arrived—though she had accepted that she would probably never see him again; their exchange had seemed so final. She wanted to be finished with this case—a case she'd taken on because she hated to see a frightened child; a child who feared he would never be believed.

"Anyway, in the grand scheme of things, most of what we learned today is only corroboration of something I know already."

"Miss, you were going to finish explaining why Miss Hunter was attacked."

Maisie nodded. "Of course, yes, you should know." Maisie looked around and pointed to a place against a wall, well away from anyone walking past. "Billy, I am going to give you some highly classified information—you won't forget it, so I can't ask you to do that, and it might not even seem terribly secret, but it is."

"Who is she? I mean—what did she do, exactly?"

"More than you can ever imagine," said Maisie. "I suppose there's probably no other way to describe her work except to say she was a spy. She was one of the best intelligence agents in the field working on behalf of France and Britain during the last war. She was part of a group reporting to Maurice, who was a linchpin between the intelligence services of Britain, France and Belgium." She put her hand on her chest, feeling her breath become short, imagining Hunter anticipating an attack to the extent that she had prepared for it by wearing what the doctor thought was a "corset" but was in fact an item of protective clothing she had used in earlier years, when the threat of death was part of her job. "Gabriella has access to a stunning depth of information—and contacts everywhere. She knew exactly what had happened to Chaput, not only in France toward the end of the last war but also in the Levant—she was there for a time, though I do not know in what capacity, and I'm not going to ask. It didn't take her long to recognize Chaput's name as the leader of a unit involved in a deadly massacre that had been the subject of investigation, in case it represented a security breach. Any official record of the subsequent inquiry was conveniently lost so the disaster would be forgotten as the years passed—it was hushed up. But Gabriella knew the Chaput name, and she knew about Payot—she has a memory like an elephant, but because I'd made the inquiry, she called a few contacts to fill in any gaps."

"But if this Chaput was a war hero anyway, how could she hurt him?"

Maisie took a deep breath and looked up at Billy, her eyes meeting his.

"Cross my heart I won't tell a soul, miss," Billy assured her.

"All right. Chaput is presently involved in subversive activities against the Germans in his country. He will be leaving England soon to continue that work and lead trained French citizens in acts designed to stop the Nazis." Maisie felt as if she were tap-dancing around the truth. "For him it's a matter of honor—I think that's what Gabriella was trying to tell me. Chaput is determined to fight for the honor of France, and to reclaim a sense of worth lost years ago. He doesn't want anything to stand in the way—and if the truth about Payot's death gets out, it could prevent him from being sent across the Channel. A volatile leader can put a whole operation at risk, and if the facts regarding the debacle in Syria—leading men into an ambush—are revealed, then he will watch others depart to do the job while he's behind a desk in London, which he hates. So all the time Gabriella was a benign academic, the past had been nicely stashed away in yesterday's box. But then someone got wind of her new book—she had written about events in Syria, though she didn't include names—and along with her inquiries on my behalf, her fate was sealed. Chaput knew she had too much on him, and that it was coming straight to me. Furthermore, his association with Hackett would come out, and along with the issue of Payot's murder and the fiasco in Syria, Chaput would not be trusted to lead a dog to a kennel, let alone French villagers into a citizen's battle with the Germans. History came to find Gabriella in the form of André Chaput—or whoever he sent to her home. He wanted his chance to atone for a past that haunted him, and was fearful it would just slip through his fingers. He was buying himself time."

"Blimey."

"And the extraordinary thing is that in this case, the past is all but untouchable. Right from the start I felt I knew who killed Claude Payot, though it's all turned out to be rather more convoluted than I might have imagined—yet my knowledge will never put the killer in court. Justice will have to look on and weep. Or perhaps not, because this is wartime, and as Caldwell would tell you, Justice is hiding out in a shelter somewhere, wounded, her head in her hands, but not yet beaten down."

Billy nodded. "Be careful, miss. You'll get on the blower when you're done with it all, won't you? I'll be waiting."

"I will. And all will be well. I believe MacFarlane knows where I am already and where I plan to go, so I will be safe."

CHAPTER 19

Maisie intended to stop at another pub known to Hackett, but decided there was no need. There was nothing to be gained from asking more questions. Later, perhaps, but not now. She knew where she was going, and she knew who she would meet there. It was as if the stones had been cast, the next moves already mapped.

She did not stop to look or linger, had no desire to touch the ground or spend even a second at the place where Freddie Hackett had witnessed the death of Claude Payot, also known as Charles d'Anjou. She stepped around the point where she believed his body had hit the ground and walked on toward the almost derelict, bomb-damaged Victorian house where Freddie Hackett had delivered a message on the evening he saw one man kill another. Arriving at the house, she knocked on the door. Feeling a burst of anxiety course through her body, she wished she had stopped on the way, found a quiet corner somewhere in a bombed-out building, so that she might temper the emotion she could only identify as dread. She was walking straight into the lair of a killer. In the few seconds remaining before every one of her senses had to expand, had to go forward before her as if they were an advance guard, protecting her, keeping her safe, Maisie closed her eyes and whispered, "Maurice, help me." She raised her fist to knock again, but the door opened.

"I've been expecting you, Miss Dobbs."

"I thought you might, Major Chaput. May I come in?"

"Please do."

Chaput stepped aside to allow Maisie to pass, though she turned to face him as soon as she could.

"There are two chairs in that room now," said Chaput. "As you know, I do not come here often. This is only the second or third time."

Maisie nodded and proceeded into what had been the parlor before the war. She picked up one of the chairs and walked with it to the window, where she could see out to the street and someone passing might have a view into the property—if anyone walked in this direction. Chaput grinned, an expression that accentuated the deep lines extending from just below his cheekbones to the sides of his mouth. He took the second chair and positioned it opposite Maisie. As he sat down, his unbuttoned jacket flapped open, revealing a pistol holstered against his chest. She leaned forward to place her bag on the floor, giving her the opportunity to cast a glance in the direction of his ankle, where another strap held a knife in place.

"So, Miss Dobbs, now you know how I am armed, where shall we begin, you and I? We find ourselves in an unfortunate situation, because you know so much about me, yet I know almost nothing about you—except that for some reason you knew exactly who I was the moment we met, didn't you?"

"A lucky guess," said Maisie, then corrected herself. "No, it was more than that. I know a killer when I see one. I've had a lot of practice."

Chaput folded his arms, his head inclined, giving the impression of a relaxed man.

"You've taken the lives of two men on British soil, Major Chaput," said Maisie. "You've used the cover of war to claim 'an eye for an eye and a tooth for a tooth.' There was no need—and without doubt no need to involve Hackett."

"Oh, but there was, Miss Dobbs, there was every *need*, as you put it. But tell me what you know—it cannot do any harm now, and I'm curious anyway. It will help me become a little more vigilant next time—though I confess you are very well connected, which I think helped you in your little investigation."

Maisie felt her jaw tense.

"All right, Major. Here we go." She drew a deep breath, and began. "In the last war you were a captain—soon to be promoted to major—and you were encamped close to a local village with a British battalion not terribly far away. However . . . however, for several days there had been an increasing level of disruption among your men. Am I right so far?"

"I'll complain when you're wrong," said Chaput.

"This part is fairly straightforward. In a local estaminet, a fight broke out between some of your men, and when one of them went for you, a British soldier stepped in. He wasn't actually trying to help you; more likely he just wanted to have a go at someone because it was in his nature. But he saved you, didn't he, and managed to get a swipe across his cheek with a knife in the process?"

"It was toward the end of the war, and my men were becoming disillusioned. As were the British and the Germans. But that cut gave my savior the permanent ticket home he wanted, so it wasn't all that bad for him." Chaput glanced at his watch. "My time is precious, so please hurry, Miss Dobbs."

"Military police broke up the fight, Hackett was removed to a dressing station and you shook his hand as he was stretchered away. You thought you would never see him again."

"Hoped I'd never see him again—dissent is a danger to everyone on the battlefield, and I'd heard one of the British military police telling him to get out, and he refused, so I know he was no better than the worst of my men."

"Which brings us to Claude Payot and his cousin, Thierry Richard, who were with you again in Damascus. What a terrible job that must have been, given the way you were ordered to fight, to protect the French mandate against uprisings from a people who were quite able to rule themselves."

"We were not the only small group with orders that were just a little different from the army."

"Be that as it may, but Payot goaded you—I know what he did, what his constant provocation led to, and how your men were killed when your full attention was compromised by a lesser man who pushed you on when everything told you to pull back, because danger lay ahead. You allowed your better judgment to be undermined."

"The actions of Payot and Richard rendered us vulnerable."

"They rendered *you* vulnerable, Major Chaput. The fact that they lived, that subversive actions initiated by Payot led to the death of all but the three of you, was a thorn in your side—and not only did you blame them, you had to live with yourself, because there was an element of truth, wasn't there, in the fact that you had a certain sympathy for the local people?"

"I am a soldier of France—I followed my orders to the letter."

"Let's not split hairs." Maisie cleared her throat. "By chance Hackett ran into you in London—or was he lurking around just in case he saw you in places where the French spent their time, various clubs and so on? He was always in need of money, so instead of just giving him a handout—and therefore admitting to a debt—you had him run the odd errand for you, usually gathering information on where your agents went when they were on their own time in London. Now, my details are a little woolly here, but I would say he kept an eye on Payot for you and marked him as an alcoholic—after all, it takes one to know one. On the night of Payot's death, Hackett followed him to get him drunk and part him from his money. I think the plan unfolded over several weeks, so during that time Payot believed he had made a friend."

Maisie shook her head and glanced out of the window before she brought her attention back to Chaput, who was silent, watching her. "It couldn't go on for too long, this playing out of the line, could it? Hackett was a drunk himself, and time became of the essence. So on the night of the murder, Hackett led Payot to you, to the place where you were waiting. You wanted to make sure Payot paid for what happened in Syria. You wanted him to suffer for making you bear indignities in front of your men—indignities that distracted you. You were the sole keeper of this particular account, and you had the unpaid note. Oh, and you also wanted him out of the way, just in case that history was brought up before your superiors. I know an official report on the Syria debacle had once been tucked away in an old records office in Damascus, before it was lost." Maisie shook her head. "But where did Hackett go? Did he watch you settle the account? Did he have any idea that his son had witnessed the whole thing?" She looked down at her hands as she rubbed the palm of her right hand across the back of her left. "Given the anxiety that festered inside young Freddie, I have wondered if indeed he saw two men taking on Payot, which is why he was at first confused between facial lines and scars, though he didn't identify his father. I believe that in the boy's mind, the killer merged with his father because he only ever knew Arthur Hackett to be a brutal man. But that is for me to talk to Freddie about, in time." She brought her focus back to Chaput. "Hackett might not have been in his cups at this point, because he helped get rid of the body, dragged it from the pavement, probably around the back of a pile of debris. Then you returned, and I believe there was also assistance from another quarter. Do I have that right?"

"Good enough."

"Someone provided a vehicle, and I think I know who that might have been. Anyway, I would imagine Hackett was almost sober at this point—he's a nasty, weak, violent drunk, so it would have been no good using him if he'd hadn't been able to control himself while he was about the business of getting Payot insensible. But later, after the body was disposed of, it was time to make sure Hackett's memory was done for. What was it? A draught to make him forget? I'm fairly sure you have a veritable medicine cabinet at your disposal."

"I have tools."

"Of course you do," said Maisie. "And now we get to the man who was killed in Scotland. Claude Payot's cousin. Richard." She sighed. "I have wavered, asking myself if he was pushed, or whether he fell. I think it was a bit of both. I believe you tormented him first—that was the initial push. You plagued him at every opportunity, letting him know that you recognized him, that you had not forgotten the fact that he aided his cousin in his quest to supplant you. You can be an intimidating man, Major Chaput, and I am sure Richard reached a point where he was terrified and thought it better to leave this earth than live one more day with you breathing down his neck. But on that fine autumn day in Scotland, you not only reminded him of his failings but attacked him and then allowed him to finish the job himself as he went over the top of that crag."

"He was a weak man. How he was ever recruited, I will never know. Women are stronger than that dolt."

"Our women agents have proven themselves to be every bit as strong, if not stronger, than men sent out to your country. And they have given their lives. Let's just remember that."

Chaput shifted in his chair before bringing his attention back to Maisie. "In the end, yes, he took his own life. And did I push him to the final act? Yes, I did, and mine was the last face he saw as I watched to make sure the fall would kill him—of course I gave him a little extra help." He scraped back his chair and stood up, pacing to the fireplace and back to the chair again. "You see, Miss Dobbs, those cousins had blood on their hands. They had the blood of every one of my men who was hacked to death that night. I vowed I would have my revenge. And do I have regret? No. I don't. Not a sou."

Maisie heard a motor car pull to a halt outside. She stood up.

"You made an error with Gabriella Hunter. She was a fine agent, someone who understands the damage wrought by war, and she was ahead of you. She will survive. For whatever length of time you have here in London, make sure she remains safe, because she knows what it is to truly honor her country."

"I made an error. I sent a neophyte, an incompetent agent, to her house."

"Which is down to you. And why did you try to scare a boy, Major Chaput? Why would you frighten a child by going to his school, when you have nothing to fear even from me, though I know what you've done?"

"Miss Dobbs, that is where *you* make an error. You see, I wasn't trying to scare the boy, I simply wanted to talk to him. His father is a monster. Hackett may have saved my life, but he did so to feed the violent devil inside him. War can make a cruel brute of the most benign soul, but I doubt Freddie's father was ever a man of good temper. The woman and her children deserve their place of refuge, but be aware, Miss Dobbs—Hackett bears a grudge."

"I will ensure their safety." Maisie stepped away from the chair toward the door. "I must go now, Major Chaput. But . . . but I wonder how you feel, Major—now you've done all you can to assuage your guilt."

"Guilt?"

"Yes. There was a feeling of inadequacy that dogged you from the time you were a young officer on the battlefield, wasn't there? You, too, were a neophyte once, and in wartime, and when you fell foul of Payot's constant digs about your ancestry, you didn't know how to deflect the rhetoric coming from a pest like him. It might have been as simple as admitting your Levantine blood, laughing about it, then singing the *Marseillaise*."

"Payot called me a traitor, Miss Dobbs, for not going forward even though I could see it would lead to a rout for us. He pressed and pushed and then said he would lead the men if I was too scared to do it."

Maisie looked into Chaput's eyes, at the misery reflected in their darkness. "I know—fear of losing face led you into the ambush. And fear is really the most omnipresent of emotions, isn't it? Fear and panic can be crippling for all concerned. Given your standing, justice will turn a blind eye, but the scales remain, weighing you up. And though you are now a different man, an even braver soldier, you will always feel your actions measured against something you hold dear, won't you?" Maisie shook her head. "Your personal honor."

She did not wait for Chaput to reply, but left the house and walked toward the motor car outside. A driver opened the rear passenger door, and she stepped in.

MacFarlane waited until she was seated before he tapped on the window, signaling the driver to proceed.

"All done, Maisie?"

"Do we wait to hear the shot?"

"No, he won't do it yet. Probably at the end of the war—unless the Gestapo get him first. He's going out on a Lysander tomorrow night."

"Thank you for coming with the car."

"I've been keeping an eye on you."

"Yes, I know."

"Got a few minutes to spare me at Baker Street?"

"Do I have a choice, Robbie?"

"No. But I like to ask. It makes me feel like more of a gentleman."

Inside his office, MacFarlane walked to the filing cabinet, opened the bottom drawer, and took out the bottle of eighteen-year-old single-malt whisky and two glasses, pouring a good two fingers' worth in each glass. He handed one to Maisie, who was seated on the other side of his desk.

"You knew the entire time," said Maisie.

"Let's not go over it all." He took a hefty swig. "Yes, I knew. Would I have liked you to drop it? Yes, I would. All that business over there with the Arabs—I don't understand it and never will. It all looks like a bloody mess dished up by too many incompetent imperialist cooks, if you ask me. Anyway, we've got a different war to be getting on with now. You've found out who did what, and now you're done."

"You could have stopped all of it," said Maisie.

"No, I couldn't. There's an important alliance here, and one I have to protect, even when I have to clean up after our allies. On a personal note, there's also the Auld Alliance, as we say in Scotland, or in the case of the French major, the Vieille Alliance with Ecosse—we've got to stick together to control the English after all, a matter of honor between Scotland and France." He raised an eyebrow. "And I'm only half joking."

"Well, even with your warped idea of honor, you should have stopped the attack on Gabriella Hunter. Weren't you having his people watched, so you knew where they were going?"

"That was unfortunate."

"Unfortunate? Robbie, she almost died! She could be dead now, and—"

"But she's not. I saw her this afternoon. Sitting up in bed. She knew the stakes, Maisie. She knew what would happen the minute she took a shovel and started digging up the past. It took just one or two telephone calls on her part. And I don't have eyes in the back of my head or as many people to deploy as you might think. All the same, if she had been in contact with me, she would have had protection—she knows who I am, and she knew how to raise the drawbridge. Maisie, she was a top intelligence agent, for pity's sake. She'll be looking over her shoulder for the rest of her life. Anyway, it appears she managed to get out a bit of useful information to you in time."

Maisie nodded.

"You know, Maisie, we will all be called to account in some way or another when this war is over. In the aftermath, actions taken in wartime aren't necessarily looked upon kindly. Those who have never been to war can be the harshest of judges—their sense of what is right taking comfort in the soft pillow of peace rather than the bed of nails that is conflict." MacFarlane refilled his glass. "Now then, before I go too poetic on you, a word about the files I gave you a few days ago."

"I rejected one." Maisie sipped her whisky and felt the heat at the back of her throat. "What's going on, Robbie? Why do you keep doing this to me? Sending me recruits I know and therefore cannot in all good conscience possibly assess."

"Keeping you on your toes, Your Ladyship. Everyone has to be tested now and again to make sure they're paying attention, even you."

Maisie rolled her eyes, then took another sip of whisky. "Is that really it?"

MacFarlane shook his head. "Not with Evernden and Jones. I knew

I could trust you to be detached, even though you maintained it was a conflict of interest. I needed you to make the final report, Maisie. We all have to follow orders we don't like—and that goes for me too."

"So what about Corporal Bright?"

MacFarlane looked at Maisie. "Guilty as charged. That one was a test, Maisie. You see, I have to know if you're standing back and not letting emotions get in the way. You've struck up a little friendship with the girl, and I had to be sure you could look at her dispassionately, whether you would just give me a bucket of reasons why you wouldn't look at the file, or whether you would give me a solid assessment. I don't know who the next person through my door will be. My next best agent could be one of your friend's sons, and I have to know you'd approach your work with clarity. We don't send people over who don't want to go. Anyway, I won't do it again, but I was honest with you—it's part of the game, Maisie. Just part of the game. Anyway, I'm curious— why did you reject Bright?"

"That's an easy one, Robbie—and you know what it is, because you've thought as much yourself. She's overconfident. She's a sparky young woman with lots of spirit, but she's got an answer for everything, and from what I've seen, she knows no fear—none at all."

"You're right." MacFarlane swirled the remaining whisky around in his glass. "Were you scared, Maisie? Going to see Chaput—were you frightened?"

Maisie reached forward and set her glass on the desk. She nodded. "Of course. I knew the man would be armed, and I hoped I had the measure of his temper, but you never know how any animal might respond when it's cornered. But I also knew he felt protected by his position here—and like any agent, he's learned to manage the emotions that come with a threat. Well, I suppose to a point. But that's what we all do, isn't it? We take the energy produced inside us by the act of being scared, and we use it to propel us forward. It's what kept men's legs moving as they ran across no-man's-land, and it's what keeps Freddie Hackett running. If he stops, then he feels the terror, which is why he was doubly petrified when he witnessed the murder."

"Explain." MacFarlane reached across to refill her glass, but she held a hand over the rim.

"There was all that adrenaline pumping around inside him. He'd been running to the sound of bombs, to the sirens and ambulances. Then he had to stop, and it was as if his engine was flooded, in the same way that an idling motor car can get too much fuel if you put your foot on the accelerator. I believe there were two men tackling Payot at first, but he thought he saw only one—it was a consequence of what had gone before in his life." She was silent, staring at her hands. "That poor boy must have seen that scar on his father's angry face in nightmares, even on those days when he wasn't striped time and again by the belt. It paralyzed him, the sheer ugliness of his father's anger."

"You sure you won't have another?" MacFarlane lifted the bottle again. "Might as well kill the bottle, eh, lass?"

Maisie nodded and pushed her glass toward him. They sat in a comfortable silence for a few moments, both too tired for their usual back-and-forth banter.

"So, what about the Yank?"

"Getting a bit personal, aren't you, Robbie?" Maisie swirled the whisky around in her glass. "Anyway, seeing as you keep tabs on me, Robbie, I would imagine you already know, or you've guessed—it's over." She looked away. "I suppose it was to be expected. We're both working hard, and—well, we've had a rocky few weeks, one minute all very happy and then seeming at odds with each other. You know how it is—that undercurrent of something brittle. And there's the war." She looked at her glass. "I wish I hadn't drunk that—I've said too much."

MacFarlane nodded. "I'll get a driver to take you home. Your flat?"

Maisie shook her head. "No. Chelstone. I want to see Anna."

MacFarlane picked up the telephone, then replaced the receiver. "Not working again—I'll just nip out to talk to the porter."

As the door banged shut behind him, Maisie leaned back in the chair and sipped her drink, already wondering how best to approach the question of Freddie Hackett and his family in light of the day's events. She sat up when MacFarlane reappeared.

"Bright will be here in about half an hour or so—bit longer than I thought. We can fill our time with idle talk, can't we, Maisie?"

The talk was far from idle, lubricated with more whisky. Maisie was surprised to note that almost an hour had passed when the porter came to the door to announce that Corporal Bright had arrived for Miss Dobbs.

"I'll leave you in this man's capable hands, Maisie," said MacFarlane. "He'll escort you out. I've paperwork to get on with. Have a good evening."

Corporal Bright stepped from the driver's seat and came to the rear passenger door, opening it for Maisie.

"Thank you, Corporal Bright."

"Shouldn't be too long a run down to Kent, Miss Dobbs."

Maisie smiled as she stepped into the vehicle.

"Hello, Maisie—my pal Mac thought I should come along for the ride."

"Mark, but—"

"Take a seat. We've got to talk."

"But—"

"But nothing. Just listen." Scott lowered his voice as the motor car pulled out into traffic. "Good."

"Mark? I thought—"

"Now that's the trouble—all this thinking, and you've reached conclusions that just aren't right." He shook his head. "And here I had all these words planned, to explain why you'd gone off in the opposite direction to the one I intended, and now I've forgotten all of them. Except about four, though I could cut it down to two."

"Mark, never mind about me getting things wrong, but you aren't making any sense, if you don't mind my saying so." Maisie felt herself become impatient, a wave of panic beginning to envelop her.

"Maisie—"

"What is it, Mark? Is something wrong?"

She reached for his hand and felt him grasp hers in return.

"Marry me."

CHAPTER 20

N ow, let me go over this again. I want to make sure I know exactly what happened, because what with Brenda going on and on about cakes and puddings and having to take the lives of a few chickens, I couldn't keep up with any of it this morning. So you had no idea that Mark was in the motor car, and that MacFarlane had arranged to have him picked up, which is why you had to sit there chatting to MacFarlane and getting a bit tight on single-malt whisky while the driver went over to the embassy?" Priscilla mixed two gin and tonics, handing one to Maisie before sitting down at the opposite end of the sofa. "There you go—it's a weak one for you as usual, though I would have thought you'd want a belter after what's gone on in the past twenty-four hours!"

Maisie laughed as she took the glass. "Weak is about all I could stand, Pris. And yes, I had no idea what was going on, though it seems Robbie knew more about the situation than I would have given him credit for. Mark had told Robbie I'd finished with him, while at the same time I thought he was so fed up with me, he'd thrown me over. I believe it's called 'irrational reasoning.' It's what happens to people when they're scared, and it happened to me. It was all very confusing, and to be honest, I was tired and consumed with a case and, well—"

"Haven't I always said, Maisie darling, that you may be very, very good at your job, but when it comes to personal matters of the heart, you are verging on incompetent. Sometimes you think about things far too much. And by the way, about these all-consuming cases—I do hope that particular situation might change."

"There are a few developments afoot—we've been talking about it, Mark and I." Maisie swirled the ice around in her drink, the words lingering in her mind. *Mark and I.* She smiled at Priscilla. "Nice having a refrigerator, isn't it?"

"Never mind my new refrigerator and the ice in your drink—what do you mean? What changes?"

"I'm going to see how Billy feels about assuming more control in the business. The majority of cases coming in since war was declared are right up his alley, and it's only occasionally that we get something more . . . more involved. We might take on a new assistant to help him out."

"And I suppose you will just swoop in for the big cases, when someone has just been offed and no one knows who did the deed. Hmmm."

"What do you mean by 'hmmm'?"

"I'd just like to be a fly on the wall while you're trying out this not-working mode, that's all. Personally, I think you will be bored stiff, and I can't see you in the local jam-making circle any more than myself. I tried, and it was a crushing bore, all about how to use local honey instead of sugar and how to make the silly jam set. I tried. Mine came out like syrup. A ghastly sweet, horrible concoction."

"Don't worry—I'm not going to join any sort of circle. And nothing much will change, Priscilla. Just a little here and there. I've decided I will be up in town at my flat for just one night each week, so I can at least be on hand as a guide for Billy in the short term, and of course if that bigger case comes in, then I'll be a little more occupied in London. The rest of the time I can work from my study at the Dower House. That's how Maurice did things in his later days, when he wanted to be in Chelstone more than London—remember I was his assistant, and I had to hold the fort at his office on Wigmore Street. In the year or so before he retired and I started my own business, he left a good number of cases to me until something came in requiring his expertise or I needed help. He called it a 'time of transition.'" Maisie set her drink on the table next to the sofa. "It will be wonderful—spending more time here, and Mark will come home to the Dower house from Friday afternoon until Monday morning, when we'll return to the flat together."

"Well, I must say, you've got that bit sorted out nicely, and in a very short time. Now then—down to more important things." Priscilla reached for a desk diary on the adjacent coffee table. "December the sixth you say, for the register office ceremony with just family and close friends, after which the wedding breakfast will be at the manor? Then the really big event will be the blessing at Chelstone church on the afternoon of the seventh, followed by a reception and dance, again at the manor but this time in the ballroom? I bet it hasn't been used in years!" She closed the book. "And I'm sure the whole village will squeeze into the church to see you and your American walk down the aisle. Pity your Mark's a divorcé, otherwise you could have done the whole thing there."

Maisie shook her head. "I didn't want a full ceremony in church anyway. The register office will do nicely. But the church blessing is a different matter . . . it seems only right, because—"

"Because that's where you married James, and it's as if he's giving you away."

"Something like that, yes."

Priscilla sighed. "Well, I'm simply relieved that it's all happening before my final operation on the eighth. I cannot imagine how I would have felt in my best dress nicely set off by a whopping great bandage around my head." She reached for a notebook. "Which reminds me, I must see that lovely seamstress in the village. No good even thinking about a new dress, as you'll need all our clothing coupons for a gown, so I'll have her do something wonderful with an old thing or two I've had tucked away at the back of my wardrobe since before the war."

"Priscilla, we have more important things to discuss—and I know you're deliberately avoiding getting down to it."

"I know. I am dreading it, Maisie. Just dreading the finality of saying good-bye to her." Priscilla turned to Maisie. "We all loved Elinor— just adored her. We're absolutely crushed."

"I know, Pris—I know." Maisie paused, allowing a few moments before continuing. "Shall we go over the arrangements? After all, we want everything to be perfect for her." Another pause. "Now then, George will pick me up next Saturday morning and then come over to collect you and Tarquin to take us to the station for the London train. We'll meet Douglas and Tom at Paddington, ready to catch the train down to Westbury. And you've spoken to Tim?"

Priscilla finished her drink. "Yes, I passed on your message that Mr. MacFarlane will be in Cambridge anyway, so he'll pick him up and give him a lift to the military chapel in Wiltshire. Given that my middle boy seems to have inherited his mother's penchant for the opposite sex in uniform, he won't miss MacFarlane's driver."

"No, he definitely won't miss her."

There was another hiatus in the conversation, until Priscilla spoke again.

"It's just so incredibly sad, isn't it? You come over to see me in the aftermath of your wonderful news, and here we are. Instead of discussing getting you married off to your dishy American, we're confirming our journey to Elinor's memorial service, so we can bid a final farewell to a young woman we all loved and who only wanted to serve her country."

Maisie reached for her friend's hand.

"Maisie?"

"Yes?"

"Will you promise me that, one day, you will tell me the truth? About Elinor, and how she died?"

Maisie said nothing, but increased her grasp of Priscilla's hand.

Priscilla nodded, wiped a tear that had begun to run across her cheek and turned to Maisie, changing the subject.

"You know what stuns me, Maisie, is that you said 'Yes.' You didn't say, 'Oh, let me give it a bit of thought until next year.' And you didn't throw excuses one after the other, you know, about how he's an American and will never understand you. You just accepted there and then."

Maisie shrugged. "I suppose I broke the habit of a lifetime. But if there's one thing about wartime—and indeed love—that I've learned the hard way, Pris, it's that you don't dither when it comes to happiness. And in this case it's not only my happiness, but that of my beautiful daughter." She put her hand against her chest, feeling a welter of emotion rise up. "You know, it's as if something is so very complete when we're all together. I see Anna in her element with this big family around her—Me, Dad, Brenda, Mark, her Auntie Pris, Douglas, the boys, Grandma Rowan and Papa Ju-Ju, which is what she's started calling Julian, much to his delight, which has surprised us all. Now she'll have a father, and I must say she is like a puppy with two tails. They've gone out this afternoon for a walk together to search for chestnuts, and you would not believe the smile on her face."

"Oh, that reminds me—talking of puppies and tails, what is that thing I saw Anna and your father with, when I came over to the house this morning?"

"Her name is Little Emma. Mark brought her back from America and had someone at the embassy look after her for him until he found an opportunity to bring her to Chelstone for Anna. She's another Alsatian. He couldn't bear the thought of Anna being so upset over losing her beloved dog. I can't say he's in Brenda's best books, given Little Emma's antics, but the dear pup is learning fast."

The conversation lulled as Priscilla mixed herself another drink, holding up the bottle to inquire whether Maisie wanted a top-up. She shook her head—she had barely touched her cocktail—and Priscilla returned to her place on the sofa.

"So, you think you've done it right this time, Maisie?"

"I believe I did it right with James, but yes, I've done it right this time too." Maisie stood up. "Sorry to leave you to drink alone, Pris, but I must be getting on now—I have work to do. My current case isn't quite finished. There are a few tasks to complete before I can close the book on it."

"Oh yes, your final accounting or whatever you call it." Priscilla stood up and accompanied Maisie to the door. "By the way, has a honeymoon been mentioned?"

"It has, but it won't be until after the war. Mark is talking about taking me to his home in America, followed by a sojourn in Hawai'i."

"Terribly exotic, I'm told." Priscilla drew Maisie to her, kissing her on both cheeks. "I just wish the rest of the bloody Yanks would come in and help us out a bit. The papers say that over seventy percent of them are in favor of war now—and that's a big change, isn't it? It's because they've seen what we're going through here on their newsreels, and they've been listening to Mr. Murrow's broadcasts from London. We've held the line against Hitler for a long time, and we're so terribly small and alone in the world, aren't we? Anyway, I'm not going to spoil your day with my moaning about this bloody war. I'm going to return to the task of learning a bit of Welsh to add to the few words I'm composing for Elinor's memorial service."

"What do you want to say?"

"I'm not completely sure, but I know how I'll begin."

Maisie waited for Priscilla to answer.

"Roedd hi'n annwyl iawn."

"Which means?"

"She was much loved."

Though excitement about her forthcoming marriage to Mark Scott had begun to consume the family, Maisie knew there would be no clear start to a new life if she did not begin her final accounting, the process by which she drew each case to a close. She often thought of it as akin to washing and ironing the laundry, folding each pressed item with care and putting it away in the linen cupboard. It was a way of closing the door on a case, as far as she could manage. Sometimes that final click took years to achieve.

Her first stop was the very place where Freddie Hackett had witnessed a murder, a killing that confused him in a part of his psyche that he might never understand. In overlaying an image of his brutal stepfather with the ultimate act of aggression, he had seen nothing more than a scarred man—a man with a terrifying disfigurement that he saw in every story he wrote in school, in every nightmare keeping him awake at night.

She had no desire to enter the bomb-damaged house where Major Chaput had created a refuge, the secret haven where he received sensitive documents and also hatched a scheme for revenge; where he had met Hackett to plan how he might take an eye for an eye and a tooth for a tooth, payment for terror that had stained him during the French occupation of Syria. Again she hoped for peace, not only in far-flung corners of the world, but in her world, a part of London that was once full of hard-working families, neighborhoods where back doors remained open to anyone who called, and children played football and hopscotch in the street.

At the pub not far from the rooms where the Hackett family had lived, she was informed by the landlord that Arthur Hackett was now in police custody for being drunk and disorderly, and that it might be some time before he was a free man, given the list of "previous" held against him. He would have no rooms to return to anyway. Following a recent bombing, the back-to-back dwellings had been condemned, and Mrs. Dunley was now with relatives in another part of London; relatives she hardly knew, according to the pub landlord.

Gabriella Hunter was sitting up in bed when the ward sister, a rotund Irish woman with a ready wit, ushered Maisie into the hospital room. She fluffed up Gabriella's pillows and smiled at Maisie. "You can stay an extra five minutes today, because this patient is the only one who can frighten me. I've seen her motley assortment of scars, and I know she didn't get them elbowing her way into a jumble sale!"

The women laughed, and after taking Gabriella's temperature and making a note on the clipboard at the end of the bed, the Irish sister left the room.

"I'm really quite a tough old boot, you know, Maisie." Gabriella reached for her hand. "And I knew it was likely to happen—I knew someone would come for me one day. You see, I know too much about too many things no one should know about, and though years have passed since I worked with Maurice, in my line of business you can never be too sure that there's not someone out there bearing a grudge, or worried that something you say might reveal too much about them. It could happen again."

"Aren't you worried about your book? Might it put you at risk?"

Hunter sighed. "It crossed my mind with rather more gravity after I was brought in here, but Joan has made sure anything inflammatory has been extinguished. I suppose you could say she's not just a good editor, but something of a censor." She smiled. "Mind you, it still might ruffle a few feathers, but as far as I'm concerned, a little feather-ruffling will keep everyone on their toes in this war."

"I think you're right," said Maisie. "By the way, did I tell you that Joan has been in touch with me again?"

"I bet I know what for."

"And I bet you do too. She knows I have Maurice's papers, and she's after a book. In fact, she's talked about a couple."

"Did you agree?"

"I'm going to see her anyway, so I'm sure it will come up. I've a lot on my plate at the present time, Gabriella, so—"

"You're doing the final accounting, aren't you?"

"Yes," said Maisie. "Just few more items on the list."

"Maurice was a stickler for it. I suppose that's why I wrote my book. We all have to do a final accounting at some point, don't we?"

Maisie was about to answer when the ward sister entered the room.

"Time for you to go, Miss Dobbs. The little alarm clock in my brain just went off."

"Thank you, Sister." Maisie stood up and leaned forward to kiss Hunter on the cheek. "Thank you for everything, Gabriella—you helped me tie up all the loose ends."

"And I think one loose end in particular. Don't leave me off the invitation list, will you?"

"Of course not—though my husband will probably corner you to ask all sorts of questions about the last war."

It was only as she left the hospital, standing outside to hail a taxicab, that Maisie realized she had said the words "my husband." She smiled.

The meeting with Dr. Duncan Jamieson took an unexpected turn almost as soon as Maisie entered his place of work.

"Maisie, the very person I need at just the right time—can you assist? I've had four brought in—bombing last night, and all found dead with not a mark on them."

"And you want to find out if the pressure caused an arrhythmia or whether the impact collapsed the lungs."

"You're ahead of me—shouldn't take long, but I've more coming in today, plus a little something on behalf of Scotland Yard, and I'd just like a hand with this family."

"Oh dear—a family," said Maisie, removing her jacket and hanging it on a hook by the door while reaching for a clean white cotton coat and a white cotton triangle of fabric, which she would use to keep her hair back. She put on a mask and began snapping rubber gloves into place as she joined Jamieson.

Once again, the pathologist addressed each of the deceased as he worked, as if they were still able to feel the cold steel of his scalpel when he made the first incision. He began a conversation with Maisie, as if the task were no more serious than repairing a leaking tap.

"So, I was right about the Frenchman then?"

"Almost—he was French Canadian, from the province of Quebec, but he'd spent a significant amount of time in France, not only with family but in the army during the last war."

"I see. And what was he doing here?"

"Oh, some sort of war work," said Maisie. "Nothing too important."

"He must have sustained injuries to cause those scars in the last war. Strange, I pegged him for a professional killer—what they called a guerrilla during the Napoleonic Wars. I'm not often wrong."

"I suppose a soldier is a professional killer, in a way."

"Yes, I suppose so." Jamieson nodded.

Maisie leaned forward to hold back blue flesh, enabling Jamieson to better reach into the heart cavity of the deceased woman.

"Hmmm. Yes," said Jamieson, as if his diagnosis regarding cause of death had been confirmed.

"As you suspected? It certainly looked like an arrhythmia."

"Extraordinary, isn't it, Maisie? The heart stops because the impact of a bomb has knocked it out of rhythm. I suppose the sad truth is that war can cause a heart to break, both literally and figuratively."

It was a few days later, while she was on the way to Pimlico to visit Grace, Freddie and Iris Hackett, that Maisie stopped for a moment along the Embankment where she had seen a Spitfire dragged up from the Thames, still with the aviator inside, a young man who was likely not yet twenty years of age and who had given his life for his country. She bowed her head, whispering the words "May he know peace" and also directing her thoughts toward the spot where Claude Payot's body had touched land again. She was interrupted by a familiar voice.

"Well, well, this is a surprise, Miss Dobbs."

Maisie opened her eyes and turned around. "Detective Chief Superintendent Caldwell—I didn't expect to see you here."

Caldwell stood next to Maisie and looked at the water. "Paying your respects?"

"Actually, I was. It was a dreadful thing to witness, the Spitfire being pulled from the water."

"Makes us all more determined to beat them, doesn't it?" said

Caldwell, removing his hat. "Whenever I've got a moment, which isn't very often, mark you, I come down here to have a silent word, you know, to thank the pilot." He pointed across the river to bombed-out buildings. "Look at that mess, the blighters taking down whole streets. Night after night, and they just keep on."

Maisie nodded. "We're doing the same to them."

"But they started it, didn't they? What with Hitler wanting to rule the world. And here we are, holding on with no help from anyone. I wonder how much longer we can do it."

"We will—I believe we will."

"From your lips to God's ears, Miss Dobbs." Caldwell replaced his hat. "Oh, by the way—I believe you owe me a report on that Hackett case."

"Give me a few days, if you don't mind."

"Just a few."

At Maisie's request, Alice Langley agreed to continue seeing Freddie Hackett once each week, simply to listen to the boy, encouraging him to talk about the traumas he'd witnessed. The plan had two functions, the first being to help Freddie recover from years of abuse at the hands of his stepfather, and then the terror of witnessing a murder. However, as Langley pointed out, young Freddie had seen enough horror while running with messages as bombs fell, and the images that festered in his psyche would take time to work their way out, splinters of memory that would rise to the surface for years. Now Maisie wanted to see Freddie at home, along with his mother and Iris.

"Miss Dobbs—Maisie—I cannot begin to explain how everything seems to have fallen into place. First of all, Iris is more settled, and your caretaker's wife has found out about a new school that she can attend, especially for children like Iris. She knows all about it on account of her niece's little girl."

"That's excellent news, Grace. Is it close?"

"Well, that's the thing—it's not. It's in Surrey, but I've got a new job too, and it's in the same place. I couldn't believe it—one thing led to another. It turns out that because the children live in, they need what they call a house mother, helping put the children down at night and looking after them."

"And what about Freddie?"

"All very good, because most of the boys and girls from his old school were evacuated to a village not far away, and he's going to join them. It's as if someone waved a magic wand to help us out. We have somewhere to live too. It's a flat at the school, so Iris can stay with us unless she wants to be with the other kiddies—and that might be better for her, in the long run. But it's even more exciting, because Freddie's PE teacher, the one who went with the evacuees to the village, is looking forward to having him there. He says that with some decent training, Freddie's got it in him to do well with his running." She looked down at her work-worn hands. "It was Mrs. Langley who put the final touches on the whole idea, because she'd worked with one of the doctors at this new school, so she asked about the job on my behalf." She paused, catching her breath. "It's funny how things work out, isn't it? I mean, it's like dominoes—you touch one and then the others start to go, and sometimes they fall in the right direction and one person knows another and it all opens up like a flower."

"I could not be happier for you, Grace."

"I might need your flat for a bit longer, six weeks perhaps, because they don't require me to start until the new year."

"Not to worry—take your time." Maisie stood up to leave.

"And I hear congratulations are in order—you're getting married!"

"How did you find out?" asked Maisie.

"Oh, a Mr. MacFarlane came round to see how Freddie was doing, and gave him five bob. Five shillings! For a boy! Such a generous person. Anyway, he told me." She stopped speaking and looked at Maisie, holding her gaze. "He said your fiancé was a good man. You deserve a good 'un, Maisie. Nothing but the best."

Maisie nodded. "Yes, he's a good man. An American, actually."

Grace Hackett laughed. "Oh, very nice, I'm sure."

MacFarlane waved to Maisie to enter as she arrived at the open door of his Baker Street office.

"Come in, lass, come in. Take a pew. Close the door behind you. I won't be a minute." He rifled through a pile of papers and stacked them to one side. "Just getting everything sorted for us to discuss a few new recruits. Now then, some news for you."

"Pascale?"

"Just arrived at Southampton airport, came in via Lisbon and Shannon. Debriefing at an undisclosed location in Hampshire. Sorry, can't tell you where."

Maisie felt the tension release through her body as she exhaled. "Oh, thank god."

"It's been a stinking ride, this one."

"I was just terrified," said Maisie, placing her hand on her forehead. "I've had to go on pretending—pretending to Priscilla, to Mark, to my dear Anna, to everyone I love, that I am having the best time of my life and that everything is tip-top, but I have been feeling sick with fear every single day in case Pascale failed to reach safety."

MacFarlane shook his head. "I'll tell you now that it was touch-

and-go at times, and that girl is a terror for not following orders. I thought you said she wasn't like her aunt."

"She's not—well, not entirely. If she didn't follow orders, there must have been a very good reason. If Priscilla decided not to follow orders, it would have been because she didn't feel like it."

MacFarlane folded his arms. "The lass isn't going out again. Not for us, anyway. That wound might not heal as well as we thought, and the Welsh girl's fate has left a bigger scar on Miss Evernden than we had hoped. But that's an early impression. We'll see."

"Please, Robbie—don't even consider sending her, even if she seems as if she's recovered. Find something else for her—training recruits, my job, anything but a resistance line."

"So you're saying you don't want to do your job anymore?"

"I don't know if I can, Robbie. I don't know if I can willfully commit another man or woman to a task charged with such terrifying uncertainty. The stakes are so high."

"Being engaged making you soft, Maisie?"

Maisie shrugged. "Perhaps."

"I'll remind you yet again that yours is not the only word, my friend. It's just one impression. Others make the final decision, Maisie."

Maisie came to her feet at the same time as Robert MacFarlane. He reached out and placed a hand on her shoulder.

"That Yank had better look after you, Maisie, or he will have to answer to me along a dark street on a stormy night."

"Oh, I think he knows that, Robbie." She drew away. "And you take care."

"I will, hen, I know how to look after myself. I'll see you at your big party on December the seventh!"

She was reaching for the door knob when MacFarlane called her back.

"Maisie!"

"Yes?"

"I forgot to tell you. Major Chaput."

"What about him?"

"He's dead. He organized an unusually destructive act of sabotage against the enemy. A Nazi train carrying vital supplies of materiel, supplies, men and—well, and you name it—was struck and completely destroyed. Chaput led a small band from the front and was killed in the act of landing a hard blow on the enemy. The other agents survived."

"He did it deliberately, didn't he?"

"He paid his debt, and he made up for his actions in Syria. He died a hero. The piper has been paid, Maisie. The scales of justice are even again."

On the day Maisie completed her final accounting, she returned to her Holland Park flat weary, yet knowing she had done what she had set out to do, which was to find a killer with scars on his face, whether natural or inflicted by a weapon. She was tired, yet buoyed by thoughts of what might come next. As she walked along the path to the front door of her garden flat, she could already hear Mark Scott singing a number from a picture he'd seen while back in the United States. The words rang out as she opened the door. *At last my love has come along . . .*

She ran into his arms, to be held in place for what seemed like ages.

"You okay, my love?"

"Yes, Mark, I'm okay."

"Happy?"

"Very much."

"Wine?"

"Love some."

"And guess what we have for dinner."

"Spaghetti."

"You know me too well."

"I certainly do."

"I cannot wait for you to be my wife. At last."

Maisie rested her head on the shoulder of the man she loved, closing her eyes as he continued the song, and they began a slow dance.

EPILOGUE

The family Elinor Jones had loved for over twenty years stood shoulder to shoulder in the small chapel. Maisie took a place next to Priscilla, and reached for her hand. Robert MacFarlane was on her other side, his voice booming during the one hymn, Elinor's favorite, which she had specified in her will. It was "Cwm Rhondda," a Welsh hymn, and as they reached the final verse, every member of the congregation raised their voice.

When I tread the verge of Jordan,
Bid my anxious fears subside;
Death of death, and hell's destruction
Land me safe on Canaan's side:
Songs of praises, songs of praises,
I will ever give to thee;
I will ever give to thee.

At the back of the chapel, Corporal Charlie Bright, who had brought MacFarlane and Tim to the barracks, stood to attention. The young woman who had received every one of Elinor's messages sent from France for the eyes of the Special Operations Executive was in the opposite pew, along with a smattering of people from the headquarters in London. They did not remain to talk after the service, and

Maisie would not have recognized them again if she passed them in the street.

There was little said between those gathered while the chaplain shook the hand of each member of the congregation as they departed the chapel. In silence they stood outside, before stepping toward the motor cars that would whisk them away to their individual destinations.

Out of the corner of her eye Maisie saw Corporal Bright beckon to her from a corner of the garden at the rear of the chapel. As Maisie joined Bright, the ATS driver turned away so no one else could discern their conversation, or see what might pass between them.

"Miss Dobbs, I have something for you."

"For me? What is it, Corporal Bright?"

"This letter is for you. The woman who died—I was the driver who took her from the house in Hampshire to the airfield. I have to do that sometimes, so I know where they're going. She gave it to me to give to you if . . . if something happened to her. She knew I'd probably find out, one way or another. You hear a lot, driving the sort of people I have as passengers." She glanced around to see if anyone was paying attention to them. "I know she didn't die driving a lorry." She handed Maisie a white envelope. "Anyway, better take this before Mr. Mac-Farlane comes over."

Maisie took the envelope and slipped it into her pocket. "You know, Corporal Bright, I wondered why our paths kept crossing. When that sort of thing happens, it sparks my curiosity, and usually there is a reason for the constant reappearance of a person as I go about my work. Yet I just couldn't work out what it was about you. Now I know. You really are a messenger."

"I s'pose you could look at it like that, but—"

"Shhh—here's comes MacFarlane," said Maisie, turning to the approaching Scotsman. "Robbie—Corporal Bright was just asking me about my engagement."

"I wanted to wish Miss Dobbs every happiness, sir, being as I was the only witness to the proposal. Are you ready to leave now, Mr. Mac-Farlane?"

MacFarlane raised an eyebrow. "When you are, Bright. Only when you are."

Corporal Charlotte Bright turned to Maisie and saluted, then began to walk toward the black motor car parked on gravel in front of the chapel.

"Interesting little exchange with Bright, was it, Maisie?"

"I have no idea what you're talking about."

"'Just asking me about my engagement,' blah, blah, blah. You'd think I was born yesterday." Robert MacFarlane smiled, then followed Corporal Bright, the messenger, toward the motor car.

Priscilla, Douglas and their sons had decided to remain in London, so Maisie traveled with the family by train as far as Paddington. There was little conversation at first, aside from a tight-mouthed "Well, that went off very well" from Priscilla. Maisie thought the journey would be long and difficult, but soon the mood in the carriage changed as Priscilla's sons began to reminisce, sharing their stories of Elinor.

"Remember when she made Tim sit on the stairs with one of her scarves wrapped around his mouth because he was cheeky?"

"And she tied his ankles with string, and he had to sit on his hands!"

"What about when she drenched Tom with a bucket of water—you'd been flicking water at her after she told you to go and make your bed, but she waited for you in the garden with that bucket until you came out to find your bicycle—ha! I thought Tarq would split open laughing!"

"Tarquin was the worst."

"I was not!"

"And she spoiled you."

"Far from it! She smacked my bottom more than once—it's a wonder I can sit down today."

"Well, you deserved it—you were a little monster. But she sorted you out!"

And so it went on, the telling of stories about Elinor, a sad journey made lighter by bittersweet remembering.

F rom Paddington Maisie took a taxi across to Charing Cross and caught a train to Tonbridge, where she would change for the branch line service to Chelstone. The solitary journey offered a welcome moment in which to read the letter from Elinor in private.

Dear Maisie,

If you are reading this, then you probably know exactly what has happened to me. I know I'm not really supposed to write this sort of letter, but I want to thank you for not striking me off the list of agents, and for entrusting me with this work even though you had your doubts. I am incredibly grateful for this chance to do something of worth. Am I scared? Yes, I am. In fact I am terrified that I will make a poor job of things. But be assured I have done my best, whatever happened to cause this letter to be handed to you.

Please look after my family. I know I was an employee, but I felt like I had a real family from the moment I was sent to work for Mrs. P., and I cannot imagine never seeing them again. I don't think she knows quite how young I was when I was sent to help her. I'd barely left school, but I knew how to look after babies. I was good with children and I soon learned how to get those boys to do what I wanted. Seeing them grow into men has made me proud, but I've feared for them. If anything I do will stop this war sooner so that my family remain safe, then I will do it. I'm terrified of losing one of those boys more than I dread death.

Look after Mrs. P. She's been so brave, and I know the skin operations frighten her.

I don't think there's more to say, Maisie, except I hope you know that I consider you my family too. You could have stopped me doing this, but you didn't, and that means the world to me.

Until we meet again.
Elinor

PS: I thought I should call you "Maisie" in the circumstances. I hope you don't mind.

Maisie read the letter one more time, then tore it into small pieces, which she placed in the envelope to burn later. Then she closed her eyes and whispered: "Roedd hi'n annwyl iawn."

George collected Maisie from the station, and although it was almost dusk, she asked him to drop her off at the end of the drive leading up to the Dower House. She took care not to draw attention to her arrival as she approached the back door and looked through the window, thankful the blackout curtains had not yet been drawn. Brenda was standing alongside the stove, while Frankie sat at the table opposite Mark Scott. Anna ran into the kitchen, clad in her pajamas and dressing gown, a puppy trailing in her wake, tugging at her belt as she clambered onto Mark's lap and pulled his arms around her.

At last, the lonely days were over.

I guess a registrar is like a justice of the peace back home. That was so fast, I'm not sure if I'm now your husband or if I just landed a job as your chef."

"Actually, Mark—what we just did means you're both," said Maisie, feeling the comfort of her new husband's arm around her as George drove them from the register office in Tunbridge Wells, then home to Chelstone Manor, where the Comptons' butler was overseeing a luncheon for a dozen guests at the manor house. When the luncheon concluded, with a round of planned speeches including a few words from Priscilla, who insisted on throwing tradition to the wind so she could extol the virtues of the bride and not let the groom forget even one of them, George would then whisk the couple away to the Mermaid Inn in Rye for the night. A larger reception would be held on the morrow, following a late-afternoon church blessing of the union. There would be a four-course supper and a party to follow, after which guests would filter out into the pitch darkness of the blackout.

"And what about that hat Priscilla was wearing? Do you Brits always go for really strange headwear when you go to a wedding?"

"She's still a bit embarrassed about the scars on her face, though I don't really think you can see them," said Maisie. "And the skin grafts she's having on Monday will help diminish the scars even more—when they heal."

"I wonder what she'll wear to the church tomorrow," said Mark.

"Oh, that's a much more elaborate affair, so she'll wear something outrageous, you can depend on that. A church wedding—or in our case a blessing—is an occasion for Priscilla to shine. As you've just seen, a register office marriage is over in minutes."

Scott nodded and kissed his new wife on the forehead. "One more question—and I didn't want to ask before, because it shows how ignorant I am, but what the heck is a wedding breakfast? I mean, are we all getting eggs over easy and bacon with hash browns?"

"Oh of course not, Mark. It's what they call the celebratory meal after the wedding. It's the first meal as a married couple."

"I suppose it was the breaking of a fast, in a way." Scott pulled her closer. "And there's another thing, and I'd hate to get off on the wrong foot as your husband, but I've got to tell you, Maisie, it was a bit of a shock when the registrar called you Margaret—how come you never told me that was your full name?"

"I've just always been 'Maisie' ever since I was a child. Anyway, I wanted to keep you on your toes. I've asked the vicar to use 'Maisie' during tomorrow's service, but the registrar was the official part. The blessing is . . . it's for the spirit."

"Hmmm. Okay, I get it. And you're sure you don't mind losing the title?"

"I rarely used it anyway." She remembered Gabriella Hunter's housekeeper. "Just occasionally when I needed to cross a tricky threshold here and there."

The Service of Prayer and Dedication, the church ceremony during which the marriage between Mark Scott and Maisie Dobbs was honored before a congregation comprising family, friends, Scott's fellow diplomatic staff from the embassy and a smattering of Maisie's colleagues, including Robert MacFarlane, had also drawn a good number of villagers, who were pressed into pews at the back of the small church. Anna and Billy's daughter, Margaret Rose, were bridesmaids, two little girls who could not stop giggling from the moment they followed the couple as they made their way along the aisle until Brenda turned and raised an eyebrow while putting her forefinger against her mouth.

As he bound the ecclesiastical stole of embroidered silk around the hands of the married couple, the vicar of Chelstone Parish Church asked the congregation to forever love and support the bride and groom as they moved forward into a life together. He blessed the marriage, completing the service with the words, "May your love sustain you, support you in times of joy and sadness, in sickness and health, good times and bad, and for all the days of your lives."

Villagers who had gathered outside applauded, and someone shouted "About time!" as Maisie and Mark Scott emerged from the church into the low winter sunshine of late afternoon. Colors of red and gold leaves not yet fallen were reflected in Maisie's cream gown, which was topped with a short matching woolen cape, while a thick band of silk embellished with pearls kept her hair in place. A photographer did his best to marshal the company, and the bridesmaids began their infectious laughter again. Robert MacFarlane's voice suddenly boomed out, and soon the assorted guests were following his orders regarding where they should stand for the photographer, who seemed both grateful for the interference and intimidated by the source.

Mark and Maisie stood up for their first dance as the band began to play "At Last," the melody they had come to refer to as their song, and after a few moments, Mark steered Maisie toward Anna, picking her up with one arm so they danced on with Anna between them, the bridesmaid who still could not stop laughing. Mark nodded toward the Americans present, who cheered and raised their glasses.

"This is just what my gang needed—a good day out and something to make them smile. They're all enjoying themselves—it's a break from London and the bombs."

Yes, it was a day to remember, a day when Maisie Dobbs felt as if she had rediscovered all she had lost years ago. She danced with every man and some of the women, laughing as she and Priscilla swept around the Chelstone Manor ballroom as if they had never been to war and never been scarred by death. She danced with each of Priscilla's sons, though Tarquin left her with bruises across her feet, and in between each dance with a guest, she was swept away again by her husband.

"Got a dance for your old man, love?" said Frankie Dobbs, as the band began to play a slow number. "This is about my speed."

"Dad! Where have you been? I've been waiting for this dance!"

"I don't need to ask if you're happy, do I, Maisie?" said Frankie as he led his daughter at a slow pace on the dance floor.

Maisie smiled. "No, you don't. Dad, I am happier than I have ever been. I have a wonderful husband and a beautiful daughter. I have you and Brenda, and I have my best friend here, and look at how fortunate I am in having Rowan and Julian cheer me on. Billy is happy, Sandra is happy. We'll all be even better when the war's over, but for now, I could not be more blessed."

"The war will pass, love. It will pass. They always do. We'll be changed, though."

Some guests were staying at the inn in the village, and a large group from the American embassy were being put up at the manor. Others were making their way home in the blackout, and all too soon the party wound down. Frankie and Brenda left a few minutes before Mark picked up Anna, who had fallen asleep under a tapestry-covered bench in the manor's grand entrance hall. Watching her new husband carry the daughter he now claimed to love at least as much as her mother,

Maisie felt she had to pinch herself in case this happiness were a dream and she might wake up at any moment.

After putting Anna to bed, she joined Mark, Frankie and Brenda at the kitchen table, where they were exchanging stories from the day, discussing who had said what and who danced with whom. As their talk turned to everyone getting a good night's sleep, the telephone began to ring.

"Probably someone lost on the road in the blackout," said Scott. "Lucky they found a telephone kiosk." He looked at Frankie. "I don't know about you, Frank, but my dogs are barking!"

"He means his feet are killing him," said Maisie as she rose from the chair and kissed her husband on the cheek, before hurrying along to the library.

She felt the color drain from her face as she listened to the caller. "Yes—yes, of course. I'll get him straightaway." She put the receiver down on the desk and ran to the kitchen.

"Maisie, what is it?" Scott's smile evaporated as he looked up.

"The call is for you, Mark. It's . . . it's very serious."

Maisie reached for her father's hand.

"I'll make a cup of tea," said Brenda, standing up and hobbling toward the stove.

"What's happened, Maisie?" asked her father.

"I didn't ask—but I—I know it's a matter of extreme gravity. It was an American, from the embassy. I could hear it in his voice . . . that something is terribly wrong." She bit her lip.

"Oh love, it's probably—" Frankie stood up and put his arm around his daughter, just as Scott returned.

"Maisie. Just a minute." Scott beckoned her from the doorway, his face drawn.

In the library, he closed the door and put his arms around her.

"A car will be here soon to pick me up, Maisie, and—"

"All that way in the blackout? The driver will never get here, and—oh, Mark, what's happened?"

Maisie felt Scott's hold become tighter.

"The Japanese have attacked our ships in Hawai'i, at a place called Pearl Harbor. I'm to return to London immediately. The ambassador delayed having embassy staff called back because it was our wedding day, but now we have to leave. We don't know how many are dead yet, but we believe it'll be in the thousands. About nineteen vessels are gone—half the Pacific Fleet was in Pearl Harbor." He released his hold and rubbed a hand across his forehead. "And I know what's going to happen next."

"Mark—?"

Scott took both her hands in his own. "We're in, Maisie. Roosevelt will declare war on Japan, and because they're an Axis power, it'll all come down like a house of cards. So we're in."

Maisie's eyes filled with tears. "I—I don't believe it. Oh Mark—I know it's what we've all talked about—but not like this."

"Maisie, right now I think everyone at the embassy is borderline terrified. We knew it would happen eventually, that the United States would join the Allies, and we know what we've got to do, and we'll do it—but it doesn't take away the fear. Controlled fear, that's what it is—and it can be pretty powerful. Over here the people have been living with it every day for over two years now. We'll take a leaf out of your book." He paused to take a deep breath, and when he continued, Maisie heard his tone change, becoming more resolute. "Let me tell you one thing, Maisie—they sure went for us when our guard was down, but they can't attack America and get away with it. I don't even know if the Japanese strike is over yet. Reports are still coming in. But you can bet the piper will be paid. The piper is always paid." He looked around the room. "I could do with a shot of Scotch."

"I'll get it." Maisie poured a glass of whisky and handed it to Scott, watching as he swirled the amber liquid against crystal before downing the measure.

"What do you think this means, Mark—for all of us?"

"Time will tell." He smiled at his bride, a smile Maisie knew was forced. "But I reckon there is one thing you Brits can look forward to."

"I can't think what it might be."

"You aren't holding the fort alone any more. You've got company coming—at last. And guess what—they're all like me."

AUTHOR'S NOTE

I t was one of my favorite authors, Susan Isaacs, who in the acknowledgments to one of her novels thanked everyone who had helped with her research, and then added (I'm paraphrasing here), "Where their facts didn't meet my fiction, I have jettisoned the facts." With that in mind I must draw readers' attention to two points in this book where I deliberately followed the lead of the inimitable Ms. Isaacs.

Under orders from Winston Churchill, Britain's Special Operations Executive (SOE) was founded in July 1940 with the intention of engaging in warfare that was far from gentlemanly. Specially trained agents were sent to France, among other locations, to set up resistance lines and to commit acts of espionage and sabotage in Nazi-occupied Europe. The first woman to be deployed by the SOE was an American citizen, Virginia Hall, in September 1941. Much has been written about the women of the SOE, but there were no more "official" deployments of women until 1942. For the sake of this work of fiction I have allowed two female characters to be sent to France as SOE agents in 1941.

I have also taken a liberty with one of my favorite songs, "At Last." Most readers will be familiar with the gorgeous, smoky version recorded by Etta James in 1961. The Glenn Miller instrumental version first appeared in the film *Sun Valley Serenade* in 1941 and was recorded with lyrics in 1942 for the film *Orchestra Wives*. I wanted that song for one scene in this novel, so I decided to manipulate the facts a bit. As Lee Child notes in his book *The Hero*, fiction comprises "stories about things that never happened to people who didn't exist." Many of the events in my novels are based on fact, and sometimes, to add depth to the experience of my fictional characters in the midst of those extraordinary events, I've found it necessary to play with time . . . just a little.

ACKNOWLEDGMENTS

Given that I tend to thank a great number of people every time I publish a novel, I will limit myself to just one named resource for this book. For the Welsh phrase "Roedd hi'n annwyl iawn," I knew I had to check with an expert. Fortunately, Anne-Marie and Tim Sweet, my dearest friends since childhood, came to the rescue—Anne-Marie is Welsh, and Tim has roots in the land of the red dragon. They immediately contacted Anne-Marie's coworker, Kath Caldwell, who is not only Welsh but studied the language at Cardiff University. Thank you, Kath, for kindly confirming the integrity of words that mean "She was much loved."

Of course, I cannot help myself thanking everyone involved in bringing this book to fruition, but in the interests of brevity, suffice it to say that you know who you are, and I appreciate everything you do, always.

A final word—once again this is a story initially inspired by my late father, Albert Winspear. Dad was a very, very fast runner, and when Britain declared war on Germany in September 1939, he was among the fastest boys in London who were chosen to run messages between Air Raid Precautions depots—the "ARP" men visited schools across London to watch boys run before plucking out the best of them. After school he would sprint to the local depot to pick up a message and then deliver message after message as fast as he could for several hours, usually through bombing raids. Those of you who have read *To Die But Once* and learned about the inspiration for that book will know what came next for my father. It is often forgotten that in wartime, children's work becomes—sadly—a vital resource.

ABOUT THE AUTHOR

JACQUELINE WINSPEAR is the author of the *New York Times* bestsellers *The American Agent, To Die But Once*, and *In This Grave Hour*, as well as twelve other bestselling Maisie Dobbs novels. Her standalone novel, *The Care and Management of Lies*, was also a *New York Times* bestseller, and a finalist for the Dayton Literary Peace Prize. In addition, Jacqueline is the author of two works of nonfiction: a memoir, *This Time Next Year We'll Be Laughing*, and *What Would Maisie Do?* a companion book to the series. Originally from the United Kingdom, Winspear now lives in California.

PLACE IN THE MAISIE DOBBS SERIES

There was never any grand plan that led me to set the Maisie Dobbs series in London and Kent, the latter being one of what are known as England's "Home Counties"—those counties immediately flanking the Greater London area. *Maisie Dobbs* unfolded in an organic way, because in terms of place, I was writing what I know. Much has been written about the importance of character development in fiction, and it's a key component of any workshop for writers—but from the very second the reader turns to the first page of a novel, it's clear that "place" is a character along with every other in the book. In developing a sense of place, the writer can take a few tips from the cinematographer: to develop an impression in the mind of the reader that is every bit as effective as zooming in with the camera to draw attention to detail, or panning across the landscape so the reader knows exactly where the protagonist stands. You want the reader to stand right there with them, to feel as if they are close to the action. As a writer, you want the reader to feel their feet on that land, in that room or on that street, and to have a sense that they share the same sky overhead as any character in the story. The author Adam Nicolson wrote about the concept of "place" in his book *Sissinghurst, An Unfinished History*, describing "place as the roomiest of containers for human meaning; place as the medium in which natural and cultural, inherited and invented, individual and communal can all fuse and fertilize." I like that—it sums up what I try to do as a writer: to bring a sense of time and place to my writing, weaving the soul of a location into the narrative for the reader to inhabit for the duration of the story.

Though readers may have an idea of what London was like in the first half of the last century—it's been depicted in enough books and films—perhaps this is where I tell you a little more about Kent. Tourists will have heard it called "The Garden of England," given the county's rich agricultural heritage, its colorful gardens and breathtaking foliage across miles of woodland, though apparently the true origin of the moniker offers another impression, and can be traced back to French prisoners during the Napoleonic Wars—they called it the "garderobe" of England. A garderobe is a medieval lavatory! A century later, during the Great War, you could hear the battlefield cannonade across the English Channel from Kent's beaches. And in World War II, the Luftwaffe called it "Hell's Corner." But to me, the county of Kent, in Britain's southeastern corner, was quite simply "home." Kent was in the crosshairs of invaders from earliest times. Romans, Saxons, Vikings, Normans, the Danes—they all came to Britain's shores, and the Kentish coast was the first landing point for those interlopers who crossed the English Channel.

Easy access to the Thames would take armies directly to London, which for Kentish folk lay at a greater distance than France. I heard many stories in childhood about the impact the conquerors had on local trade, on our architecture, on the language, our names, and how the land developed, but there was one legend I loved above all others. It was said that when the Romans first crossed the Channel with the intention of making the island part of their empire, as their ships neared the coast, the soldiers saw our heavy horses on the clifftops, grazing. Terror ran through the ranks as the men wondered, "If those are their horses, how big are their men?" So they sailed back to France to bolster their numbers. Growing up in a rural area amid the hop gardens, apple orchards, woodland and fields of Kent, I could not get enough of the stories and legends of the land I loved. Even as a child I was aware I was living in a "front line county" and that any discord with our neighbors across some twenty-eight miles of water could put us in grave danger.

My mother was evacuated from London to Kent during the war and had a spectator view of the Battle of Britain as it raged overhead. She once witnessed a Messerschmitt coming in for a crash landing, the pilot still using his guns to attack women working in a field. The locals had many stories of individual civilians being targeted by the enemy—on one occasion a woman pushing her baby boy in his pram was fired on by an enemy fighter pilot who had swooped low over the street as she was on her way to the shops. When my novel *An Incomplete Revenge* was published, a friend commented, "This book is your love letter to Kent." In some ways, perhaps it was. Yet with every book in the Maisie Dobbs series, I have woven in the London of times past—the London known to my maternal grandmother, who was born in Lambeth in the late 1800s, and the London familiar to my paternal grandfather, who was a costermonger, a man who sold fruit and vegetables from a horse-drawn cart—and now, as the series has moved on from the immediate post–World War I years, I'm focusing on the London my parents knew during World War II. They both grew up south of the River Thames between the wars, and were twelve and thirteen respectively when Britain declared war on Germany in 1939. They moved to the county of Kent as a young married couple in a bid to escape the bomb sites and the lack of housing, and to make a new start. Their memories have informed a sense of place I've been able to bring to my writing.

I had no grand plans to write fiction until Maisie Dobbs came into my life—at the time I was a writer of nonfiction, concentrating on articles and essays, and I also had a day job. The idea for *Maisie Dobbs*, my first foray into fiction, came to me while I was stuck in traffic near my home in California on a rainy day. I knew straightaway that this character was a person who would be as at home in the city as in the country, that I could explore the very best and the very worst of both places during a tumultuous era in history. As time passed—both for me and for Maisie—I've allowed my characters to venture further afield. It was while standing in a World War I "casualty clearing station" cemetery close to Ypres, in Belgium, that I knew I had to bring Maisie to that very place, and that she would see the graves of doctors and nurses who had been killed while tending the wounded. I stood in the driving rain looking at those names, knowing what would happen to her as the full weight of her wartime experience returned to haunt her.

While visiting Gibraltar several years later, I walked across the border into Spain, and I knew I had to bring Maisie Dobbs to that place, though I was not sure how the story would unfold. In Munich, walking along streets toward the conservatory of music that had once been Adolf Hitler's headquarters, and later while visiting Dachau concentration camp, I knew I would bring what I had learned to the reader through Maisie's eyes, setting *Journey to Munich* at a terrible time in history. Now, with *The Consequences of Fear*, once again readers will find themselves in London and Kent in World War II, this time in the latter part of 1941. Readers who know their history will recognize the importance of this crucial time.

Growing up as a horse-mad girl, I loved the insignia that was on all official Kent County Council buildings and correspondence. It was a rearing horse with the word "Invicta" underneath. In Latin, the word means *unconquered*. Perhaps the word could describe Maisie Dobbs and her fellow characters, as they navigate the slings and arrows of wartime Britain in a region that has seen centuries of conflict.

—Jacqueline Winspear

THE 17 INDISPUTABLE
LAWS OF TEAMWORK

Embrace Them and Empower Your Team

JOHN C. MAXWELL

THOMAS NELSON PUBLISHERS®
Nashville

Published in Nashville, Tennessee, by Thomas Nelson, Inc.

Scripture quotations noted KJV are from the KING JAMES VERSION.

ISBN 0-7852-7434-0 (hc)
ISBN   0-7852-6558-9 (ie)
Library of Congress Control Number 2001 132671

Printed in the United States of America

6 7 8 9 10 BVG 05 04 03 02 01

This book is dedicated
to the people of The INJOY Group:

You make me better than I am.
You multiply my value to others.
You enable me to do what I do best.
You give me more time.
You represent me where I cannot go.
You provide community for my enjoyment.
You fulfill the desires of my heart.
I can never thank you enough!

About the Companion Web Site

To enhance and complete your teamwork learning experience, we invite you to visit our companion Web site at www.LawsOfTeamwork.com.

Read *The 17 Indisputable Laws of Teamwork.*

Apply what you learn by following the suggestions at the end of each chapter.

Log on at the free interactive assessment developed by The INJOY Group. It will help you gauge your strengths and weaknesses when it comes to teamwork. There you will also find recommendations for ways to further your personal and professional development.

We hope you enjoy the book and the Web site, and we trust that you will embrace the Laws of Teamwork and empower your team.

Thomas Nelson Publishers and The INJOY Group

CONTENTS

What's your dream? Lilly Tartikoff's is to cure cancer. She's not a scientist—nor does she need to be. All she needs to know is the Law of Significance.

What would prompt a former U.S. president to go cross-country by bus, sleep in a basement, and do manual labor for a week? The answer can be found in the Law of the Big Picture.

3. THE LAW OF THE NICHE   28
All Players Have a Place Where They Add the Most Value

If you were the leader of the free world, how would you decide what job to give the person who's capable of doing *any* job—including yours? If you wanted everyone to win, you'd use the Law of the Niche.

4. THE LAW OF MOUNT EVEREST   42
As the Challenge Escalates, the Need for Teamwork Elevates

Tenzing Norgay and Maurice Wilson were experienced climbers with the right equipment. So why did one man die on the mountain while the other conquered it? Only one knew the Law of Mount Everest.

5. THE LAW OF THE CHAIN   58
The Strength of the Team Is Impacted by Its Weakest Link

Does it matter if thousands of your employees are doing a great job and only one person makes a wrong turn? Just ask the company that paid more than $3 billion in damages and was bound by the Law of the Chain.

6. THE LAW OF THE CATALYST   73
Winning Teams Have Players Who Make Things Happen

What do you do if December 31 is rapidly approaching and your salespeople are hopelessly behind on their goal for the year? Dave Sutherland can tell you. His team made its goal because he's always lived by the Law of the Catalyst.

The president of Enron learned about the company's multimillion-dollar venture to go on-line only two months before the launch, and it didn't bother him a bit. Why? Because he and his team were reaping the benefits of the Law of the Compass.

They were expected to crush the competition. They had the talent and the ambition to win. But instead of dominating, they self-destructed. If only they'd known about the Law of the Bad Apple.

Maybe people don't die in your organization when somebody drops the ball. But it can happen to people in this family business. That's why the Law of Countability is so important to them.

The company could have been the world's largest retailer. Instead it was forced to close its doors after 128 years of business. Why? The leaders were paying for ignoring the Law of the Price Tag.

11. THE LAW OF THE SCOREBOARD   148

The Team Can Make Adjustments When It Knows Where It Stands

Thousands of Web-based companies have failed. Many "successful" ones are still waiting to make a profit. Yet this company keeps winning and growing and making money! Why? Because it has always played by the Law of the Scoreboard.

12. THE LAW OF THE BENCH   161

Great Teams Have Great Depth

Who is usually an organization's MVP? The CEO? The chairman? The top salesperson? Would you believe it might be someone from HR? You would if you knew the Law of the Bench.

13. THE LAW OF IDENTITY   178

Shared Values Define the Team

How do you get thousands of people excited about working in warehouses, wearing bright orange, and catering to the customer's every need? Bernie Marcus and Arthur Blank did it by building their company's foundation on the Law of Identity.

14. THE LAW OF COMMUNICATION   193

Interaction Fuels Action

The team had ten leaders in ten years. Employees were burned out and bitter, and the company was bleeding cash. So how was Gordon Bethune going to save this last-place airline from crashing? He started by using the Law of Communication.

15. THE LAW OF THE EDGE 210

The Difference Between Two Equally Talented
Teams Is Leadership

The team had major problems. The participants had everything they needed to go the distance—talent, support, resources—everything but the most important thing. Their only hope for turning things around was someone who fulfilled the Law of the Edge.

16. THE LAW OF HIGH MORALE 225

When You're Winning, Nothing Hurts

What would prompt a fifty-year-old man who couldn't even swim to endure the pain of training for the toughest triathlon in the world? No, it wasn't a midlife crisis. It was the Law of High Morale.

17. THE LAW OF DIVIDENDS 243

Investing in the Team Compounds Over Time

Have you ever been tricked into taking a job? Morgan Wootten was, and as a result, he has changed the lives of thousands of kids. His life of giving will teach you everything you need to know about the Law of Dividends.

ACKNOWLEDGMENTS

Every book I write is an act of teamwork. And this one is no exception. I'd like to thank the people who helped me to create *The 17 Indisputable Laws of Teamwork:*

The INJOY Team, who helped me to think through and refine the laws.

Margaret Maxwell, my wife, best friend, and number one teammate, who gives good advice.

Linda Eggers, who always takes care of all the details of my life.

Kathie Wheat, who did such wonderful research for the book.

Stephanie Wetzel, who sharpened the manuscript by proofreading and editing every word.

Charlie Wetzel, whose writing extends my influence around the world.

INTRODUCTION

Every day, in some way, you are a part of a team. The question is not, *Will you participate in something that involves others?* The question is, *Will your involvement with others be successful?* You can find the answer to that question in this book.

Everyone knows that teamwork is a good thing; in fact, it's essential! But how does it really work? What makes a winning team? Why do some teams go straight to the top, seeing their vision become reality, while others seem to go nowhere?

These questions don't have simple answers. If they did, sports would have more back-to-back world champions, and the list of Fortune 500 companies would never change year after year.

One of the challenges of learning about teamwork is that even people who've taken a team to the highest level in their field sometimes have a hard time identifying what separates a great team from a collection of individuals who can't seem to get it together. Some will say the key to winning is a strong work ethic. But haven't you known plenty of hardworking individuals who never worked together to reach their potential? Others believe that great teams are the result of chemistry. But they often say, "I can't explain how you create it, but I definitely know it when I see it." How can you get your hands around that and learn from it to build *your* team?

As a communicator who spends countless hours speaking to live audiences every year, I am always looking for straightforward ways to teach people complex truths. That's what a communicator does—he takes something complicated and makes it simple. In 1998, I wrote *The 21 Irrefutable Laws of Leadership*. My desire was to share what I had learned from three decades of leading people. The response was overwhelming. The book landed on bestseller lists of the *New York Times* Business Books, the *Wall Street Journal, Business Week,* and the Christian Booksellers Association (CBA) marketplace. For that I am truly grateful. But more important, during the last several years as I have taught the laws throughout the United States and on five continents, I have had the delight of seeing people connect with the laws, apply them to their lives, and improve their leadership. Learning the laws changed people's lives, and I knew that I had found an effective handle for helping people learn leadership.

My desire is to make team building as simple to grasp, retain, and put into practice as leadership. I want to take the mystery out of it. That's why I've worked hard to identify the Laws of Teamwork. The wonderful thing about a law is that you can depend on it. No matter who you are, what your background is, or what circumstances you face; you can take a law to the bank.

As I teach you the laws, you will find that I often approach the subject of teamwork from a leader's point of view—that makes sense since leaders are the ones who bring teams together and lead them to victory. But you don't have to be a leader to benefit from this book. Just about everything you do depends on teamwork. It doesn't matter whether you are a leader or follower, coach or player, teacher or student, parent or child, CEO or nonprofit volunteer worker. No matter who you are, if you learn and apply the laws, your teamwork capacity will increase. The greater the number of laws that you and your teammates learn, the more likely you are to be transformed from a group of individuals into a winning team.

Teams come in all shapes and sizes. If you're married, you and your spouse are a team. If you are employed by an organization, you and your colleagues are a team. If you volunteer your time, you and your fellow workers are a team. As Dan Devine joked, "A team is a team is a team. Shakespeare said that many times." Although the gifted playwright might not have said exactly that, the concept is nonetheless true. That's why teamwork is so important.

At a recent conference where I was teaching, a young leader who was just getting started in his career came up to me and asked, "John, what's the one thing I need to know about teamwork?"

"One thing?" I replied. "That's not an easy answer to come up with."

He persisted: "But just get me started. I want only the thing that's most important."

"All right, if you insist," I said. "The one thing you need to know about teamwork is that there is more than one thing you need to know about teamwork."

At first he looked at me questioningly. Then he became a bit irritated. But then I could see a sudden understanding in his eyes.

"Oh, I get it," he said. "It's a process. Okay, okay. I'm ready to dive in. I'm willing to take the time to learn."

I want to encourage you to do the same, to devote yourself to the process of learning to be a great team member and team builder. As you read about the Laws of Teamwork and begin to apply them, I think you will find that they have a positive impact on every aspect of your life. As you proceed, also remember this: None of the laws stand alone, but they all stand together really well. The greater number of laws you learn, the better you will become.

Enjoy the process, give it your best, and never forget that no matter what you want to do in life, it takes teamwork to make the dream work.

THE LAW OF SIGNIFICANCE

One Is Too Small a Number to Achieve Greatness

Who are your personal heroes? Okay, maybe you don't have heroes exactly. Then let me ask you this: Which people do you admire most? Who do you wish you were more like? Which people fire you up and get your juices flowing? Do you admire . . .

- Business innovators, such as Jeff Bezos, Fred Smith, or Bill Gates?

- Great athletes, such as Michael Jordan, Marion Jones, or Mark McGwire?

- Creative geniuses, such as Pablo Picasso, Buckminster Fuller, or Wolfgang Amadeus Mozart?

- Pop culture icons, such as Madonna, Andy Warhol, or Elvis Presley?

- Spiritual leaders, such as John Wesley, Billy Graham, or Mother Teresa?

- Political leaders, such as Alexander the Great, Charlemagne, or Winston Churchill?

- Film industry giants, such as D. W. Griffith, Charlie Chaplin, or Steven Spielberg?

- Architects and engineers, such as Frank Lloyd Wright, the Starrett brothers, or Joseph Strauss?

- Revolutionary thinkers, such as Marie Curie, Thomas Edison, or Albert Einstein?

Or maybe your list includes people in a field I didn't mention.

It's safe to say that we all admire achievers. And we Americans especially love pioneers and bold individualists, people who fight alone, despite the odds or opposition: the settler who carves a place for himself in the wilds of the frontier, the Old West sheriff who resolutely faces an enemy in a gunfight, the pilot who bravely flies solo across the Atlantic Ocean, and the scientist who changes the world through the power of his mind.

THE MYTH OF THE LONE RANGER

As much as we admire solo achievement, the truth is that no lone individual has done anything of value. The belief that one person can do something great is a myth. There are no real Rambos who can take on a hostile army by themselves. Even the Lone Ranger wasn't really a loner. Everywhere he went he rode with Tonto!

Nothing of significance was ever achieved by an individual acting alone. Look below the surface and you will find that all seemingly solo acts are really team efforts. Frontiersman Daniel Boone had companions from the Transylvania Company as he blazed the Wilderness Road. Sheriff Wyatt Earp had his two brothers and Doc Holliday looking out for him. Aviator Charles Lindbergh had the backing of nine businessmen from St. Louis and the services of the Ryan Aeronautical Company, which built his plane. Even Albert Einstein, the scientist who revolutionized the world with his theory of relativity, didn't work in a vacuum. Of the debt he owed to others for his work, Einstein once remarked, "Many times a day I realize how much my own outer and inner life is built upon the labors of my fellow men, both living and dead, and how earnestly I must exert myself in order to give in return as much as I have received." It's true that the history of our country is marked by the accomplishments of many strong leaders and innovative individuals who took considerable risks. But those people always were part of teams.

> *The belief that one person can do something great is a myth.*

Economist Lester C. Thurow commented on the subject:

> There is nothing antithetical in American history, culture, or traditions to teamwork. Teams were important in America's history—wagon trains conquered the West, men working together on the assembly line in American industry conquered the world, a successful national strategy and a lot of teamwork put an American on the moon first (and thus far, last). But American mythology extols only the individual . . . In America, halls of fame exist for almost every conceivable activity, but nowhere do Americans raise monuments in praise of teamwork.

I must say that I don't agree with all of Thurow's conclusions. After all, I've seen the U.S. Marine Corps war memorial in Washington, D.C., commemorating the raising of the flag on Iwo Jima. But he is right about something. Teamwork is and always has been essential to building this country. And that statement can be made about every country around the world.

THE VALUE OF TEAMWORK

A Chinese proverb states, "Behind an able man there are always other able men." The truth is that teamwork is at the heart of great achievement. The question isn't whether teams have value. The question is whether we acknowledge that fact and become better team players. That's why I assert that *one is too small a number to achieve greatness.* You cannot do anything of *real* value alone. That is the Law of Significance.

> *"There are no problems we cannot solve together, and very few that we can solve by ourselves."*
>
> —LYNDON JOHNSON

I challenge you to think of *one* act of genuine significance in the history of humankind that was performed by a lone human being. No matter what you name, you will find that a team of people was involved. That is why President Lyndon Johnson said, "There are no problems we cannot solve together, and very few that we can solve by ourselves."

C. Gene Wilkes, in his book *Jesus on Leadership,* observed that the power of teams not only is evident in today's modern business world, but it also has a deep history that is evident even in biblical times. Wilkes asserts,

- Teams involve more people, thus affording more resources, ideas, and energy than would an individual.

- Teams maximize a leader's potential and minimize her weaknesses. Strengths and weaknesses are more exposed in individuals.

- Teams provide multiple perspectives on how to meet a need or reach a goal, thus devising several alternatives for each situation. Individual insight is seldom as broad and deep as a group's when it takes on a problem.

- Teams share the credit for victories and the blame for losses. This fosters genuine humility and authentic community. Individuals take credit and blame alone. This fosters pride and sometimes a sense of failure.

- Teams keep leaders accountable for the goal. Individuals connected to no one can change the goal without accountability.

- Teams can simply do more than an individual.

If you want to reach your potential or strive for the seemingly impossible—such as communicating your message two thousand years after you are gone—you need to become a team player. It may be a cliché, but it is nonetheless true: Individuals play the game, but teams win championships.

WHY DO WE STAND ALONE?

Knowing all that we do about the potential of teams, why do some people still want to do things by themselves? I believe there are a number of reasons.

1. Ego

Few people are fond of admitting that they can't do everything, yet that is a reality of life. There are no supermen or superwomen. As Kerry Walls, one of the people on my INJOY Group team, says, "Spinning more plates doesn't increase your talent—it increases your likelihood of dropping a plate." So the question is not whether you can do everything by yourself; it's how soon you're going to realize that you can't.

> *Teamwork is birthed when you concentrate on "we" instead of "me."*

Philanthropist Andrew Carnegie declared, "It marks a big step in your development when you come to realize that other people can help you do a better job than you could do alone." To do something really big, let go of your ego, and get ready to be part of a team.

2. Insecurity

In my work with leaders, I've found that some individuals fail to promote teamwork because they feel threatened by other people. Sixteenth-century Florentine statesman Niccolo Machiavelli probably made similar observations, prompting him to write, "The first method for estimating the intelligence of a ruler is to look at the men he has around him."

I believe that insecurity, rather than poor judgment or lack of intelligence, most often causes leaders to surround themselves with weak people. As I stated in *The 21 Irrefutable Laws of Leadership,* only secure leaders give power to others. That is the Law of Empowerment. On the other hand, insecure leaders usually fail to build teams because of one of two reasons: Either they want to maintain control over everything for which they are responsible, or they fear being replaced by someone more capable. In either case, leaders who fail to promote teamwork undermine their own potential and erode the best efforts of the people with whom they work. They would benefit from the advice of President Woodrow Wilson: "We should not only use all the brains we have, but all that we can borrow."

> *"We should not only use all the brains we have, but all that we can borrow."*
>
> —WOODROW WILSON

3. Naïveté

Consultant John Ghegan keeps a sign on his desk that says, "If I had it to do all over again, I'd get help." That remark accurately represents the feelings of the third type of people who fail to become team builders. They naively underestimate the difficulty of achieving big things. As a result, they try to go it alone.

Some people who start out in this group turn out okay in the end. They discover that their dreams are bigger than their capabilities, they realize they won't accomplish their goals solo, and they adjust. They make team building their approach to achievement. But some others learn the truth too late, and as a result, they never accomplish their goals. And that's a shame.

4. Temperament

Some people aren't very outgoing and simply don't think in terms of team building and team participation. As they face challenges, it never occurs to them to enlist others to achieve something.

As a people person, I find that hard to relate to. Whenever I face any kind of challenge, the very first thing I do is to think about the people I want on the team to help with it. I've been that way since I was a kid. I've

> *"People have been known to achieve more as a result of working with others than against them."*
>
> —DR. ALLAN FROMME

always thought, *Why take the journey alone when you can invite others along with you?*

I understand that not everyone operates that way. But whether or not you are naturally inclined to be part of a team is really irrelevant. If you do everything alone and never partner with other people, you create huge barriers to your own potential. Dr. Allan Fromme quipped, "People have been known to achieve more as a result of working with others than against them." What an understatement! It takes a team to do anything of lasting value. Besides, even the most introverted person in the world can learn to enjoy the benefits of being on a team. (That's true even if someone isn't trying to accomplish something great.)

A few years ago my friend Chuck Swindoll wrote a piece in *The Finishing Touch* that sums up the importance of teamwork. He said,

Nobody is a whole team . . . We need each other. You need someone and someone needs you. Isolated islands we're not. To make this thing called life work, we gotta lean and support. And relate and respond. And give and take. And confess and forgive. And reach out and embrace and rely . . . Since none of us is a whole, independent, self-sufficient, super-capable, all-powerful hotshot, let's quit acting like we are. Life's lonely enough without our playing that silly role. The game is over. Let's link up.

For the person trying to do everything alone, the game really is over. If you want to do something big, you must link up with others. *One is too small a number to achieve greatness.* That's the Law of Significance.

YOU CAN SEE THE DIFFERENCE

When you look at the way people conduct their lives, you can tell fairly quickly who recognizes and embraces the truth of the Law of Significance. That is certainly true of Lilly Tartikoff. I don't know whether Lilly always knew the value of teamwork, but I suspect she learned it early since she was once a professional ballet dancer. If dancers don't work together, then their performances never reach the caliber of Lilly's. Beginning at age seven, she spent ten hours a day, six days a week, practicing or performing ballet. As a result she became a member of the New York City Ballet Company and performed with them from 1971 to 1980.

At a tennis party in Los Angeles in 1980, Lilly met Brandon Tartikoff, the newly named president of entertainment for NBC. At that time he was the youngest network president in history at age thirty. They soon became friends. Then they began to see each other romantically. In 1982, they were married. And that started a whole new life for Lilly. She went from a nontelevision watcher to the spouse of a network executive immersed in the L.A. culture of the entertainment industry. But that adjustment was nothing compared to the other challenge she faced that year. For the second time in his life, Brandon was diagnosed with Hodgkin's disease.

AMAZING SCIENCE

On the advice of a physician friend, Brandon went to see a young oncological researcher at UCLA named Denny Slamon. In August 1982, Dr. Slamon started Brandon on two kinds of treatment, one of which was experimental. Brandon would usually be treated on a

Friday, and afterward Lilly would drive him home and take care of him while he suffered from horrible side effects all weekend. They followed that pattern for a year, and all the while Brandon continued in his role of network president. It was a difficult time for them, but they chose to face the cancer as a team, and in time Brandon recovered.

Out of that ordeal came many things. For one, Brandon's network, NBC, went from worst to first in the ratings. In his autobiography he wrote, "Cancer helps you see things more clearly. The disease, I've found, can actually *help* you do your job, and there's a very simple reason why: There's nothing like cancer to keep you focused on what's important."[1] That focus enabled him to air some of the most popular and groundbreaking shows in television's history: *The Cosby Show, Cheers, Hill Street Blues, Miami Vice, The Golden Girls, The A-Team, St. Elsewhere,* and others.

For Lilly, though, there was a different outcome. Once Hodgkin's disease had been driven from her husband's body, she didn't simply move on.

"Brandon was at the receiving end of some pretty amazing science," she observed. The medical research that had extended Brandon's life intrigued her. So when she had an opportunity to help others benefit from that same science, she couldn't say no. That occurred in 1989 when Dr. Dennis Slamon, the UCLA scientist who had treated Brandon seven years before, asked Lilly for her help.

NOBODY CAN DO IT ALONE

For years Dr. Slamon had been studying breast cancer. He believed he was on the verge of developing a radical new treatment that would not only be more effective in treating the disease than anything previously developed, but he could do it without all the usual side effects of chemotherapy. He had the expertise and skill necessary to do the work, but he couldn't do it alone. He needed someone to help with funding. He thought of Lilly. She was only too happy to agree to assist him.

The plan she developed showed keen insight into teamwork and strategic partnerships. Lilly had once worked as a beauty adviser for Max Factor, formerly connected to Revlon. She sought to get Ronald Perelman, the CEO of Revlon, together with Dr. Slamon. At first that wasn't easy, but once Perelman realized the potential of Slamon's research, he pledged $2.4 million to the scientist's work with no restrictions. It was a partnership unlike anything that had been done before. What resulted was the creation of the Revlon/UCLA Women's Cancer Research Program—and a successful new treatment for cancer was soon saving women's lives.

A TASTE OF TEAMWORK

For Lilly, cofounding the research program was just a beginning. She had gotten a taste of what teamwork could do, and she was hungry to do much more. She quickly realized that she could enlist others to her cause. She would build a larger team, and she would use her show business connections to do it. That same year she established an annual Fire and Ice Ball in Hollywood to raise money. A few years later, she enlarged her circle and partnered with the Entertainment Industry Foundation (EIF) and created the Revlon Run/Walk, first in Los Angeles, and then in New York. So far, those events have raised more than $18 million for cancer research. And in 1996, she helped create the National Women's Cancer Research Alliance.

In 1997, her husband Brandon's cancer recurred a third time, and it took his life. He was only forty-eight years old. Despite the personal setback, Lilly continues to build teams to fight cancer. When she met Katie Couric, who had lost her husband to colon cancer, Lilly was again inspired to action. With the help of Couric and the EIF, she formed the National Colorectal Cancer Research Alliance in 2000.

"When I sat down with Katie," said Lilly, "to hear that, with an early diagnosis, you could turn the cancer around, and literally, it's 90 percent curable and preventable. Well, this was like putting a steak in front of a hungry dog . . . I thought, we've got to do this. So I brought in all my partners: the Entertainment Industry Foundation and Dr. Slamon . . . and Dr. Slamon brought together an agenda and a mission . . . So we created the NCCRA [National Colorectal Cancer Research Alliance]. You have no idea how exciting and gratifying it is."[2]

An individual cannot do the incredible, significant task that Lilly Tartikoff and her partners are trying to accomplish. No single person can take on cancer. But that's true of anything worth doing. If it's significant, it takes a team. That's something Lilly realized, put into practice, and now lives by every day. *One is too small a number to achieve greatness.* That is the Law of Significance.

TEAMWORK THOUGHT

You may be good—but you're not *that* good!

BECOMING A BETTER TEAM MEMBER

What major goals are you working toward achieving right now? Write some of them here:

1. _Making YFC a community impact player by 2004_
2. _Touching thousands & engaging hundreds each year by 2004_
3. _Making YFC a diverse staff by 2004_

Now, reflect on how you are working toward these goals. What approach have you been taking to achieve them? Are you going it alone? Or are you building a team to accomplish them? _yes_

If you're not trying to be part of a team, figure out why. Is it a matter of ego? Are you insecure? Have you misjudged the size of the challenges? Or does your temperament incline you to work alone? If you answer yes to one of these questions, work to overcome the difficulty immediately. The sooner you become a team player, the sooner you will be able to achieve your dreams.

BECOMING A BETTER TEAM LEADER

Think about the greatest dream you have for your life. Now ask yourself,

- "Is it bigger than I am?"

- "Does it benefit others as well as myself?"

- "Is it worth dedicating part of my life to?"

If you answer yes to all of these questions, then think about what kinds of people should join you to achieve that dream. Make a list of the like-minded people you know who might want to join you in the process. Then invite them to take the journey with you. And be on the lookout for others who would benefit from being part of the team.

COMPANION **ONLINE** RESOURCE

Learn more about how the Law of Significance uniquely applies to you.
Take the FREE Law of Significance assessment at **LawsOfTeamwork.com**.

- Nora
- Julie
- Bud
- José
- Patrick

- Dhullio Grupe
- Carrie Sass
- Ros Waters
- Michelle Hoot

THE LAW OF THE BIG PICTURE

The Goal Is More Important Than the Role

Years ago, I was invited to participate in an important conference that was being planned by a highly respected national organization. I was one of about a dozen speakers who had been selected to speak to an audience of more than sixty thousand people drawn from all parts of the country. It was for a worthy cause that I valued, and I considered the invitation to be an honor.

Several weeks before the conference was to occur, all the speakers were scheduled to meet together along with the founder of the organization to talk strategy, discuss the topics about which we would speak, and give one another support and suggestions. I was really excited about it because the group included some extraordinary leaders. It promised to be an electric time, but the reality of the meeting turned out to be different from what I expected.

When we all got into a room together, it didn't feel like a strategy-and-support session. As we discussed the upcoming day, a few of the speakers seemed to be jockeying for position. Because they were good communicators, they understood that the speaking order, the time of day, and the amount of time allotted would make a big difference in how their messages would be received. The role each speaker was to play seemed to be of more interest than the goal of the conference.

But I also noticed something else. When one speaker briefly informed us about his topic, I sensed immediately that his speech would be the real hinge pin of the whole conference. All of the other messages would be subordinate to it. Yet the man was not fighting for the best place. He wasn't jockeying. He didn't seem to want any part of that kind of maneuvering.

In that moment when everyone was focusing on himself, I realized that we had lost sight of the big picture of why we were there. So I said to the group about this speaker, "I believe his message will be the difference maker in the lives of the people attending this conference. And I think the audience will receive it better if it's delivered when I am slated to speak. Please," I said to the person who wasn't trying to promote himself, "take my spot."

It was almost as if somebody had struck each person in the room. Suddenly everybody regained perspective. After that, instead of looking out for themselves and protecting turf, all of the speakers were willing to give everything for the common good. We all remembered that the goal was more important than our individual roles. That is the essence of the Law of the Big Picture.

WHAT'S IN IT FOR ME?

In a culture that sings the praises of individual gold medals and where a person fights for rights instead of focusing on taking responsibility, people tend to lose sight of the big picture. In fact, some people seem to believe that they *are* the entire picture: Everything revolves around their needs, their goals, and their desires. I saw a message on a T-shirt that expresses the attitude well: "My idea of a team is a whole lot of people doing what I tell them to do."

A team isn't supposed to be a bunch of people being used as a tool by one individual for selfish gain. Members of a team must have mutually beneficial shared goals. They must be motivated to work together, not manipulated by someone for individual glory. Anyone who is accustomed to pulling together people and using them to benefit only himself isn't a team builder; he's a dictator.

> *If you think you are the entire picture, you will never see the big picture.*

If you want to observe team dynamics in action, look at the world of sports where you can easily see whether people are working together. The outcome of a game is immediate and measurable. For that reason it's easy to see when an individual is thinking only of himself and not the shared goals and values of the team.

To win in sports, members of the team must always keep the big picture in front of them. They must remember that the goal is more important than their role—or any individual glory they may desire. NBA superstar David Robinson remarked, "I think any player will tell you that individual accomplishments help your ego, but if you don't win, it makes for a very, very long season. It counts more that the team has played well."

IT'S ALL ABOUT THE TEAM

The acclaimed football coach of Oklahoma during the 1950s, Bud Wilkinson, put it this way in *The Book of Football Wisdom:* "If a team is to reach its potential, each player must be willing to subordinate his personal goals to the good of the team."

> *"If a team is to reach its potential, each player must be willing to subordinate his personal goals to the good of the team."*
>
> —BUD WILKINSON

Some sports teams seem to embrace an "everyone-for-himself" mind-set. Others weave the attitude of subordination and teamwork into the fabric of everything they do. For example, football teams such as Notre Dame and Penn State don't put the names of the players on their jerseys. Lou Holtz, former coach of the Fighting Irish, once explained why. He said, "At Notre Dame, we believed the interlocking ND was all the identification you needed. Whenever anyone complained, I told them they were lucky we allowed numbers on the uniforms. Given my druthers, I would have nothing more than initials indicating what position the wearer played. If your priority is the team rather than yourself, what else do you need?"

Winning teams have players who put the good of the team ahead of themselves. They want to play in their area of strength, but they're willing to do what it takes to take care of the team. They are willing to sacrifice their role for the greater goal. That's the Law of the Big Picture.

SEEING THE BIG PICTURE

People who build successful teams never forget that every person on a team has a role to play, and every role plays its part in contributing to the bigger picture. Without that perspective the team cannot accomplish its goal, whether the team's "game" is sports, business, family, ministry, or government.

Leaders at the highest level understand the Law of the Big Picture. They continually keep the vision of the big picture before themselves and their people. An outstanding example involves Winston Churchill. It's said that during World War II when Britain was experiencing its darkest days, the country had a difficult time keeping men working in the coal mines. Many wanted to give up their dirty, thankless jobs in the dangerous mines to join military service, which garnered much public praise and support. Yet their work in the mines was critical to the success of the war. Without coal the military and the people at home would be in trouble.

So the prime minister faced thousands of coal miners one day and told them of their importance to the war effort, how their role could make or break the goal of maintaining England's freedom.

Churchill painted a picture of what it would be like when the war ended, of the grand parade that would honor the people who fought the war. First would come the sailors of the navy, he said, the people who continued the tradition of Trafalgar and the defeat of the Spanish Armada. Next would come the best and brightest of Britain, the pilots of the Royal Air Force who fended off the German Luftwaffe. Following them would be the soldiers who had fought at Dunkirk.

Then last of all would come the coal-dust-covered men in miners' caps. And Churchill indicated that someone from the crowd might say, "And where were you during the critical days of the struggle?"

And the voices of ten thousand men would respond, "We were deep in the earth with our faces to the coal."

It's said that tears appeared in the eyes of those hardened men. And they returned to their inglorious work with steely resolve, having been reminded of the role they were playing in their country's noble goal of preserving freedom for the Western world.

> "Everybody on a championship team doesn't get publicity, but everyone can say he's a champion."
>
> —EARVIN "MAGIC" JOHNSON

That's the kind of mind-set it takes to build a team. It takes the courage and the resolve to recognize that *the goal is more important than the role*. It's no small thing for people to do what's best for the team. Often it means sacrificing professional satisfaction, individual statistics, or personal glory. But as NBA star-turned-successful-businessman Earvin "Magic" Johnson says, "Everybody on a championship team doesn't get publicity, but everyone can say he's a champion."

WHAT'S UP WITH BIG PICTURE TEAMS?

So how do people start to become a more unified team? How do individuals make the shift from independent people to team players who exemplify the Law of the Big Picture? It's not something that happens overnight. It takes time. Here is my best take on how to get the process started.

1. Look Up *at the Big Picture*

Everything starts with vision. You need to have a goal. Without one you cannot have a real team. Hall of Fame catcher Yogi Berra joked, "If you don't know where you're going, you'll end up somewhere else." An individual without a goal may end up anywhere. A group of individuals without a goal can go nowhere. On the other hand, if everyone in a group embraces the vision for achieving the big picture, then the people have the potential to become an effective team.

Leaders usually have the role of capturing and communicating vision. They must see it first and then help everyone else to see it. That was what Winston Churchill did when he spoke to the coal miners during the war. That was what Dr. Martin Luther King Jr. did as he spoke to people about his dream from the steps of the Lincoln Monument in Washington, D.C. That was what GE CEO Jack Welch did when he let his people know that a division of GE that couldn't be first or second in its market wouldn't be a part of GE. The people on a team will sacrifice and work together *only* if they can see what they're working toward.

If you are the leader of your team, your role is to do what only you can do: <u>Paint the big picture for your people.</u> Without the vision they will not find the desire to achieve the goal.

2. Size Up *the Situation*

One value of seeing the big picture is that it helps you recognize how far you really are from achieving it. For someone determined to do everything alone, seeing the gulf between what is and what could be is often intimidating. But for people who live to build teams, see-ing the size of the task ahead doesn't worry them. They don't shrink from the challenge—they savor the opportunity. They can't wait to put together a team and a plan to accomplish that vision.

At a meeting of all three divisions of The INJOY Group, CEO Dave Sutherland stood before our people and outlined a few of our goals for the coming year. (Some of those goals were huge.) During that process, Dave said, "Some people see the size of the goal, and they get scared. That doesn't bother me a bit. We've already got a great team. To make it to the next level, we just need a few more people like the ones we already have." That's the mind-set of a team builder!

3. Line Up *Needed Resources*

Hawley R. Everhart believes, "It's all right to aim high if you have plenty of ammunition." That's what resources are: ammunition to help you reach a goal. It doesn't matter what kind of team you're on. You cannot make progress without the support of the appropriate equipment, facilities, funds, and so forth—whether your goal is climbing a mountain, capturing a market, or creating a ministry. The better resourced the team is, the fewer distractions the players will have as they try to achieve their goal.

4. Call Up *the Right Players*

When it comes to building a successful team, the players are everything. You can have a distinct vision, a precise plan, plenty of resources, and incredible leadership, but if you don't have the right people, you're not going to get anywhere. (I'll talk more about this in several of the other laws.) You can lose with good players, but you cannot win with bad ones.

5. Give Up *Personal Agendas*

Teams that win have players who continually ask themselves, "What's best for the rest?" They continually set aside their personal agendas for the good of the team. Their motto can be expressed by the words of Ray Kroc, founder of McDonald's, who said, "No one of us is more important than the rest of us."

A remarkable sports story from several years ago was the success of the U.S. Women's Soccer Team. They won the Olympic gold medal and the World Cup in a few brief years. A key player on that team was Mia Hamm. In her book *Go for the Goal*, she gives her perspective on her sport and the attitude a player must bring into the game to achieve the goal of becoming a champion:

> *"No one of us is more important than the rest of us."*
>
> —RAY KROC

> Soccer is not an individual sport. I don't score all the goals, and the ones I do score are usually the product of a team effort. I don't keep the ball out of the back of the net on the other end of the field. I don't plan our game tactics. I don't wash our training gear (okay, sometimes I do), and I don't make our airline reservations. I am a member of a team, and I rely on the team. I defer to it and sacrifice for it, because the team, not the individual, is the ultimate champion.

Mia Hamm understands the Law of the Big Picture. And by doing whatever it took to help her team—including washing the gear—she demonstrated that the goal was more important than the role.

6. Step Up *to a Higher Level*

Only when players come together and give up their own agendas can a team move up to a higher level. That's the kind of sacrifice required for teamwork. Unfortunately some people prefer to cling to agendas and pursue the paths of their own inflated egos instead of letting go of them to achieve something greater than themselves.

It's just as philosopher Friedrich Nietzsche said: "Many are stubborn in pursuit of the path they have chosen, few in pursuit of the goal." And that's a shame because people who think only of themselves are missing the big picture. As a result their potential goes untapped, and the people who are depending on them are bound to be let down.

SUBORDINATE ROLE FOR THE TEAM'S SUCCESS

President Abraham Lincoln once remarked, "Nearly all men can stand adversity, but if you want to test a man's character, give him power." Few people have more power than an American president. Being the so-called leader of the free world can certainly go to a person's head. But not to Jimmy Carter's. If you review his career—from the time he was a school board official to his term in the White House and beyond—you can see that he was willing to take on nearly any role to achieve a goal he believed in. He has always embraced the importance of the big picture.

There is possibly no more vivid example of the Law of the Big Picture in Carter's life than his work with Habitat for Humanity. Habitat was officially founded by Millard and Linda Fuller in 1976, though the two had been exploring the idea for many years before that, first in the U.S. and then overseas. The goal of the organization is a huge one—to eliminate poverty-level housing and homelessness from the world.

In the late seventies and early eighties, they began their bold venture. After six years they had built houses internationally in Mexico, Zaire, and Guatemala. And in the U.S., they had affiliates building houses in San Antonio, Texas; Americus, Georgia; Johns Island, South Carolina; and other locations in Florida and Appalachia. Groundwork was being laid for them to build in many other cities, but the process was a struggle. They had found a successful formula for their goal: Offer home ownership to the neediest people able to make a house payment, build low-cost housing using volunteer labor, involve the future home owner in the building process, and create no-interest loans to finance the houses. It was an inspired idea, and it was catching on. To reach the world as they desired, however, the Fullers knew they would have to take Habitat to a whole new level.

From their headquarters in the town of Americus in southern Georgia, the Fullers saw a possibility. Ten miles away in the tiny town of Plains was a man who might be able to help them: Jimmy Carter. The former U.S. president had spoken at a couple of Habitat functions. Following Carter's speaking in 1983, Millard Fuller got the idea to approach Carter about helping the project along. And in early 1984 they made contact. When Carter said he was very interested in Habitat for Humanity, Fuller decided to boldly propose a list of fifteen possible roles the former president could take, hoping he would agree to one or two. His list included serving on Habitat's board, making media contacts, helping to raise money, doing a thirty-minute video, and working on a building crew for a day.

To Fuller's surprise, Carter did not agree to do one or two items on the list. He agreed to do *everything* on it. Ironically the task that captured the attention of the public most was Carter's willingness to serve on a building crew and swing a hammer to help construct a house. At first people thought Carter would just stop by for brief publicity photos. But the former president put together a work crew, traveled with them via Trailways bus to the Brooklyn, New York, building site, worked tenaciously every day for a week, and slept in a church basement along with everyone else. That first time was in 1984. Carter has raised a team and served in similar fashion every year since then. And his dedicated service has attracted people from every walk of life to serve in similar roles.[1]

A SHARED GOAL

Habitat for Humanity is the brainchild of the Fullers, and its success is the result of the efforts of hundreds of thousands of people from around the globe. But Jimmy Carter is the one who put it on the map. His selfless service inspired people rich and poor, famous and obscure, powerful and not so powerful to see the huge goal of helping people at the lowest level of society by providing them with a decent place to live. And he inspired them to get involved.

So far Habitat and its volunteers have built more than 100,000 houses sheltering more than a half million people all over the world.[2] Why? Because they, like Carter, wanted to be part of something bigger than themselves. They understood that the goal was more important than the role. They embraced the truth of the Law of the Big Picture.

TEAMWORK THOUGHT

When you see the big picture correctly,
you serve the team more quickly.

BECOMING A BETTER TEAM MEMBER

What goal in your life is bigger than you are? Are you currently participating in something greater than yourself? If not, set aside some time to spend alone reflecting on your goals and priorities. If you are trying to accomplish something big, then ask yourself what you are willing to do to accomplish it. Are you willing to take a subordinate role if necessary for the good of the team, as President Carter did? If not, you may become a hindrance to the success of the team.

BECOMING A BETTER TEAM LEADER

Think about a team you are currently part of (preferably one with a big goal). What kind of attitude do team members have when it comes to the big picture? Are they team players who desire to do whatever it takes for the team to succeed? Or do they desire to benefit only themselves?

Begin to foster a team mind-set in others by modeling a willingness to serve the big picture rather than yourself. Then think about ways you can help your teammates to embrace the Law of the Big Picture. Motivate people by painting the big picture. Publicly honor team play. And give rewards to people who sacrifice for the good of the team.

COMPANION **ONLINE** RESOURCE

Learn more about how the Law of the Big Picture uniquely applies to you.

Take the FREE Law of the Big Picture assessment at **LawsOfTeamwork.com**.

THE LAW OF THE NICHE

All Players Have a Place Where They Add the Most Value

On January 26, 2001, the United States experienced a historic first: An African-American assumed the post of secretary of state, the highest cabinet post in the United States government. The man who took that position was Colin Powell. Columnist Carl Rowan remarked of the appointment, "To understand the significance of Powell's elevation to this extremely difficult and demanding post, you must realize that only a generation ago it was an unwritten rule that in the foreign affairs field, blacks could serve only as ambassador to Liberia and minister to the Canary Islands."

Powell's appointment was remarkable, but not just because it was groundbreaking. It was significant because, to put it simply, Colin Powell was the best individual in all of the United States to take on the role of secretary of state. George W. Bush, the president who appointed him, stated, "In this cause, I know of no better person to be the face and voice of American diplomacy than Colin Powell," citing his "directness of speech, his towering integrity, his deep respect for our democracy, and his soldier's sense of duty."[1] Bush recognizes that *all players have a place where they add the most value.* Powell's is running the State Department. That's the Law of the Niche.

A PLACE FOR HIM

A soldier's sense of duty has been a vital part of the character of Colin Powell since he was in his early twenties. Something of a late bloomer, Powell entered college uncertain of what he wanted to do with his life. But it didn't take him long to find his identity: in an ROTC unit called the Pershing Rifles at the City College of New York. It was there that he discovered real teamwork for the first time in his life. In *My American Journey,* Powell wrote:

> My experience in high school, on basketball and track teams, and briefly in Boy Scouting had never produced a sense of belonging or many permanent friendships. The Pershing Rifles did. For the first time in my life I was a member of a brotherhood . . . The discipline, the structure, the camaraderie, the sense of belonging were what I craved. I became a leader almost immediately. I found a selflessness among the ranks that reminded me of the caring atmosphere within my family. Race, color, background, income meant nothing. The PRs [Pershing Rifles] would go the limit for each other and for the group. If this was what soldiering was all about, then maybe I wanted to be a soldier.[2]

As he got closer to graduation from college, there was no doubt in his mind. He gladly chose military life.

No Ordinary Journey

In the army Powell seemed to achieve success everywhere he went and quickly rose in rank. His love was commanding troops, and when he received those assignments, he did well. Yet he was constantly tapped for special jobs and responsibilities. When that happened again and again, keeping him from leading soldiers in the field, he became frustrated. But a mentor, General John Wickham, wisely told him, "You're not going to have a conventional army career. Some officers are just not destined for it."

Wickham was right. Powell's career did turn out to be unusual. And it ultimately prepared him for a cabinet post, sharpening his gifts and giving him broad experience. As an infantry officer who did tours around the globe (including two in Vietnam), Powell learned command and leadership. His work with soldiers also taught him to communicate and connect with people. As a White House Fellow, he got his first exposure to American politics and world governments. Besides his interaction with high-level U.S. officials, he met with leaders of Japan, the Soviet Union, China, Poland, Bulgaria, and West Germany.

Powell moved to a whole new level in his post at the Pentagon during the Carter and Reagan administrations. It was there that he learned how to work with civil servants and he expanded his understanding of government and military politics. As the senior military assistant to Secretary of Defense Caspar Weinberger, Powell traveled the world and attained in-depth comprehension of the complex relationships between the United States and foreign powers.

But in the office of the national security adviser, Powell stepped into the big leagues. As the deputy assistant to the president for national security affairs, he gained valuable experience in foreign policy. In fact, he was so adept that when his boss, Frank Carlucci, was asked to be secretary of defense, Powell stepped into Carlucci's former position as national security adviser. There he not only advised President Reagan, but Powell worked side by side with Secretary of State George Shultz as the statesman negotiated nuclear missile treaties with the USSR, organized summits between heads of state, and worked with Soviet President Mikhail Gorbachev to end the cold war.

COMMAND PERFORMANCE

How does someone like Colin Powell top off a successful term as the nation's first African-American national security adviser? By achieving the military's highest rank of four stars, and then by becoming the youngest chairman of the Joint Chiefs of Staff in the history of the nation. (He was also that position's first African-American and first ROTC graduate.) And once again, Powell shone in his position. Les Aspin, former secretary of defense, commented about Powell following a meeting in the Clinton White House, "It was so clear to all of us that he could do any job in the room, up to and including president."[3]

When President-elect Bush approached him about becoming a cabinet member, there was only one logical place for him to serve, the place where he would add the most. At a town hall meeting on January 25, 2001, Powell remarked,

I didn't know I would be coming back into government when I left the Army seven years ago and went into private life . . . But when Governor Bush asked me to consider it, I was ready for it. I was anxious to see if I could serve again. I think I have something to contribute still. And when he specifically said, I would like you to go to the State Department, it was almost as if I had been preparing for this in one way or another for many, many years. My work in the Pentagon, my work as a Deputy National Security Adviser, National Security Adviser, Chairman of the Joint Chiefs of Staff, and seven years in private life watching the world change, suggested to me this is something I should do.[4]

President Bush, his cabinet, and everyone in the country have a lot to gain from Powell. Not only is he the best person for the job, but he has given the newly elected president and his team greater credibility with a constituency inclined not to trust them. Powell's appointment is tangible proof of Bush's claim to inclusiveness. But that's the power of the Law of the Niche. When the right team member is in the right place, everyone benefits.

Good things happen to a team when a player takes the place where he adds the most value. Great things happen when all the players on the team take the role that maximizes their strengths—their talent, skill, and experience. That's the power of the Law of the Niche.

WHEN PEOPLE ARE IN THE WRONG PLACE

Just about everyone has experienced being on some kind of team where people had to take on roles that didn't suit them: an accountant forced to work with people all day, a basketball forward forced to play center, a guitarist filling in on keyboard, a teacher stuck doing paperwork, a spouse who hates the kitchen taking on the role of cook.

What happens to a team when one or more of its members constantly play out of position? First, morale erodes because the team isn't playing up to its capability. Then people become resentful. The people working in an area of weakness resent that their best is untapped. And other people on the team who know that they could better fill a mismatched position on the team resent that their skills are being overlooked. Before long, people become unwilling to work as a team. Then everyone's confidence begins to erode. And the situation just keeps getting worse. The team stops progressing, and the competition takes advantage of the team's obvious weaknesses. As a result the team never realizes its potential. When people aren't where they do things well, things don't turn out well. That's the Law of the Niche.

Having the right people in the right places is essential to team building. A team's dynamic changes according to the placement of people:

The Wrong Person in the Wrong Place	=	Regression
The Wrong Person in the Right Place	=	Frustration
The Right Person in the Wrong Place	=	Confusion
The Right Person in the Right Place	=	Progression
The Right People in the Right Places	=	Multiplication

It doesn't matter what kind of team you're dealing with, the principles are the same. David Ogilvy was right when he said, "A well-run restaurant is like a winning baseball team. It makes the most of every crew member's talent and takes advantage of every split-second opportunity to speed up service."

I was reminded of the Law of the Niche by something I did a few years ago. I had been asked to write a chapter for a book called *Destiny and Deliverance,* which was tied to the DreamWorks movie *The Prince of Egypt.* It was a wonderful, delightful experience. During the writing process, I was invited to go to California and view parts of the movie while it was still in production. That made me want to do something I had never done before: attend a movie premiere in Hollywood.

My publisher managed to get me a pair of tickets for the premiere, and when the time arrived, my wife, Margaret, and I flew out to the movie capital. Movie stars and moviemakers, along with many other people in the industry, attended the high-energy event. Margaret and I enjoyed the movie—and the whole experience—immensely. In short, we had a blast.

Now, anybody who's gone to a movie, show, or sporting event with me knows my pattern. As soon as I am pretty certain about the outcome of a ball game, I hit the exit to beat the crowds. When the Broadway audience is giving the ovation, I'm gone. And the second the credits begin to roll in a movie, I'm out of my seat. As *The Prince of Egypt* came to a close, I started to get up, but not a person in the theater moved. And then something really surprising happened. As the credits rolled, people began to applaud the lesser-known individuals whose names appeared on the screen: the costume designer, the gaffer, the key grip, the assistant director. It was a moment I'll never forget—and a distinct reminder of the Law of the Niche: *All players have a place where they add the most value.* When each person does the job that's best for him, everybody wins.

Put People in Their Place

NFL champion coach Vince Lombardi observed, "The achievements of an organization are the results of the combined effort of each individual." That is true, but creating a winning team doesn't come just from having the right individuals. You may have a group of talented individuals, but if each person is not doing what adds the most value to the team, you won't achieve your potential as a team. That's the art of leading a team. You've got to put people in their places—and I mean that in the most positive way!

To be able to put people in the places that utilize their talents and maximize the team's potential, you need three things:

You Must Know the Team

You cannot build a winning team or organization if you don't know its vision, purpose, culture, or history. If you don't know where the team is trying to go—and why it's trying to get there—you cannot take the team to the height of its potential. You've got to start where the team actually is; only then can you take it somewhere.

You Must Know the Situation

Even though the vision or purpose of an organization may be fairly constant, its situation changes constantly. Good team builders know where the team is and what the situation requires. For example, when a team is young and just getting started, the greatest priority is often to gather good people. But as a team matures and the level of talent increases, fine-tuning becomes more important. At that time a leader must spend more time matching the person to the position.

You Must Know the Player

It sounds obvious, but you must know the person you are trying to position in the right niche. I mention it because leaders tend to want to make everyone else conform to their image, to approach their work using the same skills and problem-solving methods. But team building is not working on an assembly line.

As you work to build a team, evaluate each person's experience, skills, temperament, attitude, passion, people skills, discipline, emotional strength, and potential. Only then will you be ready to help a team member find his proper place.

Start by Finding the Right Place for You

Right now you may not be in a position to place others on your team. In fact, you may be thinking, *How do I find my niche?* If that's the case, then follow these guidelines:

- *Be secure.* My friend Wayne Schmidt says, "No amount of personal competency compensates for personal insecurity." If you allow your insecurities to get the better of you, you'll be inflexible and reluctant to change. And to grow, you must be willing to change.

- *Get to know yourself.* You won't be able to find your niche if you don't know your strengths and weaknesses. Spend time reflecting on and exploring your gifts. Ask others to give you feedback. Do what it takes to remove personal blind spots.

- *Trust your leader.* A good leader will help you start moving in the right direction. If you don't trust your leader, look to another mentor for help. Or get on another team.

- *See the big picture.* Your place on the team makes sense only in the context of the big picture. If your only motivation for finding your niche is personal gain, your poor motives may prevent you from discovering what you desire.

- *Rely on your experience.* When it comes down to it, the only way to know that you've discovered your niche is to try what seems right and learn from your failures and successes. When you discover what you were made for, your heart sings. It says, *There's no place like this place anywhere near this place, so this must be the place!*

> *When you discover your place, you will say, "There's no place like this place anywhere near this place, so this must be the place!"*

A Place for Everyone and Everyone in His Place

One organization that strives to match its people to the right places is the U.S. military. That is particularly true now that it employs an all-volunteer force. If each function in a military command doesn't work at top efficiency (and interact well with all the other parts), then terrible—and sometimes deadly—breakdowns occur.

Nobody is more keenly aware of that than a combat pilot. Take, for example, Charlie Plumb, who retired as a captain of the U.S. Navy. A graduate of Annapolis, he served in Vietnam in the mid-1960s, flying seventy-five missions from the aircraft carrier USS *Kitty Hawk.*

An aircraft carrier is a place where you can readily observe how all the pieces of the military puzzle come together to support each other. A carrier is often described as being like a floating city with its crew of 5,500 people, a population greater than that of some towns in which its crew members grew up. It must be self-sustaining, and each of its seventeen departments must function as a team accomplishing its mission.

Every pilot knows of the team effort required to put a jet in the air. It takes hundreds of people utilizing dozens of technical specialties to launch, monitor, support, land, and maintain an aircraft. Even more people are involved if that plane is armed for combat. Charlie Plumb undoubtedly recognized that many people worked tirelessly to keep him flying. But despite the efforts of the best-trained air support group in the world, Plumb found himself in a North Vietnamese prison as a POW after his F-4 Phantom jet was shot down on May 19, 1967, during his seventy-fifth mission.

Plumb was held prisoner for nearly six grueling years, part of the time in the infamous Hanoi Hilton. During those years, he and his fellow prisoners were humiliated, starved, tortured, and forced to live in squalid conditions. Yet he didn't let the experience break him. He now says, "Our unity through our faith in God and in our love for country were the great strength which kept us going through some very difficult times."

TURNING POINT

Plumb was released from his imprisonment on February 18, 1973, and continued his career in the navy. But an incident years after his return to the United States marked his life as surely as his imprisonment. One day he and his wife, Cathy, were eating in a restaurant when a man came to the table and said, "You're Plumb. You flew jet fighters in Vietnam."

"That's right," answered Plumb. "I did."

"It was fighter squadron 114 on the *Kitty Hawk.* You were shot down. You parachuted into enemy hands," the man continued. "You spent six years as a prisoner of war."

The former pilot was taken aback. He looked at the man, trying to identify him, but couldn't. "How in the world did you know that?" Plumb finally asked.

"I packed your parachute."

Plumb was staggered. All he could do was struggle to his feet and shake the man's hand. "I must tell you," Plumb finally said, "I've said a lot of prayers of thanks for your nimble fingers, but I didn't realize I'd have the opportunity of saying thanks in person."[5]

What if the navy had put the wrong person in the position of parachute rigger, the anonymous and the rarely thanked job that man performed during the Vietnam War? Charlie Plumb wouldn't have known about it until it was too late. And we wouldn't even know where the breakdown had occurred because Plumb wouldn't have lived to tell the tale.

Today, Charlie Plumb is a motivational speaker to Fortune 500 companies, government agencies, and other organizations. He often tells the story of the man who packed his parachute, and he uses it to deliver a message on teamwork. He says, "In a world where downsizing forces us to do more with less, we must empower the team. 'Packing others' parachutes' can mean the difference in survival. Yours and your team's!"[6]

That's just another way of communicating the Law of the Niche. Are you packing parachutes for your teammates? Or are you functioning at less than 100 percent? *All players have a place where they add the most value.* I want to encourage you to make sure you've found yours.

TEAMWORK THOUGHT

You are most valuable where you add the most value.

BECOMING A BETTER TEAM MEMBER

Have you found your niche? As you fulfill your responsibilities, do you find yourself thinking something like, *There's no place like this place anywhere near this place, so this must be the place*? If so, then stay the course and keep growing and learning in your area of expertise. If not, you need to get on track.

If you know what your niche is but aren't working in it, start planning a transition. It could be as simple as a change in duties or as complex as a change of career. No matter whether it will require six weeks or six years, you need a transition plan and a timetable for completing it. Once you're certain of your course, have the courage to take the first step.

If you have no idea what you should be doing, you need to do some research. Talk to your spouse and close friends about your strengths and weaknesses. Ask for your leader's assessment. Take personality or temperament tests. Look for recurring themes in your life. Try to articulate your life purpose. Do whatever it takes to find clues concerning where you should be. Then try new things related to your discoveries. The only way to find your niche is to gain experience.

BECOMING A BETTER TEAM LEADER

A sign of a great team leader is the proper placement of people. Use the guidelines in the chapter—know your team, the situation, and the players—to begin improving your placement process. And remember this: To help people reach their potential and maximize their effectiveness, stretch them out of their comfort zones, but never out of their gift zones. Moving people outside their gifts leads to frustration, but motivating people out of their comfort zones leads to fulfillment.

> *A sign of a great team leader is the proper placement of people.*

COMPANION ONLINE RESOURCE

Learn more about how the Law of the Niche uniquely applies to you. Take the FREE Law of the Niche assessment at **LawsOfTeamwork.com**.

THE LAW OF MOUNT EVEREST

As the Challenge Escalates, the Need for Teamwork Elevates

In 1935, twenty-one-year-old Tenzing Norgay made his first trip to Mount Everest. He worked as a porter for a British team of mountaineers. A Sherpa born in the high altitudes of Nepal, Tenzing had been drawn to the mountain from the time that Westerners began visiting the area with the idea of climbing to the mountain's peak. The first group had come in 1920. Fifteen years later, climbers were still trying to figure out how to conquer the mountain.

The farthest this expedition would go was up to the North Col, which was at an altitude of 22,000 feet. (A col is a flat area along a mountain's ridge between peaks.) And it was just below that col that the climbing party made a gruesome discovery. They came across a wind-shredded tent. And in that tent was a skeleton with a little frozen skin stretched over the bones. It was sitting in an odd position, with one boot off and the laces of the other boot between its bony fingers.

HARSHEST PLACE ON THE PLANET

Mountain climbing is not for the faint of heart because the world's highest peaks are some of the most inhospitable places on earth. Of course, that hasn't stopped people from attempting to conquer mountains. In 1786, the first climbers made it to the summit of Europe's highest mountain, Mont Blanc in France. That was quite a feat. But there's a big difference between climbing the highest of the Alps at 15,771 feet and climbing Everest, the world's highest peak at 29,035 feet, especially in the days before high-tech equipment. Everest is remote, the altitude incapacitates all but the hardiest and most experienced climbers, and the weather is ruthlessly unforgiving. Experts believe that the bodies of 120 failed climbers remain on the mountain today.[1]

The body Tenzing and the others found in 1935 was that of Maurice Wilson, an Englishman who had sneaked into Tibet and tried to climb the mountain secretly, without the permission of the Tibetan government. Because he was trying to make the ascent quietly, he had hired only three porters to climb the mountain with him. As they approached the North Col, those men had refused to go any farther with him. Wilson decided to try to make the climb on his own. That decision killed him.

MEASURE THE COST

Only someone who has climbed a formidable mountain knows what it takes to make it to the top. For thirty-two years, between 1920 and 1952, seven major expeditions tried—and failed—to make it to the top of Everest. Tenzing Norgay was on six of those expeditions, as well as many other high climbs to other mountains. His fellow climbers joked that he had a third lung because of his ability to climb tirelessly while carrying heavy loads. He became respected, and he learned a lot. The greatest lesson was that no one should underestimate the difficulty of the climb. He had seen people do it at the ultimate cost to themselves.

On one climb, for example, when conditions became difficult, Tenzing and the other Sherpas put on their crampons (spikes that attach to climbing boots). But George Frey, an experienced mountaineer, decided not to wear his because he thought he didn't need them. He slipped and fell one thousand feet to his death below. Tenzing regretted the man's death, but his view was realistic. He wrote of careless climbers, "Like so many men before them—they had held a great mountain too lightly, and they had paid the price."[2]

NOT A CASUAL STROLL

In 1953, Tenzing embarked on his seventh expedition to Everest with a British group led by Colonel John Hunt. By then, he was respected not only as a porter who could carry heavy loads at high altitudes, but also as a mountaineer and full-fledged expedition member, an honor unusual at that time for a Sherpa. The year before he had climbed to a height of 28,250 feet with a Swiss team. Up to then, that was the closest any human being had come to the top of the mountain.

Tenzing was also engaged to be the British group's sirdar for the trip, the Sherpa leader who would hire, organize, and lead the porters for the journey. That was no small task. To hope to get just two people from base camp up to the summit, the team brought ten high-altitude climbers, including a New Zealander named Edmund Hillary. Altogether, the men would require two and a half *tons* of equipment and food. Those supplies couldn't be trucked or airlifted to the base of the mountain. They had to be delivered to Kathmandu and *carried* on the backs of men and women 180 miles up and down Himalayan ridges and over rivers crossed by narrow rope-and-plank bridges to the base camp. Tenzing would have to hire between two and three hundred people just to get the supplies in the vicinity of the mountain.

Supplies needed by the party above the base camp would have to be carried up the mountain by another forty porters, each a Sherpa with extensive mountain experience. The best third of that team would continue working higher up the mountain, carrying up the 750 pounds of necessary equipment in 30-pound loads. Only Tenzing and three other porters would have the strength and skill to go to the high camps near the summit.

It Takes a Team

For each level that the climbers reached, a higher degree of teamwork was required. One set of men would exhaust themselves just to get equipment up the mountain for the next group. Two-man teams would work their way up the mountain, finding a path, cutting steps, securing ropes. And then they would be finished, having spent themselves to make the next leg of the climb possible for another team. Of the teamwork involved, Tenzing remarked,

> You do not climb a mountain like Everest by trying to race ahead on your own, or by competing with your comrades. You do it slowly

and carefully, by unselfish teamwork. Certainly I wanted to reach the top myself; it was the thing I had dreamed of all my life. But if the lot fell to someone else I would take it like a man, and not a cry-baby. For that is the mountain way.[3]

The team of climbers, using the "mountain way," ultimately made it possible for two pairs to make an attempt at reaching the summit. The first consisted of Tom Bourdillon and Charles Evans. When they tried and failed, the other team got its chance. That team consisted of Tenzing and Edmund Hillary. Tenzing wrote of the first team:

> They were worn-out, sick with exhaustion, and, of course, terribly disappointed that they had not reached the summit themselves. But still . . . they did everything they could to advise and help us. And I thought, Yes, that is how it is on a mountain. That is how a mountain makes men great. For where would Hillary and I have been without the others? Without the climbers who had made the route and the Sherpas who had carried the loads? Without Bourdillon and Evans, Hunt and Da Namgyal, who had cleared the way ahead? Without Lowe and Gregory, Ang Hyima, Ang Tempra, and Penba, who were there only to help us? It was only because of the work and sacrifice of all of them that we were now to have our chance at the top.[4]

They made the most of their chance. On May 29, 1953, Tenzing Norgay and Edmund Hillary accomplished what no other human being ever had: They stood on the summit of Mount Everest, the world's highest peak!

Could Tenzing and Hillary have made it alone? The answer is

no. Could they have made it without a great team? Again, the answer is no. Why? Because *as the challenge escalates, the need for teamwork elevates.* That's the Law of Mount Everest.

WHAT IS YOUR EVEREST?

You may not be a mountain climber, and you may not have any desire to reach the summit of Everest. But I bet you have a dream. I say that with confidence because deep down everybody has one—even the people who haven't figured out what theirs is yet. If you have a dream, you need a team to accomplish it.

How do you approach the task of putting together a team to accomplish your dream? I think the best way to start is to ask yourself three questions:

1. "What Is My Dream?"

It all starts with this question because your answer reveals *what could be.* Robert Greenleaf remarked, "Nothing much happens without a dream. For something really great to happen, it takes a really great dream."

What lies in your heart? What do you see as a possibility for your life? What would you like to accomplish during your time on this earth? Only a dream will tell you such things. As Harlem Renaissance poet Langston Hughes wrote:

> Hold fast to dreams for if dreams die,
> Life is a broken-winged bird that cannot fly.
> Hold fast to dreams for when dreams go,
> Life is a barren field frozen with snow.

If you want to do something great, you must have a dream. But a dream is not enough. You can fulfill a dream only if you are part of a team.

2. "Who Is on My Team?"

This second question tells you *what is.* It measures your current situation. Your potential is only as good as your current team. That's why you must examine who is joining you on your journey. A mountain climber like Maurice Wilson, who had only three halfhearted companions, was never able to accomplish his dream of climbing the mountain. However, someone like Tenzing Norgay, who always climbed Everest with the best mountaineers in the world, was able to make it to the top. A great dream with a bad team is nothing more than a nightmare.

3. "What Should My Dream Team Look Like?"

The truth is that your team must be the size of your dream. If it's not, then you won't achieve it. You simply cannot achieve an ultimate number ten dream with a number four team. It just doesn't happen. If you want to climb Mount Everest, you need a Mount Everest–sized team. There's no other way to do it. It's better to have a great team with a weak dream than a great dream with a weak team.

> *Your team must be the size of your dream.*

FOCUS ON THE TEAM, NOT THE DREAM

One mistake I've seen people repeatedly make is that they focus too much attention on their dream and too little on their team. But the truth is that if you build the right team, the dream will almost take care of itself.

Every dream brings challenges of its own. The kind of challenge determines the kind of team you need to build. Consider a few examples:

> *Many people focus too much attention on their dream and too little on their team.*

Type of Challenge	Type of Team Required
New Challenge	Creative Team
Controversial Challenge	United Team
Changing Challenge	Fast and Flexible Team
Unpleasant Challenge	Motivated Team
Diversified Challenge	Complementary Team
Long-term Challenge	Determined Team
Everest-sized Challenge	Experienced Team

If you want to achieve your dream—I mean really do it, not just imagine what it would be like—then grow your team. But as you do so, make sure your motives are right. Some people gather a team just to benefit themselves. Others do it because they enjoy the team experience and want to create a sense of community. Still others do it because they want to build an organization. The funny thing about these reasons is that if you're motivated by *all* of them, then your desire to build a team probably comes from wanting to add value to everyone on the team. But if your desire to build the team comes as the result of only one of these reasons, you probably need to examine your motives.

How to Grow a Team

When the team you have doesn't match up to the team of your dreams, then you have only two choices: Give up your dream, or grow up your team. Here is my recommendation concerning how to do the latter.

> *When the team you have doesn't match up to the team of your dreams, then you have only two choices: Give up your dream, or grow up your team.*

1. Develop Team Members

The first step to take with a team that's not realizing its potential is to help individual team members to grow. If you're leading the team, then one of your most important responsibilities is to see the potential that people don't see in themselves and draw it out. When you accomplish this, you're doing your job as a leader.

Think about the people on your team, and determine what they need based on the following categories:

- Enthusiastic beginner—needs direction *ROBO*
- Disillusioned learner—needs coaching
- Cautious completer—needs support *JULIE*
✓ - Self-reliant achiever—needs responsibility

Always give the people who are already on your team a chance to grow and bloom. That's what early British explorer Eric Shipton did with a young, inexperienced kid named Tenzing in 1935, and his country was rewarded eighteen years later with a successful climb of the world's highest peak.

2. Add Key Team Members

Even if you give every person on your team a chance to learn and grow, and all of them make the most of the opportunities, you may find that you still lack the talent needed to accomplish your dream. That's when it's time to recruit that talent. Sometimes all the team needs is one key person with talent in an area to make the difference between success and failure. (I'll talk more about this in the Law of the Bench.)

3. Change the Leadership

Various team challenges require different kinds of leadership. If a team has the right talent but still isn't growing, sometimes the best thing you can do is to ask someone from the team who has previously been a follower to step into a leadership role. That transition may occur only for a short season, or it may be more permanent.

> *The challenge of the moment often determines the leader for that challenge.*

The challenge of the moment often determines the leader for that challenge. Why? Because every person on the team has strengths and weaknesses that come into play. That was the case for the Everest team as they faced every stage of the journey. Colonel Hunt chose the climbers and led the expedition, casting vision, modeling unselfish service, and making critical decisions about who would take which part. Tenzing chose the porters, leading, organizing, and motivating them to build the camps at each stage of the mountain. And the climbing teams took turns leading, cutting the trail up the mountain so that Hillary and Tenzing could make the final climb to the summit. When a particular challenge emerged, so did a leader to meet it. And everyone worked together, doing his part.

If your team is facing a big challenge, and it doesn't seem to be making any progress "up the mountain," then it might be time to change leaders. There may be someone on the team more capable for leading during this season. (Learn more by reading the myths of the head table and the round table in the Law of the Edge.)

4. Remove Ineffective Members

Sometimes a team member can turn a winning team into a losing one, either through lack of skill or a poor attitude. In those cases you must put the team first and make changes for the greater good.

Tenzing faced that situation during the Everest expedition of 1953. During early days of travel, there were continual flare-ups between the porters and the British team of climbers, and as sirdar, Tenzing was constantly stuck in the middle trying to work things out. After repeatedly negotiating the peace between the two parties, Tenzing discovered that the source of the problem was two Sherpas who were stirring up dissension. He promptly fired them and sent them home. Peace was quickly restored. If your team keeps breaking down or falling short, you may need to make changes in your team.

Growing a team is demanding and time-consuming. But if you want to achieve your dream, you have no other choice. The greater the dream, the greater the team. *As the challenge escalates, the need for teamwork elevates.* That is the Law of Mount Everest.

NOT EVERY CHALLENGE IS A DREAM

The challenges that our teams face are not always ones we select. Sometimes they are thrust upon us, and we have no choice but to do the best we can with the team we have, or give up and suffer the consequences. That was certainly the case for the crew and support team for Apollo 13.

If you saw the movie *Apollo 13* starring Tom Hanks (or remember some of the coverage on television during the actual flight as I do), then you know the basic story. On April 13, 1970, at 10:07 P.M. EST, an oxygen tank in the service module of the *Odyssey* spacecraft exploded, causing the ship to lose its oxygen supply and all normal power. In addition, the ship's main engine was rendered nonfunctional. Since the ship was 200,000 miles away from earth and on a course that would put it into a permanent orbit around the moon, it was a potentially disastrous—and possibly fatal—challenge.

The astronauts in the *Odyssey*, James Lovell, John Swigart Jr., and Fred Haise, would not be able to make it back to earth on their own. Their survival depended on teamwork at a level that the space program had never experienced—and it was used to having people work together like a well-oiled machine.

TEAMWORK AT A NEW LEVEL

The flight control team on the ground immediately instructed the command crew to shut down the ailing command capsule and move into the lunar module (LM) *Aquarius* for their safety. That put the crew out of harm's way for the moment. But they still faced two major challenges:

1. Getting the command module, *Odyssey,* and the lunar module, *Aquarius,* on the quickest course home.

2. Conserving the "consumables" that kept the astronauts alive: power, oxygen, and water.

Accomplishing both would severely test everyone's abilities and know-how.

During a typical Apollo mission, Houston's mission control employed four teams of controllers, each designated by a color: white, black, gold, and maroon. Each team had technicians responsible for various specific areas required to keep the ship on course. The usual procedure was for each team to take a six-hour shift under the guidance of one of three flight directors. But with the lives of three astronauts on the line, every member of every team jumped in to help. And one team was pulled from the usual rotation by Gene Kranz, the lead flight director, and dubbed the Tiger Team. Those fifteen men worked as a crisis management team.

As Kranz gathered them together, he told them,

> For the rest of the mission, I'm pulling you men off console. The people out in that room [the other teams] will be running the flight from moment to moment, but it's the people in this room who will be coming up with the protocols they're going to be executing . . . For the next few days we're going to be coming up with techniques and maneuvers we've never tried before. I want to make sure we know what we're doing.[5]

In addition, NASA promptly sent word out to contractor representatives, such as the people at Grumman Aerospace, who had built the lunar module. (And when word got out that there was trouble with Apollo 13, virtually *everyone* in the organization showed up at the facility in the middle of the night to pitch in.) They also pulled in every top specialist and experienced astronaut they had, quickly building a coast-to-coast network of simulators, computers, and experts. NASA records state:

Astronauts Alan Shepard and Ed Mitchell operated one of the LM simulators at the Manned Spacecraft Center in Houston, and Gene Cernan and David Scott worked in the other. At Cape Kennedy, Astronaut Dick Gordon simulated emergency procedures in a third LM. One team of simulator specialists worked around the clock without a break. No procedure, no maneuver instruction, no checklist was relayed to the crew that hadn't been thoroughly proved out.[6]

As Easy As One, Two, Three

The team's first task was to figure out how to get the lunar module, which had been designed to support two men for 49.5 hours, to sustain three men for 84 hours. They did that by determining how to get the ship to run using the bare minimum number of systems, which would use less than one-fourth of its normal power.

Next, they had to get the spacecraft on a course that would return it to earth. That was no simple task since they would have to use the lunar module's tiny engine, and the guidance systems were off-line. But between the efforts of the crew, the expertise of the lunar module's manufacturer, and the calculations of Tiger Team, they were able to do it. And they also boosted the craft's speed to shorten the flight time. That would preserve precious water and energy.

The third major challenge the team faced was making the air that the crew was breathing safe. Oxygen was not a problem because the small lunar module was well supplied. But carbon dioxide was building up to dangerous levels because the small craft intended to land on the moon had not been designed to remove so much of it.

The crew on the ground worked out a clever way to adapt the lithium hydroxide filters from the command module so that they would work with the lunar module's noncompatible system.

Each time NASA's massive team faced an obstacle that threatened to leave the crew stranded in space, their pooled ingenuity, inherent tenacity, and incredible cooperation enabled them to overcome it. As a result, on April 17, 1970, the crew of the *Odyssey* made it safely home. NASA likes to call the mission a "successful failure." I call it a lesson in the Law of Mount Everest. *As the challenge escalates, the need for teamwork elevates.*

Putting men on the moon is an incredible challenge. But getting them home when things go wrong 200,000 miles away from earth is an even greater one. Fortunately for those men, the dream team was already in place when they got in trouble. And that is one of the lessons of Apollo 13. The time to build your team is not in the midst of a life-or-death challenge, but long before one can happen. If you haven't already, start building today so that when a formidable challenge occurs, you and your team will be ready.

TEAMWORK THOUGHT

The size of your dream should determine the size of your team.

BECOMING A BETTER TEAM MEMBER

What is your natural first reaction when a challenge becomes more difficult? Do you go off alone to think? Do you try to solve the problem alone? Do you stay away from other people to avoid the pressure? Or do you lean on your teammates and let them lean on you?

If you don't already do it, teach yourself to rally with your teammates. You cannot win a great challenge alone. As Tenzing asserted, "On a great mountain, you do not leave your companions and go to the top alone."[7]

BECOMING A BETTER TEAM LEADER

What kinds of adjustments do you need to make to create your dream team, one that can meet the challenges ahead? Do you need to spend more time developing your people? Do you need to add key team members? Or should you make changes to the leadership? And don't forget that you, too, need to keep growing. What's true for a teammate is also true for the leader: If you don't grow, you gotta go.

COMPANION **ONLINE** RESOURCE

Learn more about how the Law of Mount Everest uniquely applies to you. Take the FREE Law of Mount Everest assessment at **LawsOfTeamwork.com**.

5

THE LAW OF THE CHAIN

The Strength of the Team Is Impacted by Its Weakest Link

On March 24, 1989, the news broke that an environmental disaster had occurred in Alaska's Prince William Sound. The oil tanker *Exxon Valdez* had run aground on the Bligh Reef, damaging the hull of the ship and rupturing eight of the vessel's eleven cargo tanks. As a result, 10.8 million of the ship's approximately 53 million gallons of oil poured out of the ship and into the sea.

The negative impact on the area was immense. Fishing and tourism came to a halt, harming the local economy. The environment suffered. Experts estimate wildlife losses at 250,000 seabirds, 2,800 sea otters, 300 harbor seals, 250 bald eagles, 22 killer whales, and billions of eggs for food-fish species such as salmon and herring. Though it wasn't the largest oil spill on record, experts consider it to be the worst spill in history in terms of the damage done to the environment.[1]

———

Of course, Exxon, the company that owns the ship, also paid a price. The company's representatives estimate that the incident cost Exxon $3.5 *billion:*

- $2.2 billion in cleanup costs

- $300 million in claims paid

- $1 billion in state and federal settlements[2]

But that's not all. In addition to what Exxon has already paid, the company stands to lose an additional $5 billion in punitive damages, a judgment it is still attempting to reverse through the appellate process more than a decade after the incident. What was the cause of such an expensive and far-reaching accident? The answer can be found in the Law of the Chain.

THE BROKEN CHAIN

When the *Exxon Valdez* cast off from the Alyeska Pipeline Terminal on the evening of March 23, the voyage began routinely. An expert ship's pilot guided the vessel through the Valdez Narrows and then returned control of the ship to its captain, Joe Hazelwood. The captain ordered that the ship be put on a particular course, turned control over to Third Mate Gregory Cousins, and left the bridge. Thirty-five minutes later, the *Exxon Valdez* was stranded on a reef and leaking tons of oil into the sea.

Investigation following the accident painted an ugly picture: neglect of safety standards, indifference to company policy, and unwise decision making. The ship's captain had been drinking in the hours before he took command of the ship. One officer, rather than the required two, remained in the wheelhouse as the tanker navigated the Valdez Narrows and again after the pilot left the ship. (And that officer, Cousins, had been so overworked that fatigue is thought to have contributed to the navigation error that followed.) Nor was a lookout always present on the bridge while the vessel was under way.

There were also discrepancies between what Captain Hazelwood told the Vessel Traffic Center he was doing and the orders he actually gave on the ship. At 11:30 P.M., the captain radioed that he would take a course of 200 degrees and reduce speed to wind his way through the icebergs that sometimes float in the shipping lanes. Yet the engine logs showed that the ship's speed kept increasing. Nine minutes after that, the captain ordered that the ship take a course of 180 degrees and be put on autopilot, but he never informed the traffic center of the change. Then at 11:53, he left the bridge.

At four minutes after midnight, the ship was on the reef. For almost two hours, first Cousins and then Hazelwood tried to get the ship free, all the while leaking oil into the sea. In the first three hours, it's estimated that 5.8 million gallons poured from the distressed tanker. By then, the damage was done, and the weak link had caused the "chain" to break. Alaska's coastline was a mess, Hazelwood's career as a ship's captain was over, and Exxon was stuck with a public relations nightmare—and massive financial obligations.

As much as any team likes to measure itself by its best people, the truth is that *the strength of the team is impacted by its weakest link*. No matter how much people try to rationalize it, compensate for it, or hide it, a weak link will eventually come to light. That's the Law of the Chain.

YOUR TEAM IS NOT FOR EVERYONE

One of the mistakes I often made early in my career as a team leader was that I thought everyone who was on my team should remain on the team. That was true for several reasons. First, I naturally see the best in people. When I look at individuals with potential, I see all that they can become—even if they don't see it. And I try to encourage and equip them to become better. Second, I truly like people. I figure the more who take the trip, the bigger the party. Third, because I have vision and believe my goals are worthwhile and beneficial, I sometimes naively assume that everyone will want to go along with me.

But just because I wanted to take everyone with me didn't mean that it would always work out that way. My first memorable experience with this occurred in 1980 when I was offered an executive position at Wesleyan World Headquarters in Marion, Indiana. When I accepted the position, I invited my assistant to come with me to be a part of the new team I was building. So she and her husband considered my offer and went to Marion to look around. I'll never forget when they came back. As I excitedly talked about the coming challenges and how we could begin to tackle them, I began to realize from the expressions on their faces that something was wrong. And that's when they told me. They weren't going.

That statement took me completely by surprise. In fact, I was sure that they were making a mistake and told them so, doing my best to convince them to change their minds. But my wife, Margaret, gave me some very good advice. She said, "John, your problem is that you want to take everybody with you. But not everyone is going to go on the journey. Let it go." It was a hard lesson for me to learn—and sometimes it still is.

From that experience and others I've had since then, I've discovered that when it comes to teamwork . . .

1. Not Everyone Will Take the Journey

Some people don't want to go. My assistant and her husband wanted to stay in Lancaster, Ohio, where they had built relationships for many years. For other people the issue is their attitude. They don't want to change, grow, or conquer new territory. They hold fast to the status quo. All you can do with people in this group is kindly thank them for their past contributions and move on.

2. Not Everyone Should Take the Journey

Other people shouldn't join a team because it's a matter of their agenda. They have other plans, and where you're going isn't the right place for them. The best thing you can do for people in this category is wish them well, and as far as you are able, help them on their way so that they achieve success in their venture.

3. Not Everyone Can Take the Journey

For the third group of people, the issue is ability. They may not be capable of keeping pace with their teammates or helping the group get where it wants to go. How do you recognize people who fall into this category? They're not very hard to identify.

- They can't keep pace with other team members.
- They don't grow in their area of responsibility.
- They don't see the big picture.
- They won't work on personal weaknesses.
- They won't work with the rest of the team.
- They can't fulfill expectations for their area.

If you have people who display one or more of those characteristics, then you need to acknowledge that they are weak links.

That's not to say that they are necessarily bad people. In fact, some teams exist to serve weak links or help them become stronger. It depends on the team's goals. For example, when I was a senior pastor, we reached out to people in the community with food and assistance. We helped people with addictions, divorce recovery, and many other difficulties. Our goal was to serve them. It's good and appropriate to help people who find themselves in those circumstances. But putting them on the team while they are still broken and weak doesn't help them, and it hurts the team—even to the extent of making the team incapable of accomplishing its goal of service.

What can you do with people on your team who are weak links? You really have only two choices: You need to train them or trade them. Of course, your first priority should always be to try to train people who are having a hard time keeping up. Help can come in many forms: giving people books to read, sending them to conferences, presenting them with new challenges, pairing them with mentors. I believe that people often rise to your level of expectations. Give them hope and training, and they usually improve.

But what should you do if a team member continually fails to meet expectations, even after receiving training, encouragement, and opportunities to grow? My father used to have a saying: "Water seeks its own level." Somebody who is a weak link on your team might be capable of becoming a star on another team. You need to give that person an opportunity to find his level somewhere else.

THE IMPACT OF A WEAK LINK

If you are a team leader, you cannot avoid dealing with weak links. Team members who don't carry their own weight slow down the team, and they have a negative effect on your leadership. Several things may happen when a weak link remains on the team:

1. The Stronger Members Identify the Weak One

A weak link cannot hide (except in a group of weak people). If you have strong people on your team, they always know who isn't performing up to the level of everyone else.

2. The Stronger Members Have to Help the Weak One

If your people must work together as a team to do their work, then they have only two choices when it comes to a weak teammate. They can ignore the person and allow the team to suffer, or they can help him and make the team more successful. If they are team players, they will help.

3. The Stronger Members Come to Resent the Weak One

Whether strong team members help or not, the result will always be the same: resentment. No one likes to lose or fall behind consistently because of the same person.

4. The Stronger Members Become Less Effective

Carrying someone else's load in addition to your own compromises your performance. Do that for a long time, and the whole team suffers.

5. The Stronger Members Question the Leader's Ability

Anytime the leader allows a weak link to remain a part of the team, the team members forced to compensate for the weak person begin to doubt the leader's courage and discernment. You lose the respect of the best when you don't deal properly with the worst.

Many team members may be able to avoid the hard decision of dealing with subpar members, but leaders can't. In fact, one of the differences between leaders and followers is action. Followers often know what to do, but they are unwilling or unable to follow through. But know this: If

> *You lose the respect of the best when you don't deal properly with the worst.*

other people on the team make decisions for you because you are unwilling or unable to make them, then your leadership is being compromised, and you're not serving the team well.

STRENGTHENING THE CHAIN

Weak team members always take more of the team's time than strong ones. One reason is that the more competent people have to give their time to compensate for those who don't carry their share of the load. The greater the difference in competence between the more accomplished performers and the less accomplished ones, the greater the detriment to the team. For example, if you rate people on a scale from 1 to 10 (with 10 being the best), a 5 among 10s really hurts the team where an 8 among 10s often does not.

Let me show you how this works. When you first put together a group of people, their talents come together in a way that is analogous to addition. So visually a 5 among 10s looks like this:

$$10 + 10 + 10 + 10 + 5 = 45$$

The difference between this team and great ones with five 10s is like the difference between 50 and 45. That's a difference of 10 percent. But once a team comes together and starts to develop chemistry, synergy, and momentum, it's analogous to multiplication. That's when a weak link really starts to hurt the team. It's the difference between this:

$$10 \times 10 \times 10 \times 10 \times 10 = 100{,}000$$

and this:

$$10 \times 10 \times 10 \times 10 \times 5 = 50{,}000$$

That's a difference of 50 percent! The power and momentum of the team may be able to compensate for a weak link for a while, but not forever. A weak link eventually robs the team of momentum—and potential.

Ironically, weak links are less aware than stronger members of their weaknesses and shortcomings. They also spend more time guarding their turf, saving their positions, and holding on to what they have. And know this: When it comes to interaction between people, the weaker person usually controls the relationship. For example, someone with a good self-image is more flexible than a person with a poor self-image. An individual with a clear vision acts more readily than someone without one. A person with superb ability and high energy accomplishes more and works longer than an individual with lesser gifts. If the two people journey together, the stronger member must constantly work with and wait on the weaker one. That controls what happens on the journey.

If your team has a weak link who can't or won't rise to the level of the team—and you've done everything you can to help the person improve—then you've got to take action. When you do, heed the advice of authors Danny Cox and John Hoover. If you need to remove somebody from the team, be discreet, be clear, be honest, and be brief. Then once the person is gone, be open about it with the rest of the team while maintaining respect for the person you let go.[3] And if you start to have second thoughts before or afterward, remember this: As long as a weak link is part of the team, everyone else on the team will suffer.

No Weak Links!

Nobody particularly wants to have a weak link on a team, someone who causes the team to fail at its objectives. Yet we've all had to work with weaker team members. And sometimes good experiences have come out of it. There is rich personal reward to be reaped by helping a teammate go from being a weak link to a solid team member—and sometimes even to becoming a star player. But for good or bad, dealing with subpar performers is an inevitable part of being on any team, right? There's no such thing as a team that has no weak links, is there?

As I already mentioned, the goal of the team often determines how well it can work with a weak link. Sometimes the stakes for a team are so high that its members cannot afford to have a weak link. And that is the case for the U.S. Navy SEALs. The jobs they do are so demanding that a weak person on the team will get everyone on the team killed.

In recent years the SEALs have generated a lot of popular interest. They've been the subject of numerous novels and movies. They've captured people's imaginations because they are considered the best of the best. As one former SEAL remarked, "No group of men is closer to perfection in their chosen field."

The SEALs were first commissioned by President John F. Kennedy in 1962. They evolved from the underwater demolition teams who were developed during World War II to clear the amphibious landing areas of obstacles in such locations as Omaha and Utah Beaches in Normandy and later on the islands of the Pacific. Like all the special operations forces in the various branches of the U.S. military, they are experts in weapons, hand-to-hand combat, and demolition, and they have trained to parachute from airplanes. But their expertise is in operations based on and in water. That's the origin of their name: SEALs indicates that they are capable of operating in the SEa, from the Air, and on Land.

Forging the Chain

The key to the success of the SEALs is their training—the real emphasis of which is not learning about weapons or gaining technical skills; it's about strengthening people and developing teamwork. Weapons change, and so do methods of conducting operations, but the intense mental and physical training has remained much the same for all the years that the SEALs have been in existence. Peter J. Schoomaker, commander in chief of U.S. Special Operations Command, says, "Everything but our core values are on the table; we have to be ready to change anything but those values to get the job done. The core value for a SEAL Team is the people."[4]

Having the right people on the team starts with the selection process. Only a certain kind of person will even apply to go through SEAL training. And of those who apply, only one in ten is accepted. (The navy recommends that candidates be running at least thirty miles a week and swimming long distances *before* they apply.) Those who do make it into the program then undergo twenty-six weeks of intense physical, psychological, and mental stress. The physical and emotional rigors of that training make marine boot camp look like a picnic. John Roat, who went through the training, was one of the first members of the newly formed SEAL teams in 1962. He said that more than 1,300 men tested to get into the training, but the program accepted only 134. The bar for physical training was so high that people began dropping out the first day. And he saw that as a good thing. He explained:

> There were still some 130 guys when the instructors broke us up into ten-man boat crews and gave us our boats . . . The men of each crew carried their boat on their heads, and until a crew got its ducks in a row, everyone in it suffered. There was no chance of a boat crew's learning how to work as a team until it got rid of the men who didn't belong in training. Until they were gone, they were just an added harassment factor. Sounds cold, but that's life.[5]

For the first five weeks, the training is torturous and the physical demands incredible. Then comes Hell Week, five days of constant physical and mental challenges where the trainees are kept awake and training for all but four or five hours during the entire week. It's the trial that eliminates remaining weak links and at the same time forges the class into a real team. Roat described the impact of that part of the training:

> Each training class still learns the same things during Hell Week: You can go farther than you ever thought possible, but you can't do it alone, and everyone left standing belongs there. Hell Week has changed less than any part of training, for one simple reason: The instructors cannot find a better way. You can't pick the ones who can

hack it by their looks. No written test will find out if a man is a Team player. If it was possible to get good operators by letting some shrink interview trainees and say yea or nay, the navy would love it. The big problem is, the psychologists can't predict who will survive five-plus days of no sleep, with constant harassment, and impossible physical demands with an easy way out. That's still the test.[6]

SEAL training is so intense that there have been classes from which *no one* completed the training. In the end, 49 of the 134 people who started training with Roat graduated. The hearts of those who made it through the stress and pain can be represented by the words of one of Roat's classmates: "I couldn't quit; I would have let my classmates down. I just couldn't do it."

Many people consider the Navy SEALs to be the elite among the already elite company of special operations forces in the U.S. military. Their interaction is the definition of teamwork, and they depend upon each other at a level that most people cannot understand and will never experience. Their survival depends on it. And for that reason, they cannot afford to have any weak links.

Although you may never have to face the pressures that SEALs do, you can be sure of this: *The strength of the team is impacted by its weakest link.* No matter what kind of team you're on, that's always true. That's the Law of the Chain.

❧

TEAMWORK THOUGHT

The team cannot continually cover up its weakness.

BECOMING A BETTER TEAM MEMBER

Most people's natural inclination is to judge themselves according to their best qualities while they measure others by their worst. As a result, they point to areas where their teammates need to grow. But the truth is that every person is responsible for his own growth first.

Take a hard look at yourself. Using the criteria from the chapter, examine yourself to see where you may be hindering the team. Mark the box under the word *Self* for any issue that applies to you. And if you have real courage, ask your spouse or a close friend to evaluate you by marking the boxes listed under the word *Friend.*

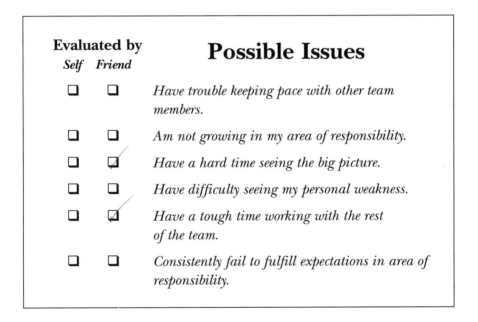

Evaluated by Self Friend	**Possible Issues**
❑ ❑	*Have trouble keeping pace with other team members.*
❑ ❑	*Am not growing in my area of responsibility.*
❑ ☑	*Have a hard time seeing the big picture.*
❑ ❑	*Have difficulty seeing my personal weakness.*
❑ ☑	*Have a tough time working with the rest of the team.*
❑ ❑	*Consistently fail to fulfill expectations in area of responsibility.*

If you (or the other person who evaluated you) checked more than one box, you need to put yourself on a growth plan so that you don't hinder your team. Talk to your team leader or a trusted mentor about ways you can grow in any weak area.

BECOMING A BETTER TEAM LEADER

If you're a team leader, you cannot ignore the issues created by a weak link. For the various kinds of teams, different solutions are appropriate. If the team is a family, then you don't simply "trade" weak people. You lovingly nurture them and try to help them grow, but you also try to minimize the damage they can cause to other family members. If the team is a business, then you have responsibilities to the owner or stockholders. If you've offered training without success, then a "trade" might be in order. If the team is a ministry and training has made no impact, then it might be appropriate to ask the weak people to sit on the sidelines for a while. Or they might need some time away from the team to work on emotional or spiritual issues.

No matter what kind of situation you face, remember that your responsibilities to people come in the following order: to the organization, to the team, and then to the individual. Your own interests—and comfort—come last.

COMPANION ONLINE RESOURCE

Learn more about how the Law of the Chain uniquely applies to you.

Take the FREE Law of the Chain assessment at **LawsOfTeamwork.com**.

THE LAW OF THE CATALYST

Winning Teams Have Players Who Make Things Happen

Most teams don't naturally get better on their own. Left alone, they don't grow, improve, and reach championship caliber. Instead, they tend to wind down. The road to the next level is always uphill, and if a team isn't intentionally fighting to move up, then it inevitably slides down. The team loses focus, gets out of rhythm, decreases in energy, breaks down in unity, and loses momentum. At some point, it also loses key players. And it's only a matter of time before it plateaus and ultimately declines into mediocrity. That's why a team that reaches its potential always possesses a catalyst.

> *Catalysts are get-it-done-and-then-some people.*

THE DEFINITION OF A CATALYST

Catalysts are what I call get-it-done-and-then-some people. The most outstanding one I've ever had the privilege of seeing in action is Michael Jordan. In the opinion of many people (including me), he is the greatest basketball player ever to play the game, not only because of his talent, athleticism, and understanding of the game, but also because of his ability as a catalyst. His résumé as an amateur, and as a professional with the Chicago Bulls attests to that ability:

- Won NCAA Division I Championship (1982)

- Named the *Sporting News* College Player of the Year twice (1983, 1984)

- Received the Naismith and Wooden Awards (1984)

- Won 2 Olympic gold medals (1984, 1992)

- Won 6 NBA world championships (1991, 1992, 1993, 1996, 1997, 1998)

- Selected NBA Rookie of the Year (1985)

- Selected to the NBA All-Rookie Team (1985)

- Selected for All-NBA First Team a record 10 times (1987, 1988, 1989, 1990, 1991, 1992, 1993, 1996, 1997, 1998)

- Holds the NBA record for highest career scoring average (31.5 points per game)

- Holds the NBA record for most seasons leading the league in scoring (10)

- Holds the NBA record for most seasons leading the league in field goals made (10) and attempted (10)

- Ranks 3rd in NBA history in points (29,277), 3rd in steals (2,306), and 4th in field goals made (10,962)

- Voted NBA Defensive Player of the Year (1985; after being criticized that he was "only" an offensive player)

- Selected to the All-NBA Defensive First Team 8 times (1988, 1989, 1990, 1991, 1993, 1997, 1998)

- Named NBA MVP 5 times (1988, 1991, 1992, 1996, 1998)

- Named NBA Finals MVP 6 times (1991, 1992, 1993, 1996, 1997, 1998)

- Named 1 of the 50 greatest players in NBA history

Statistics make a strong statement about Jordan, but they really don't tell the whole story. For that, you had to see him in action. When the Bulls needed to get the team out of a slump, the ball went to Jordan. When a player needed to take the last shot to win the game, the ball went to Jordan. Even if the team needed to get things going in practice, the ball went to Jordan. No matter what the situation was on the court, Jordan was capable of putting the team in the position to win the game. That's always the case for championship teams. *Winning teams have players who make things happen.* That's the Law of the Catalyst.

STILL MAKING THINGS HAPPEN

As you know, Michael Jordan has retired from basketball as a player. But he is still in the game. In early 2000, Jordan became part owner and president of basketball operations of the Washington Wizards. Only a week after becoming part of the organization, Jordan put on a number 23 Wizards jersey and joined the team for a practice.

Wizards forward Tracy Murray, who guarded Jordan during some drills, remarked afterward, "He's definitely moving the same way . . . dunking the ball, shooting a jump shot, fade away. Still got the same game, hasn't gone anywhere."

Nobody expected his talent to be diminished, especially not just two years after his retirement. But his ability as a catalyst hadn't diminished either. Murray continued, "And as soon as he sets foot in that gym, he starts talking trash, so of course the intensity is going to pick up."

Every catalyst brings intensity to the table. One commentator remarked of Jordan's visit to the court, "By being himself, he turned a Wizards practice into something it hasn't been in a while—energetic and fun."

"Which is what we should expect every day," was Jordan's reaction. "Actually, I told them they shouldn't have to wait for me to come out to show the energy that they had today. I just tried to keep them focused, challenge them, say whatever I have to say. If they can play hard against me, they can play hard against anybody. It was fun."[1]

That's the way it always is for a catalyst. Having fun. He loves stirring up the team, making things happen, doing whatever it takes to push the team to the next level. When a catalyst does that consistently, the team becomes expectant, confident, elevated, and ultimately amazed. That's the Law of the Catalyst. *Winning teams have players who make things happen!*

THREE KINDS OF PLAYERS

When crunch time comes, a catalyst becomes critical, whether it's the salesperson who hits the impossible goal, the ballplayer who makes the big play, or the parent who gets a child to believe in himself at a critical moment in life. A team can't reach big goals or even break new ground if it doesn't have a catalyst.

My experience with teams has taught me that what is true for sports is also the case for business, ministry, and family relationships. When the clock is running down and the game is on the line, there are really only three kinds of people on a team:

1. People Who Don't Want the Ball

Some people don't have the ability to come through for the team in high-pressure situations, and they know it. As a result, they don't want the responsibility of carrying the team to victory. And it shouldn't be given to them. They should be allowed to play in their areas of strength.

2. People Who Want the Ball But Shouldn't

A second group contains people who can't carry the team to victory. The problem is that *they don't know* that they can't. Often the cause is that these players' egos are greater than their talent. These people can be dangerous to a team.

3. People Who Want the Ball and Should

The final group, which is by far the smallest, consists of people who want to be "go to" players at crunch time and who can actually deliver. They are able to push, pull, or carry the team to new levels when the going gets tough. They are the catalysts.

Every team needs catalysts if it wants to have any hope of winning consistently. Without them, even a team with loads of talent cannot go to the highest level. I saw an illustration of this in the late 1990s and again in 2000 with the Atlanta Braves. They had the best starting pitchers in baseball. They had strong hitters, Gold Glove fielders, and talent in the bull pen. They possessed team members who had been league MVP or rookie of the year. But they lacked the catalytic players they needed to become World Series champions.

CHARACTERISTICS OF A CATALYST

It's easy to point out a team's catalyst after he has made an impact on the group and spurred the members on to victory, especially in the world of sports. You can point to particular moments when the person went to a whole new level and took the team there at the same time. But how do you recognize a catalyst *before* the fact? How do you look for catalytic people for your current team?

No matter what kind of "game" you're playing or what kind of team you're on, you can be sure that catalysts have certain characteristics that make them different from their teammates. I've observed that these nine are often present in the catalysts with whom I've interacted. They are . . .

1. Intuitive

Catalysts sense things that others don't sense. They may recognize a weakness in an opponent. They may be able to make an intuitive leap that turns a disadvantage into an advantage. They are able to use whatever it is they sense to help the team succeed.

For different kinds of teams, the way the intuition plays out changes. That makes sense because the goal of the team determines what the team values. Another reason is that people are most intuitive in their areas of natural strength. So for a small business, the catalyst may be an entrepreneur who can smell an opportunity when no one else is aware of it. For a ministry or other nonprofit organization, the catalyst may be a person who intuitively recognizes leadership and can recruit talented volunteers. For a football team, it may be a quarterback who senses that a defense isn't adjusting well and calls the play that wins the game. In each case the situation is different, but the result is the same: A catalyst senses an opportunity, and as a result, the team benefits.

2. Communicative

Catalysts say things that other team members don't say in order to get the team moving. Sometimes they do it to share with their teammates what they have sensed intuitively so that they will be better prepared to meet the challenge. Other times their purpose is to inspire or incite other team members. And they usually know the difference between when a teammate needs a boost—and when he needs a boot.

Anytime you see a team of people suddenly turn around or crank their play up to another level, you'll see someone on the team talking, directing, inspiring others. You'll see it, too, with strong political leaders. People such as Churchill, Roosevelt, and Kennedy changed the world with their words. They were catalysts, and catalysts communicate.

3. Passionate

Catalysts feel things that others don't feel. They are passionate about what they do, and they want to share that love with their teammates. Sometimes the passion explodes as a controlled fury to achieve goals in their area of passion. Other times it manifests itself as a contagious enthusiasm. But however it comes out, it can inspire a team to success.

Legendary baseball player Pete Rose of the Cincinnati Reds has experienced his share of problems, but he was certainly one of the great catalysts of his sport in the twentieth century. He was once asked which goes first on a baseball player: his eyes, his legs, or his arm. Rose's response was telling. He said, "None of these things. It's when his enthusiasm goes that he's through as a player." And he's also through as a catalyst.

4. Talented

Catalysts are capable of doing what others cannot do because their talent is as strong as their passion. People rarely become catalysts outside an area of expertise and gifting. That's the case for two main reasons. First, talent knows what it takes to win. You can't take the team to the next level when you haven't mastered the skills it takes to succeed on a personal level. It just doesn't happen.

The second reason people must have talent in an area where they desire to be a catalyst is that part of being a catalyst is influencing other team members. You can't do that if you have no credibility with them because of your own poor performance. Part of being a catalyst is sharing your gift with others to make them better. You can't give what you don't have.

5. Creative

Another quality commonly found in catalysts is creativity. Catalysts think things that others do not think. While most team members may do things by rote (or by rut), catalysts think differently from their teammates. They are constantly looking for fresh, innovative ways to do things.

Business and sports team consultant Carl Mays asserts that "creativity involves taking what you have, where you are, and getting the most out of it." Sometimes what they come up with can change the tempo of a game. Other times their ability to rewrite the rules changes the whole way the game is actually played.

6. Initiating

I enjoy creative people, and I've worked with many through the years. In fact, I consider myself to be creative, especially in the areas of writing and teaching. But my experience with creative people has taught me something about them: While all creative people have more than enough ideas, not all of them are good at implementing those creative thoughts.

Catalysts don't have this problem. They do things that others cannot do. Not only are they creative in their thinking, but they are disciplined in their actions. They delight in making things happen. That initiative can take almost any form: a baseball manager arguing with an umpire to stir up his players, a parent changing jobs or moving the family to help a struggling child, or a business owner putting up financial incentives for employees to break through barriers. So they initiate. And as a result they move the team as they move themselves.

7. Responsible

Catalysts carry things that others do not carry. My friend Truett Cathy, the founder of Chick-Fil-A, has a saying: "If it's to be, it's up to me." That could very well be the motto for all catalysts.

Not long ago a commercial appeared on television that showed a pair of consultants giving a company's CEO advice on how he could take his business to the next level. They explained how the company's computer system should be overhauled, how the distribution system could be improved, and how marketing channels could be changed to make the company much more effective and profitable.

The CEO listened carefully to everything they had to say, and finally he smiled and said, "I like it. Okay, do it."

The consultants looked confused for a moment, and one of them stammered, "We don't actually *do* what we recommend."

Catalysts are not consultants. They don't recommend a course of action. They take responsibility for making it happen.

8. Generous

Catalysts give things that others don't give. A true mark of people's taking responsibility is their willingness to give of themselves to carry something through. Catalysts display that quality. They are prepared to use their resources to better the team, whether that means giving time, spending money, or sacrificing personal gain.

> *Catalysts are not consultants. They don't recommend a course of action. They take responsibility for making it happen.*

A vivid example of someone giving of himself for the team can be found in the life of New York businessman Eugene Lang. On June 25, 1981, Lang stood before sixty-one graduating sixth graders in P.S. 121, the East Harlem elementary school from which he had graduated decades before. He knew that statistically, 75 percent of the children would probably drop out of school during the next six years and would never graduate from high school. And he wanted to try to do something to change that.

He began by encouraging them to work hard, telling them that if they did, success would follow. But then on the spur of the moment, Lang moved from consultant to catalyst. He promised those kids that if they would stick with it and graduate from high school, he would provide each of them with scholarship money for college. That promise was the start of what became the "I Have a Dream" program.

Four years later, all 61 students were still in school. Six years later, 90 percent of the 54 kids who remained in touch with Lang graduated from high school, and two-thirds of them went on to college. Today, I Have a Dream sponsors 160 projects in 57 cities, and it touches the lives of 10,000 kids—all because Lang decided to become a catalyst.[2]

9. Influential

Catalysts are able to lead teammates in a way that others cannot. Team members will follow a catalyst when they won't respond to anyone else. In the case of a highly talented team member who is not especially gifted in leadership, he may be an effective catalyst in an area of expertise. But people with natural leadership ability will have influence far beyond their own team.

Michael Jordan, once again, is a wonderful example. Obviously he had influence with his teammates in Chicago. But his influence stretched far beyond the Bulls. I got a taste of that firsthand at the NBA 2001 All-Star Game. I had the pleasure of speaking at the chapel for players and officials before the game, and later I got to spend time with the referees who had been picked to officiate. During my talks with them, I asked what player they respected the most in terms of his honesty. Their answer was Michael Jordan.

One ref then recounted that in a close game, Danny Ainge, whose team was playing against the Bulls, made a shot near the three-point line. The officials had given Ainge only two points for the basket since they were not sure whether he was outside the three-point line. During the timeout immediately after the shot, one of the refs asked Jordan whether his opponent's score had been a valid three-point shot. Jordan indicated that it was. They gave Ainge the three points. Jordan's integrity—and influence—caused them to reverse their call.

When you see many of those nine qualities in someone on your team, then take heart. When crunch time comes, he is likely to step up to a whole new level of performance and attempt to take the team there too.

My Own Go-to Guy

At my company, The INJOY Group, a number of team members are catalysts within the organization. But none are stronger than Dave Sutherland, the CEO.

Dave came on board in 1994 as the president of ISS, the division of The INJOY Group that helps churches with fund-raising through capital campaigns. Just prior to his coming on board, I had given serious thought to shutting down that arm of the organization. ISS wasn't supporting itself financially, it was draining time and resources from other more productive areas of the company, and it wasn't having the positive influence I had hoped for. But I believed that Dave Sutherland's leadership could make a difference. And soon after I hired him, I began seeing progress at ISS.

The second year that Dave was with me, the company had some pretty aggressive goals. That year the company's goal had been to partner with eighty churches, more than twice as many as it had the previous year. And each partnership could come only after a personal presentation to a church's board and their acceptance of our offer to help.

One day during the first week of December, I stopped by Dave's office and spoke to his wife, Roxine, who works with Dave as his assistant. I hadn't seen Dave in a while, and I asked where he was.

"He's on the road making a presentation," she said.

I thought that was a little odd because the company had several key people whose job it was to make the presentations to churches.

"On the road? When will he be back?" I asked.

"Well, let's see," said Roxine, "when he left the Monday after Thanksgiving, we still needed twenty-four more churches to reach our goal. Dave said he won't be home until we reach it."

And reach it he did. Dave was on the road until December 19. But that was no great surprise. My writer, Charlie Wetzel, told me that in a sales and marketing career that spans three decades, Dave has *never* missed a goal. Not once.

His tenacity and ability serve Dave well. But they also serve the team well. By reaching that goal, Dave made every person on the team a winner that year. And everyone in the company used the momentum he created to take ISS to a whole new level. A year later, ISS became the second largest company of its type in the world. And by the end of the year 2000, it had helped more than one thousand churches across America raise more than $1 billion.

When you have a Michael Jordan or a Eugene Lang or a Dave Sutherland, your team always has a chance to win. They are get-it-done-and-then-some people. Why is that important? Because *winning teams have players who make things happen.* Without them, a team will never reach its potential. That is the truth of the Law of the Catalyst.

TEAMWORK THOUGHT

Games are won by get-it-done-and-then-some people.

BECOMING A BETTER TEAM MEMBER

How are you when it comes to crunch time on your team? Do you want the ball, or would you rather it was in someone else's hands? If there are more talented and effective catalysts on your team, then you should not want to be the go-to player in a pinch. In those cases, the best thing you can do is get an "assist" by helping to put those people into position to benefit the team. But if you avoid the spotlight because you are afraid or because you haven't worked as hard as you should to improve yourself, then you need to change your mind-set.

Start to put yourself on the road to improvement by doing the following things:

1. *Find a mentor.* Players become catalysts only with the help of people better than themselves. Find someone who makes things happen to help you along the way.

2. *Begin a growth plan.* Put yourself on a program that will help you develop your skills and talents. You cannot take the team to a higher level if you haven't gotten there.

3. *Get out of your comfort zone.* You won't know what you're capable of until you try to go beyond what you've done before.

If you follow these three guidelines, you still may not become a catalyst, but you will at least become the best you can be—and that's all that anyone can ask of you.

BECOMING A BETTER TEAM LEADER

If you lead a team, you need catalysts to push the team to its potential. Use the list of qualities in the chapter to begin identifying and enlisting people who can get it done and then some. If you see that potential in some of your current teammates, encourage them to take initiative and become positive influencers on the team. If the people on the team can't or won't step up to that level of play, then start recruiting people from outside the team. No team can go to the highest level without a catalyst. *Winning teams have players who make things happen.*

COMPANION ONLINE RESOURCE

Learn more about how the Law of the Catalyst uniquely applies to you.
Take the FREE Law of the Catalyst assessment at **LawsOfTeamwork.com**.

THE LAW OF THE COMPASS

Vision Gives Team Members Direction and Confidence

For nearly a hundred years, IBM has been a rock of American business standing firm in a stream of competition. Even during the Great Depression of the 1930s, while thousands of companies were disappearing, IBM kept growing. The source of its strength was business and technological innovation.

INTRODUCING TECHNOLOGY

For a half century, IBM continually broke ground in the area of computers, beginning in the 1940s with its Mark I. In the 1950s and 1960s, the firm introduced innovation after innovation. By 1971, IBM was receiving $8 billion in annual revenues and employed 270,000 people. When people thought of blue-chip companies, IBM is likely the first one they pictured.

But for all its history of advances, by the late 1980s and early 1990s, the company was struggling. For a decade IBM had been slow to react to technological changes. As a result, by 1991, it suffered $8 billion in *losses* every year. And even though IBM fought to regain ground technologically, consumers' favorable perceptions of the company were at an all-time low. Where IBM had once been seen as dominant, people looked upon it as hopelessly behind the times—a slow-moving dinosaur among new companies that moved like chee-tahs. If something didn't change, IBM was going to be in big trouble.

Then in 1993, IBM got a new CEO, Lou Gerstner. He quickly began recruiting key members for his team, IBM's executive com-mittee. Perhaps the most important addition was Abby Kohnstamm, whom he invited to be IBM's senior vice president of marketing.

INTRODUCING . . . A COMPASS

Kohnstamm was eager to get started. She believed the company's products were strong enough, but its marketing was weak. When she arrived at IBM, what she found was much worse than she had expected. Not only was IBM failing to reach customers effectively; when it came to the marketing department, employees weren't even sure who did what or why. For example, when Kohnstamm asked how many employees were in the marketing area, she couldn't get the same answer from any two employees. Greg Farrell of *USA Today* described the situation: "The company was a fragmented, decen-tralized organization with more than a dozen quasi-autonomous businesses, and 70 ad agency partners worldwide."[1]

Kohnstamm immediately dismissed all those agencies and hired one to replace it: Ogilvy & Mather Worldwide. Her desire was to give the entire IBM team a single unifying theme for the hardware, software, and services they had to offer. Before long, she had found it. The company adopted the concept of e-business. Kohnstamm asserts, "E-business is the single focal point for the company, and is the single largest marketing effort ever undertaken by IBM."[2]

The vision seems to be working. Steve Gardner, an ad agency owner who once promoted Compaq, says, "The most stunning thing about e-business was that it transformed IBM from perceived laggard to leader in the Internet space without any real change in its lines of products or services. That's an astonishing achievement."[3]

Where once IBM was struggling, it now has renewed direction and confidence. Bill Etherington, senior vice president and group executive over sales and distribution, notes that the marketing focus has had an incredibly positive effect on IBM's employees. And he should know. He's been with IBM for thirty-seven years. He says, "We all had enthusiasm for this wonderful campaign. It had an edge to it and portrayed the company in a much more modern light."[4] Maureen McGuire, vice president of marketing communications, agrees: "The campaign has galvanized employees. We're trying to get all those people to sing the same song, read from the same book." For a company that hadn't sung for a long time, that's a momentous achievement. And it just goes to show you, *vision gives team members direction and confidence.* That's the power of the Law of the Compass.

DON'T GET LOST

Have you ever been part of a team that didn't seem to make any progress? Maybe the group had plenty of talent, resources, and opportunities, and team members got along, but the group just never *went* anywhere! If you have, there's a strong possibility that the situation was caused by lack of vision.

Great vision precedes great achievement. Every team needs a compelling vision to give it direction. A team without vision is, at worst, purposeless. At best, it is subject to the personal (and sometimes selfish) agendas of its various teammates. As the agendas work against each other, the team's energy and drive drain away. On the other hand, a team that embraces a vision becomes focused, energized, and confident. It knows where it's headed and why it's going there.

> *Great vision precedes great achievement.*

Field Marshal Bernard Montgomery, a leader of troops during World War II who was called a "soldier's general," wrote that "every single soldier must know, before he goes into battle, how the little battle he is to fight fits into the larger picture, and how the success of his fighting will influence the battle as a whole." People on the team need to know why they're fighting. Otherwise, the team gets into trouble.

THE LEADER'S RESPONSIBILITY

Field Marshal Montgomery was adept at connecting with the soldiers on his team and casting vision for their battles. That ability brought him and them success. He understood that leaders must be vision casters. Author Ezra Earl Jones points out,

> Leaders do not have to be the greatest visionaries themselves. The vision may come from anyone. The leaders do have to state the

vision, however. Leaders also have to keep the vision before the people and remind them of the progress that is being made to achieve the vision. Otherwise, the people might assume that they are failing and give up.

If you lead your team, then you are responsible for identifying a worthy and compelling vision and articulating it to your team members. However, even if you are not the leader, identifying a compelling vision is still important. If you don't know the team's vision, you can't perform with confidence. You can't be sure you and your teammates are going in the right direction. You can't even be sure that the team you're on is the right one for you if you haven't examined the vision in light of your strengths, convictions, and purpose. For everyone on the team, the vision needs to be compelling.

CHECK YOUR COMPASS!

How do you measure a vision? How do you know whether it is worthy and compelling? You check your compass. Every team needs one. In fact, every team needs several. A team should examine the following six "compasses" before embarking on any journey.

A team's vision must be aligned with:

1. A Moral Compass (Look Above)

Millionaire philanthropist Andrew Carnegie exclaimed, "A great business is seldom if ever built up, except on lines of strictest integrity." That holds true for any endeavor. There's only one true north. If your compass is pointing in any other direction, your team is headed the wrong way.

A moral compass brings integrity to the vision. It helps all the people on the team to check their motives and make sure that they are laboring for the right reasons. It also brings credibility to the leaders who cast the vision—but only if they model the values that the team is expected to embrace. When they do, they bring fuel to the vision, which keeps it going.

2. An Intuitive Compass (Look Within)

Where integrity brings fuel to the vision, passion brings fire. And the true fire of passion and conviction comes only from within.

In *The Leadership Challenge,* James Kouzes and Barry Posner explain that "visions spring forth from our intuition. If necessity is the mother of invention, intuition is the mother of vision. Experience feeds our intuition and enhances our insight." A vision must resonate deep within the leader of the team. Then it must resonate within the team members, who will be asked to work hard to bring it to fruition. But that's the value of intuitive passion. It brings the kind of heat that fires up the committed—and fries the uncommitted.

> *"A great business is seldom if ever built up, except on lines of strictest integrity."*
>
> —ANDREW CARNEGIE

3. A Historical Compass (Look Behind)

There's an old saying that I learned when I lived in rural Indiana: "Don't remove the fence before you know why it's there." You never know: There might be a bull on the other side! A compelling vision should build on the past, not diminish it. It should make positive use of anything contributed by previous teams in the organization.

Anytime you cast vision, you must create a connection between the past, the present, and the future. You must bring them together. People won't reach for the future until they have touched the past. When you include the history of the team, the people who have been in the organization a long time sense that they are valued (even if they are no longer the stars). At the same time, the newer people receive a sense of security, knowing that the current vision builds on the past and leads to the future.

> *People won't reach for the future until they have touched the past.*

What is the best way to do that? You tell stories. Principles may fade in people's minds, but stories stick. They bring relationships to the vision. Tell stories from the past that give a sense of history. Tell stories about the exciting things that are happening now among team members. And tell the story of what it will be like the day that the team fulfills the vision. Stories are like thumbtacks that help to keep a vision in front of people.

4. A Directional Compass (Look Ahead)

Poet Henry David Thoreau wrote, "If one advances confidently in the direction of his dreams, and endeavors to live the life which he has imagined, he will meet with a success unexpected in common hours." As I already mentioned, vision provides direction for the team. Part of that direction comes from a sense of purpose. Another comes from having goals, which bring targets to the vision.

A goal motivates the team. NFL referee Jim Tunney commented on this when he said, "Why do we call it a goal line? Because eleven people on the offensive team huddle for a single purpose—to move the ball across it. Everyone has a specific task to do—the quarterback, the wide receiver, each lineman, every player knows exactly

what his assignment is. Even the defensive team has its goals too—
to prevent the offensive team from achieving its goal."

5. A Strategic Compass (Look Around)

A goal won't do the team much good without steps to accomplish
it. Vision without strategy is little more than a daydream. As Vince
Abner remarked, "Vision isn't enough—it must be combined with venture. It is not enough to stare up the steps; we must step up the stairs."

The value of a strategy is that it brings process to the vision. It
identifies resources and mobilizes the members of the team. People
need more than information and inspiration. They need instruction in what to do to make the vision become reality and a way to
get there. A strategy provides that.

6. A Visionary Compass (Look Beyond)

The vision of the team must look beyond current circumstances
and any obvious shortcomings of current teammates to see the
potential of the team. A truly great vision speaks to what team members can become if they truly live out their values and work according to their highest standards.

If you are your team's leader, getting
people to reach their potential means challenging them. As you know, it's one thing
to have team members show up. It's
another to get them to grow up. One of the
things about having a far-reaching vision is
that it brings "stretch" to the team.

Without a challenge many people
tend to fall or fade away. Charles Noble
observed, "You must have a long-range

> *"You must have a
> long-range vision to
> keep you from being
> frustrated by short-
> range failures."*
>
> —CHARLES NOBLE

vision to keep you from being frustrated by short-range failures." That's true. Vision helps people with motivation. That can be especially important for highly talented people. They sometimes fight lack of desire. That's why a consummate artist like Michelangelo prayed, "Lord, grant that I may always desire more than I can accomplish." A visionary compass answers that prayer.

Someone said that only people who can see the invisible can do the impossible. That shows the value of vision. But it also indicates that vision can be an elusive quality. If you can confidently measure the vision of your team according to these six "compasses," and you find them all aligned in the right direction, then your team has a reasonably good chance at success. And make no mistake. Not only can a team fail to thrive without vision—it cannot even survive without it. The words of King Solomon of ancient Israel, reputed to be the wisest man who ever lived, are true: "Where there is no vision, the people perish."[5] *Vision gives team members direction and confidence,* two things they cannot do without. That is the critical nature of the Law of the Compass.

ONE OF THE BEST TEAMS IN THE WORLD

People often think of vision as pointing to the achievement of a specific goal. Although that is often true, vision doesn't always have to be that narrow. Sometimes the vision provides direction and values that are strong, but the possible achievements that can be attained are left somewhat open-ended. When that is the case, yet the vision is strong in its guidance, it can create a team atmosphere where members believe the sky's the limit.

That is what's happening at Enron. In the last several years, the global energy company has really blossomed, and it has received incredible recognition for its efforts. For example, here are a few honors it has received:

- No. 25 on *Fortune* magazine's all-star list of global most admired companies (2000)

- No. 29 on *Fortune*'s list of fastest-growing companies (2000)

- Named five times to *Fortune*'s list of most innovative companies (1996–2000)

- Twice named to *Fortune*'s one hundred best companies to work for in America (1999, 2000)

- Named to *Global Finance*'s list of world's best global companies

- Named the world's leading power company by *Forbes Global Business* (1999)

- Honored as having America's best sales force by *Sales & Marketing Management*'s annual survey (1999)

- Included as one of *Wired* magazine's forty new blue-chip companies (1999)

If you don't read the financial pages and you're not in the energy field, you may not be familiar with the name Enron (unless you are a Houston Astros fan, since the team's new ballpark is named Enron Field). The company was formed in 1985 when Houston Natural Gas (HNG) and Internorth, Inc., of Omaha merged to form a new company. They made that move because of the easing of government regulation in the energy industry, which was causing their businesses to shift from being just merchants of natural gas to being transporters of the fuel as well. Because of that, companies in the natural gas business needed access to reserves. By merging the two companies, spokesman Don Wright concluded, "We're border to border and coast to coast. We can swap gas just about any place in the United States right now. You can't make it as a regional or several-state business."[6]

One Company . . . but One Team?

When the two companies came together, their people did not experience an easy transition. It was like trying to mix oil and water. They were based in two locations: Houston and Omaha. They had very different company cultures: HNG's management was hands-on while Internorth's was decentralized. And the companies' executives didn't mix well either: HNG's leaders were innovators in their forties while Internorth's were traditionalists in their fifties and sixties. They were one company, but the question remained whether they could become a unified team.

Ken Lay of HNG, who was then forty-two years old, was soon given the task of leading the company and unifying the two teams. After working at it for almost a year, Lay conceded that it was "tougher to put the companies together than I anticipated." To do the job right, he wanted greater authority to make changes and unify the team. The board told him he could have it if he was willing to give up his employment contract (which had a built-in golden parachute). Lay gladly tore up his contract.

Confident Direction Toward Future Innovation

Early on, the vision of Enron was to become the premier natural gas pipeline in North America. The company achieved that. A decade later the desire was to become the world's leading energy company. It can be argued that the firm has achieved that too. But over the years what has emerged is a much broader vision. That vision is derived from the company's values: The company's greatest assets are the people on the team, and the most sought-after quality is innovation. As Jeff Skilling, president, COO, and CEO of Enron, says, "You should always value the ability to move and change, because that creates options, and options are valuable . . . I prefer a smart person to an asset."[7]

Having a vision for innovation and placing value on people have paid off for Enron. In 2000, the company's revenues were $101 billion, and its assets were $53 billion. More than 40 percent of Enron's market value came from businesses that were less than three years old.[8] And voluntary employee turnover in the company is a remarkable 6 percent.[9]

Perhaps the shining example of the empowerment of Enron's vision is the story of the entrance into on-line trading of natural gas and electricity called EnronOnline in 1999. It was the brainchild of Louise Kitchen, who was then the head of European gas trading for Enron. She collaborated with Greg Whalley of Enron North America and John Sherriff, chief of Enron Europe. For seven months they worked together on the $15 million initiative to make Enron an on-line commodities broker. The most amazing thing about it: Jeff Skilling didn't even know about the huge multimillion-dollar venture until two months before the launch. The result? It made Enron the largest e-commerce company in the world.

In what kind of company do employees have the confidence and ability to do such things? In a company that practices the Law of the Compass. Security and freedom come from the kind of vision communicated by Enron. *Vision gives team members direction and confidence.* And when they have direction and confidence, the team is able to develop its potential and go to a whole new level.

TEAMWORK THOUGHT

When you see it, you can seize it.

BECOMING A BETTER TEAM MEMBER

What is the vision for your team? You'd be surprised how many individuals are part of a group that works together but isn't clear about why. For example, that was the case when I became the leader of Skyline Church in the San Diego area. The church's board was comprised of twelve people. When I asked each member to articulate the church's vision the first time we met, I got eight different answers. A team can't move forward in confidence if it has no compass!

As a member of your team, you need a clear understanding of its vision. If the team doesn't have one, then help it to develop one. If the team has already found its compass and course, then you need to examine yourself in light of it to make sure there is a good match. If there isn't, you and your teammates are going to be frustrated. And everyone will probably be best served by a change.

BECOMING A BETTER TEAM LEADER

If you are the leader of your team, then you carry the responsibility for communicating the team's vision and keeping it before the people continually. That's not necessarily easy. Jack Welch, CEO of General Electric, observed, "Without question, communicating the vision, and the atmosphere around the vision, has been, and is continuing to be, by far, the toughest job we face."

I have found that people need to be shown the team's compass clearly, creatively, and continually. Whenever I endeavor to cast vision with the members of my team, I use the following checklist. I try to make sure that every vision message possesses . . .

❏ *Clarity:* brings understanding to the vision (answers what the people must know and what I want them to do)

❏ *Connectedness:* brings the past, present, and future together

❏ *Purpose:* brings direction to the vision

❏ *Goals:* bring targets to the vision

❏ *Honesty:* brings integrity to the vision and credibility to the vision caster

❏ *Stories:* bring relationships to the vision

❏ *Challenge:* brings stretching to the vision

❏ *Passion:* brings fuel to the vision

❏ *Modeling:* brings accountability to the vision

❏ *Strategy:* brings process to the vision

The next time you prepare to communicate vision to your people, use this checklist. Make sure you include each component, and I believe your team members will find the vision more accessible and will more readily buy into it. And if they do, you will see that they have greater direction and confidence.

COMPANION **ONLINE** RESOURCE

Learn more about how the Law of the Compass uniquely applies to you.

Take the FREE Law of the Compass assessment at **LawsOfTeamwork.com**.

8

THE LAW OF THE BAD APPLE

Rotten Attitudes Ruin a Team

rowing up, I loved basketball. It all started for me in the fourth grade when I saw a high school basketball game for the first time. I was captivated. Soon after that my dad poured a cement driveway along the side of our house and put a goal up on the garage for me. From that day until I went to college, I could usually be found practicing my shooting and playing pickup games on that small home court.

By the time I got to high school, I had become a pretty good player. I started on the junior varsity team as a freshman, and when I was a sophomore, our JV team had a 15-3 record, which was better than that of the varsity. We were proud of that—maybe a little too proud. I say that because of something that happened during my sophomore year.

One of the traditions on the team was that our coach, Don Neff, would give Ohio State basketball tickets to some of the players who had performed especially well during the season. Those players were almost always seniors, and they were always on the varsity. But that year I was one of the players offered Buckeye tickets. What was my response? Was I grateful and humbled by Coach Neff's recognition? No, I told him I thought he should let the JV play the varsity for *all* the tickets. Needless to say, he never allowed that game to be played.

The next year, critics who followed high school basketball in Ohio thought our team had a chance to win the state championship in our division. I guess they looked at the players who would return as seniors from the previous year's varsity team and saw the talent that would be moving up from the JV, and they figured we would be a powerhouse. And we did have a lot of talent. How many high school teams in the late 1960s could say that all but a couple of players on the team could dunk the ball? But the season turned out far different from everyone's expectations.

FROM BAD TO WORSE

From the beginning of the season, the team suffered problems. There were two of us juniors on the varsity who had the talent to start for the team: John Thomas, who was the team's best rebounder, and me, the best shooting guard. We thought playing time should be based strictly on ability, and we figured we deserved our place on the team. The seniors, who had taken a backseat to the previous year's seniors, thought we should be made to pay our dues and wait.

What began as a rivalry between the JV and varsity the year before turned into a war between the juniors and the seniors. When we scrimmaged at practice, it was the juniors against the seniors. In games the seniors wouldn't pass to the juniors and vice versa. We judged our success not by whether the team won or lost, but by whether the juniors' stats were better than those of the seniors. If we outshot, outpassed, and outrebounded the seniors, then we thought we had "won" the game, regardless of the outcome against our opponent.

The battles became so fierce that before long, the juniors and the seniors wouldn't even work together on the court during games. Coach Neff had to platoon us. The seniors would start, and when a substitution became necessary, he'd put not one but *five* juniors in the game. We became two teams on one roster.

I don't remember exactly who started the rivalry that split our team, but I do remember that John Thomas and I embraced it early on. I've always been a leader, and I did my share of influencing other team members. Unfortunately, I have to confess that I led the juniors in the wrong direction.

What started as a bad attitude in one or two players made a mess of the situation for everyone. By the time we were in the thick of our schedule, even the players who didn't want to take part in the rivalry were affected. The season was a disaster. In the end, we finished with a mediocre record and never came close to reaching our potential. It just goes to show you, *rotten attitudes ruin a team.* That's the Law of the Bad Apple.

TALENT IS NOT ENOUGH

From my high school basketball experience I learned that talent is not enough to bring success to a team. Of course, you need talent. My friend Lou Holtz, the outstanding college football coach, observed, "You've got to have great athletes to win . . . You can't win without good athletes, but you can lose with them." But it also takes much more than talented people to win.

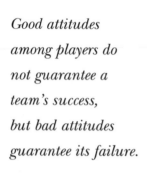

Good attitudes among players do not guarantee a team's success, but bad attitudes guarantee its failure.

My high school teammates were loaded with talent, and if that were enough, we could have been state champions. But we were also loaded with rotten attitudes. You know which won the battle between talent and attitude in the end. Perhaps that is why to this day I understand the importance of a positive attitude and have placed such a strong emphasis on it for myself, for my children as they were growing up, and for the teams I lead.

Years ago I wrote something about attitude for *The Winning Attitude.* I'd like to share it with you:

> Attitude . . .
>
> It is the "advance man" of our true selves.
>
> Its roots are inward but its fruit is outward.
>
> It is our best friend or our worst enemy.
>
> It is more honest and more consistent than our words.
>
> It is an outward look based on past experiences.
>
> It is a thing which draws people to us or repels them.
>
> It is never content until it is expressed.
>
> It is the librarian of our past.
>
> It is the speaker of our present.
>
> It is the prophet of our future.[1]

Good attitudes among players do not guarantee a team's success, but bad attitudes guarantee its failure.

The following five truths about attitudes clarify how they affect a team and teamwork.

1. Attitudes Have the Power to Lift Up or Tear Down a Team ✓

In *The Winner's Edge* Denis Waitley stated, "The real leaders in business, in the professional community, in education, in government, and in the home also seem to draw upon a special cutting edge that separates them from the rest of society. The winner's edge is not in a gifted birth, in a high IQ, or in talent. The winner's edge is in the attitude, not aptitude."

Unfortunately, I think too many people resist that notion. They want to believe that talent alone (or talent with experience) is enough. But plenty of talented teams out there never amount to anything because of the attitudes of their players.

Various attitudes may impact a team made up of highly talented players:

Abilities	+	Attitudes	=	Result
Great Talent	+	Rotten Attitudes	=	Bad Team
Great Talent	+	Bad Attitudes	=	Average Team
Great Talent	+	Average Attitudes	=	Good Team
Great Talent	+	Good Attitudes	=	Great Team

If you want outstanding results, you need good people with great talent and awesome attitudes. When attitudes go up, so does the potential of the team. When attitudes go down, the potential of the team goes with it.

2. An Attitude Compounds When Exposed to Others ✓

Several things on a team are not contagious. Talent. Experience. Willingness to practice. But you can be sure of one thing: Attitude is catching. When someone on the team is teachable and his humility is rewarded by improvement, others are more likely to display similar characteristics. When a leader is upbeat in the face of discouraging circumstances, others admire that quality and want to be like her. When a team member displays a strong work ethic and begins to have a positive impact, others imitate him. People become inspired by their peers. People have a tendency to adopt the attitudes of those they spend time with—to pick up on their mind-set, beliefs, and approaches to challenges.

The story of Roger Bannister is an inspiring example of the way attitudes often "compound." During the first half of the twentieth century, many sports experts believed that no runner could run a mile in less than four minutes. And for a long time they were right. But then on May 6, 1954, British runner and university student Roger Bannister ran a mile in 3 minutes 59.4 seconds during a meet in Oxford. Less than two months later, another runner, Australian John Landy, also broke the four-minute barrier. Then suddenly dozens and then hundreds of others broke it. Why? Because the best runners' attitudes changed. They began to adopt the mind-set and beliefs of their peers.

Bannister's attitude and actions compounded when exposed to others. His attitude spread. Today, every world-class runner who competes at that distance can run a mile in less than four minutes. Attitudes are contagious!

3. Bad Attitudes Compound Faster Than Good Ones

There's only one thing more contagious than a good attitude— and that's a bad attitude. For some reason many people think it's chic to be negative. I suspect that they think it makes them appear smart or important. But the truth is that a negative attitude hurts rather than helps the person who has it. And it also hurts the people around him.

A wise baseball manager once remarked that he never allowed the positive players to room with the negative ones on the road.

When he created the team's room assignments, he always put the negative ones together so that they couldn't poison anyone else.

To see how quickly and easily an attitude or mind-set can spread, just think about this story from Norman Cousins. Once during a football game, a doctor at the first aid station treated five people for what he suspected might be food poisoning. Since their symptoms were similar, he tried to track down what they had in common. He soon discovered that all five people had bought drinks from a particular concession stand at the stadium.

> *There's only one thing more contagious than a good attitude—and that's a bad attitude.*

The physician wanted to do the responsible thing, so he requested that the game's announcer advise people in the stadium to avoid buying drinks from the particular vendor because of the possibility of food poisoning. Before long, more than two hundred people complained of food poisoning symptoms. Nearly half the people's symptoms were so severe that they were taken to the hospital.

The story doesn't end there, however. After a little more detective work, it was discovered that the five original victims had eaten tainted potato salad from one particular deli on the way to the game. When the other "sufferers" found out that the drinks in the stadium were safe, they experienced miraculous recoveries. That just goes to show you, an attitude spreads very quickly.

4. Attitudes Are Subjective, So Identifying a Wrong One Can Be Difficult

Have you ever interacted with someone for the first time and suspected that his attitude was poor, yet you were unable to put your finger on exactly what was wrong? I believe many people have that experience.

The reason people doubt their observations about others' attitudes is that attitudes are subjective. Someone with a bad attitude may not do anything illegal or unethical. Yet his attitude may be ruining the team just the same.

People always project on the outside how they feel on the inside. Attitude is really about how a person is. That overflows into how he acts. Allow me to share with you common rotten attitudes that ruin a team so that you can recognize them for what they are when you see them.

An inability to admit wrongdoing. Have you ever spent time with people who *never* admit they're wrong? It's painful. Nobody's perfect, but someone who thinks he is does not make an ideal teammate. His wrong attitude will always create conflict.

Failing to forgive. It's said that Clara Barton, the founder of modern nursing, was once encouraged to bemoan a cruel act inflicted on her years earlier, but Barton wouldn't take the bait.

"Don't you remember the wrong that was done to you?" the friend goaded.

"No," answered Barton, "I distinctly remember forgetting that."

Holding a grudge is never positive or appropriate. And when unforgiveness occurs between teammates, it's certain to hurt the team.

Petty jealousy. An attitude that really works against people is the desire for equality that feeds petty jealousy. For some reason the people with this attitude believe that every person deserves equal treatment, regardless of talent, performance, or impact. Yet nothing could be farther from the truth. Each of us is created uniquely and performs differently, and as a result, we should be treated as such.

The disease of me. In his book *The Winner Within*, highly successful NBA coach Pat Riley writes about the "disease of me." He says of team members who have it, "They develop an overpowering belief in their own importance. Their actions virtually shout the claim,

'I'm the one.'" Riley asserts that the disease always has the same inevitable result: "The Defeat of Us."[2]

A critical spirit. Fred and Martha were driving home after a church service. "Fred," Martha asked, "did you notice that the pastor's sermon was kind of weak today?"

"No, not really," answered Fred.

"Well, did you hear that the choir was flat?"

"No, I didn't," he responded.

"Well, you certainly must have noticed that young couple and their children right in front of us, with all the noise and commotion they made the whole service!"

"I'm sorry, dear, but no, I didn't"

Finally in disgust Martha said, "Honestly, Fred, I don't know why you even bother to go to church."

When someone on the team has a critical spirit, everybody knows it because everyone on the team can do no right.

A desire to hog all the credit. Another bad attitude that hurts the team is similar to the "disease of me." But where the person with that disease may simmer in the background and create dissension, the credit hog continually steps into the spotlight to take a bow—whether he has earned it or not. His attitude is opposite that of NBA Hall of Fame center Bill Russell, who said of his time on the court, "The most important measure of how good a game I played was how much better I'd made my teammates play."

> *Most bad attitudes are the result of selfishness.*

Certainly there are other negative attitudes that I haven't named, but my intention isn't to list every bad attitude—just some of the most common ones. In a word, most bad attitudes are the result of selfishness. If one of your teammates puts others down, sabotages teamwork, or makes himself out to be more important than the team, then you can be sure that you've encountered someone with a bad attitude.

5. Rotten Attitudes, Left Alone, Ruin Everything

Bad attitudes must be addressed. You can be sure that they will always cause dissension, resentment, combativeness, and division on a team. And they will never go away on their own if they are left unaddressed. They will simply fester and ruin a team—along with its chances of reaching its potential.

Because people with bad attitudes are so difficult to deal with and because attitudes seem so subjective, you may doubt your gut reaction when you encounter a bad apple. After all, if it's only your *opinion* that he has a rotten attitude, then you have no right to address it, right? Not if you care about the team. *Rotten attitudes ruin a team.* That is always true. If you leave a bad apple in a barrel of good apples, you will always end up with a barrel of rotten apples.

President Thomas Jefferson remarked, "Nothing can stop the man with the right mental attitude from achieving his goal; nothing on earth can help the man with the wrong mental attitude." If you care about your team and you are committed to helping all of the players, you can't ignore a bad attitude. If you do, you will find out the hard way about the Law of the Bad Apple.

YOUR BEST FRIEND OR WORST ENEMY

Attitude colors everything someone does. It determines how an individual sees the world and interacts with other people. A person's attitude—positively if it's good, negatively if it's not—always

impacts his performance, regardless of talent, track record, or circumstances.

One of the most remarkable stories I've ever read that illus-
trates the Law of the Bad Apple came out of the San Francisco
Bay area. Evidently the principal of a school called in three teachers to inform them of an experiment that the district would be
conducting.

"Because you are the finest teachers in the system," she said,
"we're going to give you ninety selected high-IQ students. We're
going to let you move these students through this next year at their
pace and see how much they can learn."

The faculty and students were delighted. During the next year,
they had a wonderful experience. By the end of the last semester,
the students had achieved 20 to 30 percent more than any other
group of students in the area.

After the year was completed, the principal called in the teachers and told them, "I have a confession to make. I have to confess
that you did not have ninety of the most intellectually prominent
students. They were run-of-the-mill students. We took ninety students at random from the system and gave them to you."

The teachers were pleased. If the students were only average,
that showed that the teachers had displayed exceptional skill and
expertise.

"I have another confession," the principal continued. "You're
not the brightest of the teachers. Your names were the first three
names drawn out of a hat."

If the students and the teachers had been picked at random,
then what had enabled them to make greater progress than any
other group in the system? It was the attitudes of the people
involved. Because the teachers and students expected to succeed,

they increased their potential for success. Attitude had made all the difference.

If you want to give your team the best chance for success, then practice the Law of the Bad Apple. Trade your bad apples for good ones and you have a chance, because *rotten apples ruin a team.*

TEAMWORK THOUGHT

Your attitude determines the team's attitude.

BECOMING A BETTER TEAM MEMBER

The first place to start when it comes to attitude is yourself. How are you doing? For example, do you . . .

❑ Think the team wouldn't be able to get along without you?

❑ Secretly (or not so secretly) believe that recent team successes are really attributable to your personal efforts, not the work of the whole team?

❑ Keep score when it comes to the praise and perks handed out to other team members?

❑ Have a hard time admitting when you make a mistake? (If you believe you're not making mistakes, you need to check this!)

❑ Bring up past wrongs from your teammates?

❑ Believe that you are being grossly underpaid?

If you could place a check next to any of them, then you need to check your attitude.

Talk to your teammates, and find out if your attitude is doing damage to the team. Talk to your leader. And if you really think your pay is inequitable, you need to talk it out with your employer and find out where you stand. Anytime a relationship is unequal, it cannot last—whether you are giving more than you get or getting more than you deserve. In either case, the relationship will break down.

Warning! I have one word of caution: If you leave your position because you believe you are undervalued, and you don't succeed in your new situation, then you most likely overestimated your value or underestimated what the organization was doing to help you succeed.

BECOMING A BETTER TEAM LEADER

If you think you have a bad apple on your team, you need to take the person aside and discuss the situation with him. Doing it the right way is important. Take the high road: As you approach him, share what you have observed, but give him the benefit of the doubt. Assume that your perception might be wrong and you want clarification. (If you have several people with bad attitudes, start with the ringleader.) If it truly is your perception and the team is not being hurt, then you haven't done any damage, and you have smoothed the relationship between you and the other person.

However, if it turns out that your perception was correct and the person's attitude is the problem, give him clear expectations and an opportunity to change. Then hold him accountable. If he changes, it's a win for the team. If he doesn't, remove him from the team. You cannot allow him to remain because you can be sure his *rotten attitude will ruin the team.*

COMPANION ONLINE RESOURCE

Learn more about how the Law of the Bad Apple uniquely applies to you.

Take the FREE Law of the Bad Apple assessment at **LawsOfTeamwork.com**.

THE LAW OF COUNTABILITY

Teammates Must Be Able to Count on Each Other When It Counts

One of the many strong points of Atlanta, Georgia, where I moved my family and my companies in 1997, is that it's a sports town. I don't get the chance to go to a lot of games, but there are few things I like better than attending a sporting event with all of the energy and excitement. Watching a team with a friend or two is a joy, whether it's the Braves (baseball), the Hawks (basketball), the Falcons (football), or the Thrashers (hockey).

When the announcement was made that Atlanta would be getting a hockey team, plans were set in motion to build the team a new arena. The old Omni, where the Hawks had played since the early 1970s, was slated to be demolished and replaced on the same site by the Philips Arena. It would be an 18,000-seat state-of-the-art entertainment complex with box seating, which could host not only hockey and basketball but also concerts and other events.

Tearing down the Omni wasn't going to be a routine process. First, it needed to be done quickly so that construction could begin on the new arena. Second, because the old structure had a cantilevered roof, taking the building apart in opposite order from the way it was constructed was out of the question. It would be far too dangerous for the demolition crews. That left only one choice: blowing it up.

EXPLOSIVE FAMILY BUSINESS

When demolition crews need help blowing up a building—or more accurately imploding a building—they inevitably turn to the Loizeaux family, the people who pioneered the safe demolition of buildings using explosives. They are owners and founders of Controlled Demolition Incorporated (CDI). The company was founded by Jack Loizeaux who had started a company in the 1940s removing tree stumps with dynamite. In 1957, he blasted his first building. And in the 1960s, he began CDI. Since that first demolition—an apartment building in Washington, D.C., his company has demolished more than seven thousand structures worldwide.

CDI is a family operation. Jack and his wife, Freddie, ran the business in the beginning. It wasn't long before they were joined by their sons, Mark and Doug. When Jack retired in 1976, his sons took over the operation. Today, they are joined by several of Mark's children, including his daughter Stacey, in her early thirties, who has worked in the field since age fifteen and is already an expert in her own right.

LIKE THREADING A NEEDLE

When the Loizeauxs were contacted for the job, they quickly discovered that the demolition wouldn't be easy because of the Omni's proximity to other buildings. On one side was the World Congress Center, which is used for conventions. On another side was a station for MARTA (Atlanta's mass-transit rail system). On the third was the CNN Center from which cable and radio programming broadcasts twenty-four hours a day. And CNN Plaza was a mere thirteen feet away from the Omni! A mistake could damage the MARTA line and shut it down at one of its busiest stations. Or it could put CNN news service temporarily out of business. And of course in a worst-case scenario, the Omni could topple in the wrong direction and take down the CNN building itself. It would take every bit of the Loizeauxs' expertise and fifty years of experience to do the task right.

Using explosives to take down a building is always a dangerous undertaking. Each project is different and requires a custom-made strategy. Holes are drilled in strategic places in many parts of the structure, such as in columns, and filled with appropriate amounts of explosive material. Then those blast points are often wrapped in chain-link fence (to catch the big pieces upon detonation) and wrapped in a special fabric that helps contain the explosion. "It allows the concrete to move, but it keeps the concrete from flying," says Stacey Loizeaux. "We also sometimes put up a curtain around the entire floor, to catch stuff that gets through these first two layers. That's really where your liability is."[1] Often, earthen berms are also erected around the building to protect nearby people and structures.

Obviously there is risk anytime someone works with explosives. But the greatest danger comes in the way explosives are rigged to go off. To get the building to fall in on itself, the Loizeauxs and their crew have to precisely sequence the charges, often using delays that differ from one another by the tiniest fractions of a second. That was the case for the Omni, where first the roof needed to fall straight down, then three of the walls would need to fall inward, and then the fourth wall outward. And on July 26, 1997, at 6:53 A.M., that's exactly the way it happened. The demolition took ten seconds.

When it comes to blowing up a building the way the Loizeauxs do, everything has to go right—from analyzing the building, to planning the demolition, to transporting the explosives, to rigging the devices, to preparing the building for the safety of the surrounding area. If anyone on the crew fails to get his part right and lets the other members of the team down, not only does the CDI team fail in its objective, but it also puts a lot of people and property in danger. *Teammates must be able to count on each other when it counts.* That's the Law of Countability.

HOLDING EACH OTHER ACCOUNTABLE

The importance of the Law of Countability is clearest when the stakes are high. But you don't have to be in an explosive situation for the law to come into play. The person running a business who is trying to get out a product on schedule depends on her vendors to deliver on their promises during crunch time. The waiter trying to please his customer counts on the kitchen staff to prepare the food properly. The mom getting ready for a job interview has to know that her baby-sitter will show up as promised. If there is a breakdown in countability, then the account is lost, the customer goes away unhappy, and the job goes to some other candidate. *Teammates must be able to count on each other when it counts.*

I was reminded of how often we encounter examples of the Law of Countability, even in small things, when I was on a trip to South Africa. I was there to teach at a conference sponsored by EQUIP, my nonprofit organization. I was waiting in the hotel lobby for my ride to the conference, and I was having some trouble with a cough. That's usually no big deal, but when you're preparing to speak for five or six hours straight, it's not a great way to start the day. As the conference team and I got

> *"We don't work for each other; we work with each other."*
>
> —STANLEY C. GAULT

under way, Erick Moon, a member of the team, pulled a Ricola cough drop (my brand) out of his pocket and handed it to me. When he saw my surprise, he said simply, "We're all carrying them for you, just in case."

Stanley C. Gault asserted, "We don't work for each other; we work with each other." That is the essence of countability—it's the ability and desire for teammates to work together toward common goals. But that doesn't happen on its own. Nor is countability a given. It has to be earned. Team members who can depend on each other only during the easy times have not developed countability.

THE FORMULA FOR COUNTABILITY

I believe that there is a formula for countability. It's not complicated, but its impact is powerful. Here it is:

Character + Competence + Commitment +

Consistency + Cohesion =

Countability

When every team member embraces each of these five qualities, within himself and with others, the team can achieve the countability that is necessary to succeed.

1. Character

In *The 21 Irrefutable Laws of Leadership*, I wrote about the Law of Solid Ground, which says that trust is the foundation of leadership. That law is really about character. In the book I state, "Character makes trust possible. Trust makes leadership possible. That is the Law of Solid Ground."[2]

> *"There is no substitute for character. You can buy brains, but you cannot buy character."*
>
> —ROBERT A. COOK

In a similar way, countability begins with character because it is based on trust, which is the foundation for all interaction with people. If you cannot trust someone, you will not count on him. As Robert A. Cook remarked, "There is no substitute for character. You can buy brains, but you cannot buy character."

Anytime you desire to build a team, you have to begin by building character in the individuals who make up the team. For example, my friend Lou Holtz, who coaches football at the University of South Carolina, introduces the players on his team to a list of twelve covenants at the beginning of the season to help them understand the team culture he is trying to create. Here are the covenants:

USC—12 Covenants

1. We will accomplish what we do together. We share our success, and we never let any one of us fail alone.

2. We are all fully grown adults. We will act as such, and expect the same from the people around us.

3. We will not keep secrets. Information that affects us all will be shared by all of us, and we will quickly and openly work to separate fact from fiction.

4. We will not lie to ourselves or to each other. None of us will tolerate any of us doing so. We will depend on each other for the truth.

5. We will keep our word. We will say what we mean, and do what we say. We trust the word of others to be good as well.

6. We will keep our head. We will not panic in the face of tough times. We will always choose to roll up our sleeves rather than wring our hands.

7. We will develop our abilities and take pride in them. We will set our own standards higher than our most challenging opponent, and we will please our fans by pleasing ourselves.

8. We will treat our locker room like home and our teammates like friends. We spend too much time together to allow these things to go bad.

9. We will be unselfish and expect that everyone else will exhibit this same quality. We will care about each other without expectations.

10. We will look out for each other. We truly believe that we are our brother's keeper.

11. We are students at USC, and as such we will strive to graduate. We take pride in our grade point average and expect our teammates to do the same.

12. Losing cannot and will not be tolerated in anything we do. Losing to us is to be shamed, embarrassed, and humiliated. There is no excuse for losing a football game at USC.

When you read through the twelve points, did you notice anything? Most of them touch on issues of character. Holtz knows that if he doesn't lay a solid foundation of character within the young men on his team, he can't build anything of value on top of it.

> *"Write and publish what you want, but the only missions, values, and ethics that count in your company are those that manifest themselves in the behavior of all the people, all the time."*
>
> —BARRY GIBBONS

Barry Gibbons, in his book *This Indecision Is Final*, asserted, "Write and publish what you want, but the only missions, values, and ethics that count in your company are those that manifest themselves in the behavior of all the people, all the time."[3]

2. Competence

I spent over twenty-five years as a pastor, so I know the church world very well, and I have seen people in the religious community who act as if character is the only thing that matters. I don't think that's true. What you do is also important, as Scripture makes clear.[4] Character is the most important thing, but it's not the only thing.

If you have any doubts about that, consider this. If you had to go into surgery because of a life-threatening illness, would you be happier having a good surgeon who was a bad person or a good person who was a bad surgeon? That puts it in perspective, doesn't it? Competence matters. And if the person is going to be on the same team with you, you want competence *and* character.

3. Commitment

Having fair-weather team members doesn't make for a very pleasant team experience. When times are tough, you want to know that you can count on your teammates. You don't want to be wondering whether they're going to hang in there with you.

Dan Reiland, who is a vice president at The INJOY Group, shared with me the table on the next page that indicates the commitment of various team members.

Teams succeed or fail based on teammates' commitment to one another and the team. My friend Randy Watts, who pastors a church in Virginia, sent me a note after a conference where I taught the Law of Countability. He wrote:

> Years ago, a friend of mine attended the Virginia Military Institute, known for its rugged physical, mental, and emotional training. He told me that all the incoming freshmen are separated into companies. One of their training obstacles is to race up House Mountain, which is very steep and more than a challenge. The motivation for climbing: If you finish last, you run again. Not you, but your whole company! This makes for team commitment. If a person in your company twists an ankle or breaks a leg, other members of his company carry him! It is not enough to be the first man on top of the mountain; everyone on the team has to make it.

Real teamwork requires that kind of commitment. When teammates can't make it, you carry them the rest of the way for the sake of the team.

Level	Type of Teammate	Description
1. Green Beret Colonel	Committed Team Leader	*Dedicated to the cause. Focused on the big picture. Has a whatever-it-takes attitude.*
2. First Lieutenant	Team Achiever	*Buys into the spirit and culture of the organization. Is self-motivated and productive.*
3. OCS Graduates	Genuine Team Player	*Has passion and enthusiasm. Arrives early and stays late. Is not yet a proven leader.*
4. Private	Formal Team Member	*Enjoys being on the team. Wants to stay. Serves out of duty. Not yet a high achiever.*
5. Boot Camp Recruit	Begrudging Follower	*Will work, but only with a kick in the seat of the pants.*
6. Deserter	Nonfollower	*Won't do anything. Needs to be court-martialed.*
7. Sniper	Dangerous Follower	*Works, but makes life difficult for team. Will shoot teammates if given the chance.*

4. Consistency

Every once in a while somebody comes along who defines consistency for the rest of his teammates. In the case of the Atlanta Braves, I believe that person is Greg Maddux. If you follow baseball, then you probably know about him. Maddux is a first-rate pitcher, and he has the awards—and statistics—to prove it. He has won more than 200 games, including 176 games in the 1990s, the most of any pitcher in major-league baseball. He is the only pitcher besides Cy Young and Gaylord Perry to have won 15 or more games in 13 consecutive seasons. He is the only pitcher in baseball's history to have won the Cy Young Award four years in a row (1992–95).

For all of Maddux's awards for pitching and noteworthy stats, do you know what has been his most remarkable honor? He has been recognized as the National League's best fielder in his position by receiving a Gold Glove *ten years in a row!*

Many great pitchers are not known for their fielding. When a difficult ball is hit to a pitcher, or when the pitcher has to cover first base on a tough play to the right side of the infield, many times the other players on the team hold their collective breath. If anyone on the field is likely to make a fielding mistake, it's the pitcher. But not Maddux. He works at his fielding with the same fantastic work ethic that has made him an outstanding pitcher. The result is a career that has seen only fourteen errors in fifteen years (with two seasons of error-free fielding).

If you want your teammates to have confidence in you, to know they can count on you day in and day out, then use someone like Maddux as your example. Consistency is key.

5. Cohesion

Teammates need to develop cohesion. That's the ability to hold together, no matter how difficult the circumstances become. Navy SEAL John Roat describes cohesion this way:

Unit cohesion is one of those terms that everyone thinks they understand. In truth, most people don't have a clue. It is definitely not about everybody liking each other or being nice. It means you have a pride in the ability of your group to function at a higher level than possible for the individual. The unit doesn't shine because you're a member, you shine because you're good enough to be a member.[5]

There's an old saying when it comes to teams: Either we're pulling together or we're pulling apart. Without cohesion people aren't really a team because they're not pulling together. They're merely a group of individuals working for the same organization.

> *There's an old saying when it comes to teams: Either we're pulling together or we're pulling apart.*

Novelist and civil rights activist James Baldwin asserted, "The moment we break faith with one another, the sea engulfs us and the light goes out." When it comes down to it, countability is being able to have faith in your teammates, no matter what happens. When the chips are down, you can turn to the people on your team. Let's face it: You can't do anything that counts unless you have countability. *Teammates must be able to count on each other when it really counts.*

BROKEN TRUST

When you see a major example of broken trust that destroys countability on a team, you know it instantly. When parents run out on their children, a spouse is guilty of infidelity, or children callously deceive their parents, it is a violation of countability in the family. When employees embezzle money, or leaders abuse the power entrusted to them by people in their organization, it undermines countability in a business. And when an officer in a government agency is guilty of espionage, it not only hurts his teammates; it breaks trust with the people in an entire nation.

When the news broke in early 2001 that an FBI agent had been caught passing highly classified national security information to Russia and the former Soviet Union, the first thing I thought of was the Law of Countability. The man in this case was Robert Philip Hanssen, a counterintelligence agent who had made a career with the FBI.

Hanssen is suspected of having given the KGB (and the organization that replaced it called the SVR) sensitive information on more than twenty occasions. That information totaled more than six thousand pages of material, including counterintelligence investigative techniques, sources, methods, and operations.[6] And just as in the case of Aldridge Ames, the CIA counterintelligence officer convicted of espionage in 1994, the information illegally passed by Hanssen is believed to have precipitated the deaths of field agents working for the U.S. government.[7]

Nobody likes a traitor. In fact, in America, the name Benedict Arnold is still associated with treachery and betrayal, even though his actions occurred more than two hundred years ago. (And few remember that Arnold was a brilliant military leader.) But what makes Hanssen's case especially distasteful is that the betrayer was a member of a team that maintains high standards of conduct because of the trust given to it by the people. The FBI identifies its core values as "rigorous obedience to the Constitution of the United States; respect for the dignity of all those we protect; compassion; fairness; and uncompromising personal and institutional integrity."[8] FBI Director Louis J. Freeh said of Hanssen:

A betrayal of trust by an FBI agent, who is not only sworn to enforce the law but specifically to help protect our nation's security, is particularly abhorrent. This kind of criminal conduct represents the most traitorous action imaginable . . . It also strikes at the heart of everything the FBI represents—the commitment of over 28,000 honest and dedicated men and women in the FBI who work diligently to earn the trust and confidence of the American people every day.[9]

In other words, *teammates must be able to count on each other when it counts.* Robert Hanssen broke the trust that makes countability possible. And it may be decades before we find out how much damage he did to the country. That's a terrible thought, but that's the price that sometimes has to be paid when someone breaks the Law of Countability.

TEAMWORK THOUGHT

The greatest compliment you can receive is being counted on.

BECOMING A BETTER TEAM MEMBER

People often say that imitation is a compliment. In regard to teamwork I believe the highest compliment you can receive is trust from your teammates when it really counts.

How do your teammates feel about you? In Chapter 6 we talked about how catalysts step up to a higher level of play when crunch time comes. You may or may not be the type of player who can make things happen and then some when the game is on the line. That's okay. But can you be depended on to do *your* part, whatever that is, when your teammates need you? Do you perform and follow through in such a way that the team considers you someone they can count on? How are you doing in each of the areas examined in the chapter?

- Is your integrity unquestioned (character)?

- Do you perform your work with excellence (competence)?

- Are you dedicated to the team's success (commitment)?

- Can you be depended on every time (consistency)?

- Do your actions bring the team together (cohesion)?

If you are weak in any of these areas, talk to a mentor or trusted friend to get suggestions concerning how you can grow in that area.

BECOMING A BETTER TEAM LEADER

Developing countability and cohesion among team members is not always an easy task. And it takes time. If you are responsible for leading your team, use the suggestions of William A. Cohen in *The Art of the Leader* for building a team that is able to count on each member when it counts:

1. Develop pride in group membership.

2. Convince your group that they are the best.

3. Give recognition whenever possible.

4. Encourage organizational mottos, names, symbols, and slogans.

5. Establish your group's worth by examining and promoting its history and values.

6. Focus on the common purpose.

7. Encourage your people to participate in activities together outside of work.[10]

The more of these activities you embrace, the greater countability you will develop.

COMPANION **ONLINE** RESOURCE

Learn more about how the Law of Countability uniquely applies to you.

Take the FREE Law of Countability assessment at **LawsOfTeamwork.com**.

10

THE LAW OF THE PRICE TAG

The Team Fails to Reach Its Potential When It Fails to Pay the Price

O n December 28, 2000, one of the nation's oldest retailers, Montgomery Ward and Company, announced that it would be filing Chapter 7 bankruptcy and closing its doors forever. That announcement saddened the people of Chicago, for Ward had been an institution in that city for more than a century. What's even sadder is that the company's failure might have been avoided if leaders had learned and practiced the Law of the Price Tag before it was too late.

The retailing chain's early history is really quite remarkable. The company was founded in 1872 by Aaron Montgomery Ward, a young salesman who had worked for various dry goods merchants throughout the Midwest and South. While he was working in rural areas far from cities or large towns, he discovered that many consumers in remote areas were at the mercy of local merchants who often overcharged them for merchandise. That gave him an idea. Railroads and mail service were improving by that time. What if he bought dry goods directly from manufacturers for cash and sold them for cash via mail order to rural consumers, thus eliminating the middlemen who were gouging those customers?

PAYING THE FIRST PRICE

In 1871, Ward saved enough money from his work as a salesman to purchase some merchandise and print a one-page price list that he planned to mail out to a bunch of farmers who belonged to a fraternal organization. But before he could follow through with his plan, the devastating Chicago fire of 1871 destroyed his stock and price sheets. The setback didn't stop Ward. He convinced two sales colleagues to join him as partners, began rebuilding his stock, and reprinted the price sheet, which would become the world's first general merchandise mail-order catalog. And in 1872, at age twenty-eight, Ward opened for business.

At first, Ward was only moderately successful. In fact, a year into the business, his two partners got cold feet and asked to be bought out. Ward paid them off, then took his friend George Thorne into the business as a full partner. Together they worked hard, taking orders and shipping out merchandise by rail. Meanwhile, in 1875, Ward and Thorne came up with a novel idea. They decided to include a new credo in their catalog. It said, "Satisfaction Guaranteed or Your Money Back." And the business took off.

Ward's tenacity and willingness to pay the price twice for starting his own business came to fruition less than a decade later. The company that had begun with $1,600 of capital in 1872 had sales of

$300,000 in 1878. Nine years after that, the company's sales rose to $1 million. By the turn of the century, Montgomery Ward and Company's catalog, which would come to be known as the "Wish Book," grew to five hundred pages and was being mailed to more than a million people every year. And the company's headquarters was a new building on Michigan Avenue in Chicago—the biggest skyscraper west of New York City.[1]

STOPPING PAYMENT

Then in 1901, Montgomery Ward retired in order to spend the final years of his life working to make Chicago a better place. During the first two decades of the new century, the company continued to thrive. But in the late 1910s, things began to change. Ward's success had prompted the start of another Chicago-based company in 1886: Sears, Roebuck, and Co. It, like Montgomery Ward and Company, was a catalog-based merchant that catered to rural customers. Back when both companies began business, most of the U.S. population lived in rural areas. But the country was changing. Cities were filling up. When the 1920 census was completed, it showed that for the first time in the nation's history, the majority of the population lived in urban centers—and shopping habits were changing as a result.

Robert E. Wood, a former army quartermaster general, was brought in to run Montgomery Ward in 1919, and he saw the coming boom in retail sales. He wanted to begin opening stores in cities where people could shop in person, but the owners were unwilling to go along with the idea.[2] They simply would not pay the price to make the change.

PASSED BY

Knowing where the future lay in the business, Wood left Ward. In 1924, he went on staff at Sears as vice president. He convinced the people who ran Sears to take a chance on retail store sales. They agreed to open one store in Chicago as a test the following year. It was an immediate success. Two years later, Sears had opened 27 stores. By 1929, the company had built more than 300. Even during the depression, Sears continued to expand, and in 1931, Sears retail store sales surpassed catalog sales.[3] Wood became the company's chairman, a position he held until 1954, and Sears became the most successful department store chain in the country.

Montgomery Ward and Company never really recovered from that early error. It opened some retail stores, but it wasn't aggressive enough to overtake Sears. *The team fails to reach its potential when it fails to pay the price.* Time after time, Ward failed to pay the price. During the depression, the company hoarded cash and stopped expansion while Sears gained more ground. After World War II when other stores began moving to the suburbs, Ward failed to seize the opportunity to try to get back on top. Each time the market changed, the company's leaders didn't pay the price necessary to win a market. For the last twenty-five years of the twentieth century, they struggled to keep their doors open. Finally, after 128 years in business, Montgomery Ward closed. That's what can happen when people violate the Law of the Price Tag.

PRICE POINTS

If a team doesn't reach its potential, seldom is ability the issue. It's rarely a matter of resources either. It's almost always a payment issue. Montgomery Ward and Company had plenty of resources, and it had the talent it needed, including the leader who could move the team forward. The problem was that the company's owners were unwilling to get out of their comfort zone, take a risk, and try to break new ground.

One of the reasons teams fail to pay the price to reach their potential is that they misunderstand the Law of the Price Tag. They honestly don't know how it works. Allow me to give you four truths about this law that will help to clarify it in your mind.

1. The Price Must Be Paid by Everyone

In *Straight Talk for Monday Morning*, Allan Cox observed:

You have to give up something to be a member of a team. It may be a phony role you've assigned to yourself, such as the guy who talks too much, the woman who remains silent, the know-it-all, the know-nothing, the hoarder of talented subordinates, the non-sharer of some resource such as management information systems (MIS), or whatever. You give up something, to be sure, such as some petty corner of privilege, but gain authenticity in return. The team, moreover, doesn't quash individual accomplishment; rather it empowers personal contributions.[4]

> *If everyone doesn't pay the price to win, then everyone will pay the price by losing.*

People who've never had the experience of being on a winning team often fail to realize that *every* team member must pay a price. I think some of them think that if others work hard, they can coast to their potential. But that is never true. If everyone doesn't pay the price to win, then everyone will pay the price by losing.

2. The Price Must Be Paid All the Time

Many people have what I call destination disease. I describe it in my book *The 21 Indispensable Qualities of a Leader.*

> Some people mistakenly believe that if they can accomplish a particular goal, they no longer have to grow. It can happen with almost anything: earning a degree, reaching a desired position, receiving a particular award, or achieving a financial goal.
>
> But effective leaders cannot afford to think that way. The day they stop growing is the day they forfeit their potential—and the potential of their organization. Remember the words of Ray Kroc: "As long as you're green, you're growing. As soon as you're ripe, you start to rot."[5]

Destination disease is as dangerous for a team as it is for any individual. It makes us believe that we can stop working, stop striving, stop paying the price—yet still reach our potential. But as Earl Blaik, former football coach at the United States Military Academy, observed, "There is no substitute for work. It is the price of success." That truth never goes away. That's why President Dwight D. Eisenhower remarked, "There are no victories at bargain prices." If you want to reach your potential, you can never let up.

> *"There are no victories at bargain prices."*
>
> —DWIGHT D. EISENHOWER

3. The Price Increases If the Team Wants to Improve, Change, or Keep Winning

As I mentioned in the introduction of this book, there are few back-to-back champions in sports. And few companies stay at the top of *Forbes* magazine's lists for a decade. Becoming a champion has a high price. But remaining on top costs even more. And improving upon your best is even more costly. The higher you are, the more you have to pay to make even small improvements. World champion sprinters improve their times not by seconds, but by hundredths of a second.

No one can move closer to his potential without paying in some way to get there. If you want to change professions, you have to get more education, additional work experience, or both. If you want to run a race at a faster pace, you must pay by training harder and smarter. If you want to increase earnings from your investments, you put in more money or take greater risks. The same principle applies to teams. To improve, change, or keep winning, as a group the team must pay a price, and so must the individuals on it.

4. The Price Never Decreases

Most people who quit don't give up at the bottom of the mountain; they stop halfway up it. Nobody sets out with the purpose of losing. The problem is often a mistaken belief that a time will come when success will suddenly get cheaper. But life rarely works that way.

Maybe that kind of thinking was the problem with Montgomery Ward and Company. In 1919, when the decision

> *Most people who quit don't give up at the bottom of the mountain; they stop halfway up it.*

makers had the chance to make Ward one of the first big companies to open a chain of retail stores, they probably evaluated what it would cost them—in terms of time, money, effort, change—and they thought that it was too great a price to pay. So they passed on the opportunity.

A few years later when Sears began to breeze past Ward, the cost to compete was even higher. The company paid to get into retail store sales, yet it was still behind. That price continued to go up year after year, especially as Sears beat Ward in securing prime locations. Even as late as the 1970s and 1980s, Ward paid more and more to improve, yet fell farther and farther behind. The company dabbled in various niches, trying to compete against Wal-Mart, Target, and Circuit City, but it kept getting clobbered. The leaders thought the price would be less the next time— but it kept going up and up.

> When it comes to the Law of the Price Tag, I believe there are really only two kinds of teams who violate it: those who don't realize the price of success, and those who know the price but are not willing to pay it.

When it comes to the Law of the Price Tag, I believe there are really only two kinds of teams who violate it: those who don't realize the price of success, and those who know the price but are not willing to pay it. No one can force a team member to have the will to succeed. Each person must decide in his own heart whether the goal is worth the price that must be paid. But every person ought to know what to expect to pay in order for a team to succeed.

THE PRICE OF TEAMWORK

For that reason, I offer the following observations about the cost of being part of a winning team. To become team players, you and your teammates will have at least the following required of you:

Sacrifice

There can be no success without sacrifice. James Allen observed, "He who would accomplish little must sacrifice little; he who would achieve much must sacrifice much." When you become part of a team, you may be aware of some of the things you will have to give up. But you can be sure that no matter how much you expect to give for the team, at some point you will be required to give more. That's the nature of teamwork. The team gets to the top only through the sweat, blood, and sacrifice of its team members.

Time Commitment

Teamwork does not come cheaply. It costs you time—that means you pay for it with your life. It takes time to get to know people, to build relationships with them, to learn how you and they work together. Teamwork can't be developed in microwave time. Teams grow strong in a Crock-Pot environment.

Personal Development

Your team will reach its potential only if you reach your potential. That means today's ability is not enough. Or to put it the way leadership expert Max DePree did: "We cannot become what we need to be by remaining what we are." That desire to keep striving,

> *Your team will reach its potential only if you reach your potential.*

to keep getting better, is a key to your ability, but it is also crucial for the betterment of the team. That is why UCLA's John Wooden, a marvelous team leader and the greatest college basketball coach of all time, said, "It's what you learn after you know it all that counts."

Unselfishness

People naturally look out for themselves. The question "What's in it for me?" is never far from their thoughts. But if a team is to reach its potential, its players must put the team's agenda ahead of

> *"When you give your best to the world, the world returns the favor."*
>
> —H. JACKSON BROWN

their own. Some people see the big picture more easily than others do and realize that they will receive more if they give more. For others, that is more difficult—especially if they already have a track record of high achievement. But H. Jackson Brown's Boomerang Theory is true: "When you give your best to the world, the world returns the favor." And if you give your best to the team, it will return more to you than you give, and together you will achieve more than you can on your own.

Certainly there are other prices individuals must pay to be part of a team. You can probably list several specific ones you've paid to be on a team. The point is that people can choose to stand on the sidelines of life and try to do everything solo. Or they can get into the game by being part of a team. It's a trade-off between independence and interdependence. The rewards of teamwork can be great, but there is always a cost. You always have to give up to go up.

About a month ago I was teaching the 17 Laws of Teamwork to a group of businesspeople in Atlanta, and after I taught the Law of the Price Tag, Virgil Berry came up to me and slipped me a note. It said, "John, the price tag for failure is greater than the price of success. The price for accepting failure is poverty, depression, dejection, and a downtrodden spirit." The people at Montgomery Ward know that all too well. *The team fails to reach its potential when it fails to pay the price.*

WHAT PRICE FOR A NATION?

Paying a high price does not always guarantee victory. Many teams sacrifice dearly, only to fall short of their goals. But sometimes great sacrifice is rewarded with great results. That was the case for the Revolutionary Army of the newly formed United States and its commander, George Washington, during the winter of 1777 in Valley Forge, Pennsylvania.

The year 1777 was not a particularly successful one for General Washington and his troops. Following defeats at Brandywine, Paoli, and Germantown and the loss of Philadelphia to the British, Washington and eleven thousand soldiers straggled into Valley Forge on December 19 of that year. The troops were demoralized, and they were facing the prospect of a bitter winter with minimal shelter and comforts.

What those men probably wanted most was to go home and forget about the war for freedom. But if they did, the cost would be high. Positioned as they were, they could keep an eye on the British troops under General Howe in Philadelphia. More important, they were in a place where they could defend York, Pennsylvania, to which the Continental Congress had fled when the capital fell to the British. If the men at Valley Forge didn't pay the price, the government would fall, the army would be disbanded, and the Revolutionary War would be lost.

Conditions were horrible. The men were ill-equipped and poorly supplied. A few days after their arrival, Washington wrote to the Continental Congress, saying, "2,898 men were unfit for duty because they were barefoot or otherwise naked [insufficiently clothed for the harsh weather]." Things were so bad that sentries had to stand on their hats to ward off frostbite in their feet. By February 1, 1778, only 5,000 men were available for service.[6]

PAYING THE PRICE—AND THEN SOME

Miraculously, the troops didn't give up. They bore the brunt of the difficult winter. But they did more than just hang on and survive. They took the time to become better soldiers. Prior to their stay at Valley Forge, they were disorganized and untrained. To remedy that, General Washington employed the talents of a former officer in the Prussian army, Baron von Steuben.

First, von Steuben imposed organization on the camp and introduced improved sanitation. Then, under his instruction, one company of men was transformed into a crack team of soldiers. They in turn helped to train the other companies of men. Von Steuben also standardized the military maneuvers throughout the army so that the men could work better as a team, no matter which officers commanded them. By the time the army mobilized in June of 1778, it was a match for any group of soldiers, even the British, who were considered by some to be the best in the world.

Washington's army went on to win battles against a British army with far superior numbers. And his soldiers fought in the Battle of Yorktown, the decisive battle that turned the war in favor of the newly formed country. Those of us who live in the United States are grateful to them, for the price they paid more than two hundred years ago paved the way for us to live in a country of great freedom and opportunity. While it's true that *the team fails to reach its potential when it fails to pay the price,* it's also true that when the price *is* paid, the rewards can be abundant. That's the blessing of the Law of the Price Tag.

TEAMWORK THOUGHT

You seldom get more than you pay for.

BECOMING A BETTER TEAM MEMBER

If you are an achiever, then you probably have lots of dreams and goals. Write down some of the things you desire to accomplish in the next one to five years:

1. _Hire a diverse Staff_

2. _Reach Kids in South Storkton_

3. _Preach & Teach more_

4. _____

5. _____

6. _____

7. _____

8. _____

9. _____

10. _____

Now, which of them are you willing to give up? You always need to be ready to ask yourself that question when you are part of a team. When your personal goals conflict with the greater goals of your team, you have three choices:

1. *Put down the goal* (because the team is more important).

2. *Put off the goal* (because it's not the right time).

3. *Part with the team* (because it's better for everyone).

The one thing you have no right to do is to expect the team to sacrifice its collective goals for yours.

BECOMING A BETTER TEAM LEADER

If you lead a team, then you must convince your teammates to sacrifice for the good of the group. The more talented the team members, the more difficult it may be to convince them to put the team first.

Begin by modeling sacrifice. Show the team that you are . . .

- Willing to make financial sacrifices for the team.
- Willing to keep growing for the sake of the team.
- Willing to empower others for the sake of the team.
- Willing to make difficult decisions for the sake of the team.

Once you have modeled the willingness to pay a price for the potential of the team, you have the credibility to ask others to do the same. Then when you recognize sacrifices that teammates must make for the team, show them why and how to do it. Then praise their sacrifices to their teammates.

COMPANION
ONLINE
RESOURCE

Learn more about how the Law of the Price Tag uniquely applies to you.

Take the FREE Law of the Price Tag assessment at **LawsOfTeamwork.com**.

THE LAW OF THE SCOREBOARD

The Team Can Make Adjustments When It Knows Where It Stands

I n the previous chapter, you read about Montgomery Ward and Company, an American business that fell on hard times because it failed to heed the Law of the Price Tag. For a couple of decades, it looked as if another American institution was headed for a similar disaster: Walt Disney Productions.

THE MOUSE THAT ROARED

The company was founded by Walt Disney and his brother, Roy, in the 1920s. They began doing silent animation shorts and grew the company into one of the most loved and respected entertainment companies in the world. They continually broke new ground. They produced the first talking cartoon and the first color cartoon, both featuring Mickey Mouse, who has since become an American icon. *Snow White,* the first feature-length animated movie ever, was a radically innovative idea. While it was being made, many called it "Disney's folly." When it was released in 1937, it became the most successful film ever made up to that time. (Some say it's the most successful of all time!)

During the next two decades, Walt Disney Productions made wonderful movies that became classics. It expanded into television production. And it opened the world's first theme park. The name Disney became synonymous with creative family entertainment.

THE COMPANY THAT WHIMPERED

But after Walt died in 1966, the company started down a very bumpy road. Where Walt Disney Productions had once stood for innovation, it came to be marked by imitation—of its own past successes. Don Bluth, who left Disney in 1979, commented, "We felt like we were animating the same picture over and over again, with the faces changed a little."[1]

Instead of trying to look forward and break ground, Card Walker, who oversaw movie production, always asked himself, "What would Walt have done?" People at the studio began to joke morbidly, "We're working for a dead man."[2] The company cranked out more formula movies that didn't make a profit, and revenues continued to shrink. In 1981 the film division had an income of $34.6 million. In 1982 its income had fallen to $19.6 million. In 1983 it incurred a loss of $33.3 million. And the value of Disney stock was plummeting.

During that period, many American corporations were becoming victims of hostile takeovers, where Wall Street raiders would gain control of the company, cut it into pieces, and sell off its parts at a profit for themselves and their backers. Since Disney's stock value was down and it carried little debt, it became ripe for a hostile takeover.

In 1984, Disney narrowly avoided one takeover attempt and was facing the threat of yet another when its board of directors finally took a realistic look at where Disney stood. They decided that if the company was to survive, it would require radical changes, including something it had never done in its history—bringing in someone from outside Disney to run the company.

GETTING BACK INTO THE GAME

The people selected to turn around Disney were Michael Eisner as chairman and CEO and Frank Wells as president and COO. Concerning their challenging task, Eisner remarked,

> Our job wasn't to create something new, but to bring back the magic, to dress Disney up in more stylish clothes and expand its reach, to remind people why they loved the company in the first place . . . A brand is a living entity, and it is enriched or undermined cumulatively over time, the product of a thousand small gestures.[3]

Eisner was writing about his work on the Disney brand, but his remarks describe the approach he and Wells took to revitalizing the entire company. That involved a variety of strategies.

For one thing, they changed the name of the organization from Walt Disney Productions to the Walt Disney Company, reflecting the diversity of its interests. They brought together all of the organization's corporate executives and division heads for a weekly lunch to promote cohesiveness and to share ideas across divisions. They also hired key leaders, such as Jeffrey Katzenberg, to run their movie and television operations.

GOAL!

In a matter of a few years, Disney once again became a vital player in the entertainment industry. The almost-dead television division produced hits such as *The Golden Girls* and *Home Improvement*. The movie division, which had recently produced few movies and lost so much money, produced more movies in greater volume, with twenty-seven of its first thirty-three turning a profit. Before long, the company had four movie divisions: Disney, Touchstone, Hollywood Pictures, and Miramax. In late 1987, Disney became the number one studio at the box office for the first time in its history. And the animation division once again set the pace for the industry by creating films such as *The Little Mermaid, Beauty and the Beast, Aladdin,* and *The Lion King.*

Eisner and Wells expanded the company's efforts into new areas. They increased land development and built numerous new hotels at Walt Disney World. In 1987 they also opened retail stores in malls for the first time. Four years later, Disney owned 125 stores, which were generating $300 million in annual revenue. And of course, they improved the theme parks through expansion, innovation, and strategic partnerships with people such as George Lucas and Steven Spielberg. When they took over the company in 1984, the parks generated income of $250 million. By 1990, their income reached $800 million.

In 2000, the Walt Disney Company had revenues of $25.4 billion with $2.9 billion in net income (more than double the figures from 1984).[4] Disney has done more than just turn itself around. It has become an entertainment giant and one of the most powerful corporations in the world. For many of the years when the company was struggling, its team members looked at its history and the memory of its dead founder to gauge what to do. What they needed to do was to look at the scoreboard. *The team can make adjustments when it knows where it stands.* Eisner and Wells brought that ability to the company. They understood and implemented the Law of the Scoreboard.

UNDERSCORING THE SCOREBOARD

Every "game" has its own rules and its own definition of what it means to win. Some teams measure their success in points scored; others in profits. Still others may look at the number of people they serve. But no matter what the game is, there is always a scoreboard. And if a team is to accomplish its goals, it has to know where it stands. It has to look at itself in light of the scoreboard.

> *If a team is to accomplish its goals, it has to know where it stands.*

Why is that so important? Because teams that succeed make adjustments to continually improve themselves and their situations. For example, think about how a football team approaches a game. Before the competition starts, the team spends a tremendous amount of time planning. Players study hours of game film. They spend days figuring out what their opponent is likely to do, and they decide the best way to win. They come up with a detailed game plan.

As the game begins, the game plan is very important, and the scoreboard means nothing. But as the game goes on, the game plan means less and less, and the scoreboard becomes more and more significant. Why? Because the game is constantly changing. You see, the game plan tells what you *want* to happen. But the scoreboard tells what *is* happening.

WHY THE SCOREBOARD?

No team can ignore the reality of its situation and win. For years, Disney clung tenaciously to an out-of-date game plan while the world and the entertainment industry kept changing around it. The Disney team never really gave a hard look at the scoreboard. As a result they kept losing. That's what happens when you ignore the Law of the Scoreboard.

For any kind of team, the scoreboard is essential in the following ways:

1. The Scoreboard Is Essential to Understanding

In sports, players, coaches, and fans understand the importance of the scoreboard. That's why it is so visible at every stadium, arena, and ball field. The scoreboard provides a snapshot of the game at any given time. Even if you arrive at a game halfway into it, you can look at the scoreboard and assess the situation well.

> *The scoreboard provides a snapshot of the game at any given time.*

I'm often surprised by how many people outside sports try to succeed without a scoreboard. Some families operate their households without budgets, yet wonder why they are in debt. Some small-business owners go year after year without tracking sales or creating a balance sheet and wonder why they can't grow the business. Some pastors busy themselves with worthy activities, but never stop to measure whether they are reaching people or performing according to biblical standards.

2. The Scoreboard Is Essential to Evaluating

I believe that personal growth is a key to success. That's why I've taught lessons on growth at conferences and in books for more than twenty years. A key principle I teach is this:

$$\text{Growth} = \text{Change}$$

This sounds overly simple, doesn't it? But people sometimes lose sight of the fact that they cannot grow and remain the same at the same time. Most people are in a position that could be described by something Coach Lou Holtz once said: "We aren't where we want to be; we aren't where we ought to be; but thank goodness we aren't where we used to be."

But when it comes to growth, change alone is not enough. If you want to become better, you have to change in the right direction. You can do that only if you are able to evaluate yourself and your teammates. That is another reason for the scoreboard. It gives you continual feedback. Competing without a scoreboard is like bowling without pins. You may be working hard, but you don't really know how you're doing.

3. The Scoreboard Is Essential to Decision Making

Once you've evaluated your situation, you're ready to make decisions. In football, the quarterback uses information from the scoreboard to decide what play to call. In baseball, the scoreboard helps the manager know when to bring in a relief pitcher. In basketball, it can be used to determine whether to call a timeout.

That was the case at Disney. First Eisner looked at the company to understand its overall position. Then he evaluated individual areas for their effectiveness. Only then was he able to make sound decisions concerning how to get Disney back into the game.

4. The Scoreboard Is Essential to Adjusting

The higher the level on which you and your team are competing, the smaller the adjustments become to achieve your best. But making key adjustments is the secret to winning, and the scoreboard helps you to see where the adjustments need to be made.

One of the people on my staff is employing a unique scoreboard to help him make the adjustments required to go to the next level. That person is Kevin Small, the president of INJOY. Kevin is a real go-getter with high energy and enthusiasm. Being a young leader, he also has weak areas he needs to work on. To help him with that, he has engaged a personal coach to advise him, to help him read the scoreboard in his life, and to hold him accountable for growth. And it's really helping him. The small adjustments Kevin is making are taking him to another level and moving him closer to fulfilling his already tremendous potential.

5. The Scoreboard Is Essential to Winning

In the end, nobody can win without the scoreboard. How do you know when the game is on the line without the scoreboard? How do you know when time is running out unless you check the scoreboard? How will you know if it's cruise time or crunch time unless you have the scoreboard as a measuring device? If your desire is to take a leisurely drive with some friends, then you don't need to worry about a thing. But if you're trying to win the Indy 500, then you and your team *must* know how you're doing!

Some organizations view the scoreboard as a necessary evil. Others try to ignore it—something they cannot do for long and still do well in their profession. And some organizations make checking the scoreboard such an integral part of their culture that they are continually able to recognize and seize opportunities leading to huge success.

High Touch in a High-Tech World

That is certainly the case for eBay. I'm not a technical person. I don't have a computer—I don't even know how to use one—so I have not used eBay. I first heard about it from friends who are collectors. They talked about being able to find things they wanted through auctions held on the Internet. They seemed to be having fun with it, but to tell the truth I didn't pay much attention. Then I started seeing articles about eBay in the financial pages, and I read about the company's president and CEO, Meg Whitman.

Ebay is an e-commerce company that specializes in connecting buyers and sellers of goods on-line. It was founded by Pierre Omidyar in his San Jose, California, living room in September of 1995 with the idea of helping people find used, rare, or collectible items. The idea took off and became so successful that Omidyar soon recognized that he was in over his head. That's when he hired Meg Whitman, who had an MBA from Harvard and tremendous leadership experience as a general manager at Hasbro, president and CEO of FTD, and senior vice president of the Walt Disney Company.

An article in *Time* magazine explains eBay's success this way:

> As an online middleman between buyers and sellers, eBay is building an empire that bricks and mortar could not have touched. "If Buy.com goes down, you can still go to Circuit City," says Meg Whitman, . . . CEO of eBay. But if eBay crashes, there's nowhere else to go. And because eBay's job is connecting people—not selling them things—it isn't lumbered with a traditional retailing cost structure . . . "Ebay is the only e-tailer that really fulfills the promise of the Web," says Faye Landes, an e-commerce analyst at Sanford C. Bernstein & Co.[5]

The real genius of eBay is its mastery of the Law of the Scoreboard. It constantly makes adjustments because it knows where it stands, and that is what keeps it ahead. In the case of eBay, the scoreboard is the desires and interests of its customers—and potential customers. Sensing that many people are uneasy with conducting monetary transactions on the Internet, eBay made trust, safety, and privacy hallmarks of the company. Knowing that people wanted to get specific feedback on the individuals selling merchandise on the site, eBay created a unique rating system that allows subscribers to exchange information. The company even created a special Consumer Insights Group to track what people want.

LEARNING FROM THE CUSTOMER

Over the last three years, eBay has learned everything it can about its users and what they want while keeping its finger on the pulse of larger consumer trends. The company has expanded from being a place to trade Beanie Babies to a multifaceted auction service that offers among other services:

- Special local trading for difficult-to-ship items

- Global auction service that covers 150 countries (including a strong presence in Europe)

- A business-to-business exchange for products and services

- An automobile auction site

- Real estate services

And in 2000, when eBay saw that a new start-up company called Half.com was thriving by selling used CDs, books, movies, and video games at set prices, eBay bought the company and added it to its holdings.[6]

The result is that eBay has received highly favorable recognition and hundreds of awards, including *Business Week* Entrepreneur of the Year, E-Retailer of the Year Award from *E-Retailer*, and a place on the list of *Forbes* magazine's one hundred most dynamic companies in America. In 2000, it had 22.5 million registered users, controlled 80 percent of the on-line auction market, and had revenues of $430 million (up 92 percent from 1999).

While other Internet-based companies are struggling to survive and searching for ways to finally make a profit, eBay seems poised to keep growing—and winning. Why? Because the eBay team always has an eye on the scoreboard. And *the team can make adjustments when it knows where it stands.* That's the Law of the Scoreboard.

TEAMWORK THOUGHT

When you know what to do, then you can do what you know.

BECOMING A BETTER TEAM MEMBER

What is the scoreboard in your business or field? How do you measure your progress? Is it the bottom line? Is it the number of people you reach? Is it the level of excellence or innovation with which you do your work? How do you keep score?

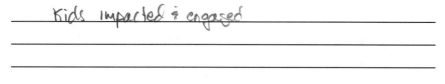

When you know what to do, then you can do what you know.

Take some time to identify how your team keeps score. Write the criteria here:

Kids imparted & engaged

Now think about how you should be measuring yourself individually. What should you be keeping track of to make sure you are doing your best? Write the criteria here:

National Office

BECOMING A BETTER TEAM LEADER

If you lead the team, you have primary responsibility for checking the scoreboard and communicating the team's situation to its members. That doesn't necessarily mean you have to do it all by yourself. But you do need to make sure that team members continually evaluate, adjust, and make decisions as quickly as possible. That's the key to winning.

Do you have a system to make sure that happens? Or do you generally rely on your intuition? Using intuition is fine—as long as you have some fail-safe backups to make sure you don't let the team down.

Evaluate how consistently and effectively you consult your scoreboard. If you're not doing it as well as you should, then create a system that helps you to do it or empowers the leaders on your team to share the responsibility.

COMPANION **ONLINE** RESOURCE

Learn more about how the Law of the Scoreboard uniquely applies to you.

Take the FREE Law of the Scoreboard assessment at **LawsOfTeamwork.com**.

THE LAW OF THE BENCH

Great Teams Have Great Depth

Have you ever heard the expression "It's not over until the fat lady sings," or Yogi Berra's famous comment, "It ain't over till it's over"? Would you be surprised to know that sometimes it *is* over before it's over—and you can know when that is if you know the Law of the Bench?

Let me give you an example. One Saturday in September of 2000, I went to a football game with some friends: Kevin Small, the president of INJOY; Chris Goede, who used to play professional ball; and Steve Miller, my wonderful son-in-law. We were looking forward to an exciting game between the Georgia Tech Yellow Jackets and the Florida State Seminoles, even though FSU was a very strong favorite. There's an intense rivalry between all Georgia and Florida college teams, so the teams can get pretty pumped up.

And on that day, we weren't disappointed. The teams were battling, and the score was close. Tech was playing its heart out.

ONLY A MATTER OF TIME

But as the third quarter came to a close, I said, "Come on, guys. This one is over." I sometimes leave games early because I hate to be stuck in traffic. Of course, if a game is really close or is likely to have some historic significance (such as a no-hitter in baseball), I stay to the end. On that day, the guys were surprised by my desire to leave, especially since the game was close and Tech had finally pulled ahead, 15 to 12.

"You don't want to see the end of the game?" asked Chris, a little curious.

"No, this game is over," I said. "Let's go to the car."

On our way back, we talked about it. It's true that Tech was hanging in there against FSU, especially when it came to the way the Yellow Jackets were playing defense. That was no easy task because the Seminoles had a powerful offense. But I had noticed throughout the course of the game that while Tech's starters were still in the game, FSU had been substituting many players from the bench— and the team's level of play had not been negatively affected. Because of that, I knew it was only a matter of time before Tech's players would be worn down by the powerful bench of FSU. And sure enough, the final score was 26 to 21 with FSU on top. That's the impact of the Law of the Bench. *Great teams have great depth.*

A great starter alone is simply not enough if a team wants to go to the highest level.

THE ROLE OF THE BENCH

It's not difficult to see the importance of having well-trained, capable reserve players who sit on the bench in sports. In major-league baseball, the teams who win championships do so because they have more than just a good pitching rotation and solid fielding. They possess a bull pen with strong players who can substitute or pinch-hit off the bench. In the NBA, players and fans have long recognized the impact of the bench by talking about the all-important sixth man, the person who makes a significant contribution to the team's success yet isn't one of the five starters on the basketball court. And today's professional football coaches express the need to have two highly skilled quarterbacks capable of winning games on their teams. A great starter alone is simply not enough if a team wants to go to the highest level.

Any team that wants to excel must have good substitutes as well as starters. That's true in any field, not just sports. You may be able to do some wonderful things with a handful of top people, but if you want your team to do well over the long haul, you've got to build your bench. A great team with no bench eventually collapses.

DEFINING THE BENCH

In sports, it's easy to define which people are the starters and which make up the bench. But how do you define them in other fields? I want to suggest the following definitions:

Starters are frontline people who directly add value to the organization or who directly influence its course.

The bench is made up of the people who indirectly add value to the organization or who support the starters.

A team's starters are the people most often in the spotlight, and as a result, they get most of the credit, and the people on the bench are liable to be neglected or overlooked. In fact, the people most likely to discount or discredit the contribution of the bench may be the starters. Some key players enjoy reminding the substitutes that they are "riding the pine." But any starter who minimizes the contribution of the bench is self-centered, underestimates what it takes for a team to be a success, and doesn't understand that *great teams have great depth.*

A leader who truly understood the Law of the Bench was UCLA's John Wooden, the "Wizard of Westwood," whose teams won ten college basketball national championships. Coach Wooden valued every person on his teams and the contribution that each person made. No coach did a better job of keeping his teams playing at the highest level over the long haul than Wooden. He observed, "Unselfishness is a trait I always insisted upon. I believed that every basketball team is a unit, and I didn't separate my players as to starters and subs. I tried to make it clear that every man plays a role, including the coach, the assistants, the trainer and the managers."[1]

THE BENCH IS INDISPENSABLE

Every human being has value, and every player on a team adds value to the team in some way. These truths alone should be enough to make team members care about the bench players. But there are also more specific reasons to honor and develop the players who may not be considered starters. Here are several:

1. Today's Bench Players May Be Tomorrow's Stars

Rare are the people who begin their careers as stars. And those who do sometimes find that their success is like that of some child actors. After a brief flash in the pan, they are never able to recapture the attention they got early on.

Most successful people go through an apprenticeship or period of seasoning. Look at someone like quarterback Joe Montana, who was inducted into the NFL Hall of Fame in 2000. He spent two years on the bench as a backup before being named the San Francisco 49ers starter. And as he was breaking records and leading his team to numerous Super Bowls, the person who sat on the bench as a backup to him was Steve Young, another top-notch quarterback.

> *Every human being has value, and every player on a team adds value to the team in some way.*

Some talented team members are recognized early for their positive potential and are groomed to succeed. Others labor in obscurity for years, learning, growing, and gaining experience. Then after a decade of hard work, they become "overnight successes." With the way people like to move from job to job today—and even from career to career—good leaders should always keep their eyes open for emerging talent. Never be in a hurry to pigeonhole anyone on your team as a nonstarter. Given the right encouragement, training, and opportunities, nearly anyone who has the desire has the potential to emerge someday as an effective player.

2. The Success of a Supporting Player Can Multiply the Success of a Starter

When every team member fulfills the role that best suits his talents, gifts, and experience and excels in that role, then the team really hums. The achievement of the whole team makes the starters flourish, and the achievement of the starters makes the team flourish. The whole team really is greater than the sum of its parts. Or to put it the way John Wooden did: "The main ingredient of stardom is the rest of the team."

> *"The main ingredient of stardom is the rest of the team."*
>
> —JOHN WOODEN

You have probably seen teams led by people who don't understand this truth. For example, they have million-dollar salespeople spending half of their time bogged down in paperwork rather than making calls on potential clients. If the organization would hire someone who enjoyed administrative tasks, not only would the salespeople be happier and more productive, but the gains in sales would more than make up for the cost of that support person.

We follow this rule at ISS, my company that provides consulting to churches for fund-raising. We employ consultants whose skills and backgrounds are truly one in a million. They work with hundreds of individual churches out in the field every year, and that is where they need to be to use their strengths. However, each consulting job requires numerous letters, instruction manuals, and other printed materials. And to accomplish that, ISS employs a team of talented support people who do a fabulous job with that work. When each person is allowed to work in an area of strength, the entire team wins.

3. There Are More Bench Players Than Starters

If you read through the roster of any successful team, you will see that the starters are always outnumbered by the other players on the team. In professional basketball, twelve people are on the team, but only five start. Major-league baseball teams start nine but carry forty players. In pro football, twenty-two people start on offense and defense, but each team is allowed to have fifty-three players in all. (College teams often have more than one hundred!)

You find similar situations in every field. In the entertainment industry, the actors are often known, but the hundreds of crew members necessary to make a movie aren't. In ministry, everyone recognizes the people up front during a worship service, but it takes scores of people working behind the scenes to bring that service together. For any politician or corporate executive or big-name fashion designer that you know about, there are hundreds of people toiling quietly in the background to make the person's work possible. Nobody can neglect the majority of the team and hope to be successful.

4. A Bench Player Placed Correctly Will at Times Be More Valuable Than a Starter

I think if you asked most people how they would classify administrative assistants as team members, they would tell you that they consider them to be bench players since their primary role is support. I would agree with that—although in some cases, administrative people have direct influence on an organization.

Take, for example, my assistant, Linda Eggers. Over the years, Linda has done just about everything at INJOY. She has been the company's bookkeeper. She used to run our conferences. She did marketing and product development. She is a very talented person. I think Linda is capable of doing just about anything. But she has chosen to take a supporting role as my assistant. And in that position, she makes a huge impact. Today my company has more than two hundred employees. I respect and value all of them. But if I lost everything tomorrow and I could keep only five or six people with whom to start over from scratch, Linda would be one of the people I would fight to keep. Her value as a support person makes her a starter.

5. A Strong Bench Gives the Leader More Options

When a team has no bench, the only option of its leader is moving the starters around to maximize their effectiveness. If a starter can't perform, the team is out of luck. When a team has a weak bench, the leader has a few options, but they are often not very good. But when a team has a great bench, the options are almost endless.

> When a team has a great bench, the options are almost endless.

That's why someone like Bobby Bowden, the coach at FSU, was able to wear down Georgia Tech. If one of his players got hurt, he had someone to replace him. If his opponent changed defenses, he had offensive players in reserve to overcome the challenge. No matter what kind of situation he faced, with a strong bench he had options that would give the team a chance to win.

6. The Bench Is Usually Called Upon at Critical Times for the Team

When an army is in trouble, what does it do? It calls up the reserves. That's the way it is in every area of life. You don't need the bench when things are going well; you need it when things aren't going well. When the starter gets hurt and the game is in jeopardy, a substitute steps in. That person's effectiveness often determines the team's success.

If your team is experiencing a tough time, then you know the importance of having a good bench. But if you are experiencing a smooth period, then now is the time to develop your backup players. Build the bench today for the crisis you will face tomorrow.

TODAY'S ACTIONS BUILD TOMORROW'S TEAM

As you think about the starters and the bench players on your team, recognize that the future of your team can be predicted by three things:

1. Recruitment: Who Is Joining the Team?

Adlai E. Stevenson offered this advice: "There are only three rules of sound administration: Pick good men, tell them not to cut corners, and back them to the limit; and picking good men is the most important." You cannot build a winning team without good players.

When it comes to recruiting, there are really only two kinds: You find the player for the position, or you find the position for the player. In the first situation, you have a position open, and you look for someone to fill that position. That is the typical way most recruiting works. But sometimes even when you don't have a position open, you find a potential player who is so good that you simply cannot pass up the opportunity to get him on the team.

I was in the second situation last year. When I discovered that John Hull might be interested in coming to work for The INJOY Group, I didn't have a specific position for him. But he is such a high-impact player that I brought him aboard. And in a matter of a few months, he became the president of EQUIP, the nonprofit organization I founded, when its original president, Ron McManus, desired to lead another department for me. If I hadn't asked John to come aboard when I did, the team might have missed out on a wonderful leader.

2. Training: Are You Developing the Team?

You cannot solve tomorrow's problems with today's solutions. If

> *You cannot solve tomorrow's problems with today's solutions.*

you want the team to succeed as it meets new challenges, you have to prepare it. That means helping starters to maximize their potential and training the people on the bench to become starters when their time comes.

If you have leadership responsibility for your team, then take the initiative to make sure everyone on the team is growing and improving.

3. Losses: Who Is Leaving the Team?

The only place that never loses people is the cemetery. Losing team members is inevitable. But the good news is that you can choose the members you lose. If you keep nonproductive people, the productive ones become frustrated and leave. If you remove the people who don't add value, then the whole team gets better. It's just like trimming trees: If you don't cut the deadwood, eventually the whole tree falls. But if you remove the deadwood, the tree becomes healthier, the healthy branches produce more, and there's room for productive new branches on the tree.

The best way to describe how to grow and improve the team

and its bench is what I call the revolving door principle. Here's the way it works: A team will always have gains and losses. People are constantly coming into an organization while others leave it. The key to its future success is gaining a more effective person with each loss.

Let's say, for example, that you can rate every person's effectiveness on a scale of 1 to 10, with 10 as the highest. As the revolving door turns, if your team is losing 4s but gaining 8s, then your future looks bright. If you're losing 8s and gaining 4s, then the future looks bleak. And if you're losing 4s and gaining other 4s, then you're wearing your team out with activity but making no progress.

PHASES OF AN ORGANIZATION AND
ITS REVOLVING DOOR

Any team that is avoiding stagnation by trying to improve will go through changes, and as the revolving door moves, different kinds of people will come and go during various phases. For example, when an organization is new and just getting started, it recruits strongly. It has no one to lose and is glad to gain anyone. The good news is that as people come on board, a team is being formed. The bad news is that the people the team is gaining are not always good.

When a team asks for commitment, some team members leave the team. But that's good. Commitment drives away the uncommitted, while it makes those who stay even stronger in the commitment they already possess.

Once the team has a committed core and begins to grow, it again gains people. The people who join the team are often attracted to it because of the level of commitment they see in existing players. That

Type of Team	Gain or Loss	Nature of Loss or Gain
New Team	More Gains Than Losses	Gains Are Not Always Positive
Committed Team	More Losses Than Gains	Losses Are Positive
Growing Team	More Gains Than Losses	Gains Are Positive
Successful Team	More Losses Than Gains	Losses Are Not Positive
Legacy Team	More Gains Than Losses	Gains Are Positive

builds the team's ability and drives it to achieve—and leads to its success.

However, once a team becomes successful, some members will want to leave to try to find greater success on their own. That's a critical time for a team. If you can give people intriguing challenges and share both responsibilities and rewards with them, you may be able to persuade them to stay. (If you can't, you'll probably have to rely on your backup players, and then you'll find out what kind of bench you've built!)

If you can sustain growth in the midst of success and repeat the process while continually building your bench, then you can create a legacy team. That's what organizations such as General Electric, Disney, and Home Depot have done. Their sustained growth and reputations for success continue to draw good people to them.

WHO IS YOUR MVP?

The key to making the most of the Law of the Bench is to continually improve the team. As you bring on better players, first improve your starters. Then build your bench. Do that long enough and you will build a great team because *great teams have great depth.* That's the Law of the Bench.

Building a great team is a process that takes a tremendous amount of work, and the bigger the organization gets, the harder the task becomes. I'm acutely aware of that because in the last three and a half years, The INJOY Group has grown from less than fifty people to more than two hundred! When you're experiencing that kind of explosive growth, your HR person may be your MVP.

Let me tell you about the person most responsible for keeping the revolving door moving in the right direction in my company. Her name is Stacy Buchanan. Two and a half years ago, an acquaintance of hers who was a headhunter directed her to The INJOY Group. At the time, we were looking for a senior accountant, and Stacy had an extensive background in accounting, having done much of the groundwork to become a CPA. She had also worked for six years at an internationally known nonprofit organization and spent several years teaching.

> *The key to making the most of the Law of the Bench is to continually improve the team.*

BOLD MOVE

Stacy believed with all her heart that she belonged at The INJOY Group, and she really wanted to work with us. So she came in and interviewed with us. But the last thing in the world she wanted to do was go back into accounting. Christine Johnson, a longtime INJOY employee who was functioning as our HR manager at the time, was interviewing Stacy. Christine could tell that she was an "eagle" and didn't want her to get away. So she introduced Stacy to the COO, Dick Peterson. As they talked, he, too, could tell she was a tremendous catch. Finally he asked her, "What do you want to do?"

Stacy gathered her courage and replied, "To tell you the truth, Dick, I want Christine's job: recruiting."

That was music to Christine's ears. She was dutifully recruiting new employees, but she didn't really enjoy it—nor did it utilize her greatest strengths. She and Dick were happy to create a position for Stacy as a recruiter, thus freeing Christine to focus on administration and management. In the thirty months since then, Stacy has hired nearly two hundred people for the company—both starters and bench players. And she does a fantastic job.

"I know I am going to sound like a preacher with my six Ps," says Stacy, "but this will give you an idea of how I place people. I analyze the following areas:

1. *Personality:* I use the DISC test, a diagnostic tool that indicates whether someone's personality is driving, influencing, supporting, or calculating.

2. *Passion:* I find out what motivates them—results, relationships, money, recognition, affirmation, impact, or security.

3. *Pattern:* I look for patterns in their successes and their failures. I figure out whether they work best alone or on a team.

4. *Potential:* I try to see what they might accomplish given the

right direction, motivation, coaching, and leadership. I particularly gauge whether they are maintainers or builders.

5. *Profile:* I gauge whether they will fit our culture and whether they are really INJOY material.

6. *Placement:* Finally I try to measure where they fit—which team will both benefit from them and add value to them.

Stacy has done a wonderful job of building our team through recruiting. And now she has expanded her role into the area of training. She has played an instrumental role in starting the nine mentoring groups that are currently in place at The INJOY Group. Stacy summarizes her work by saying, "My desire is to see people play the music that is contained in their souls."

If you want your team to become the very best it can be, then you need to concentrate on the people you're gaining, the ones you're losing, and the ones you're developing. That's the only way to build a great team. It has to be solid at every level. And never lose sight of the Law of the Bench. Remember, *great teams have great depth.*

TEAMWORK THOUGHT

Better players make you a better player.

BECOMING A BETTER TEAM MEMBER

How would you define yourself: a bench player or a starter? If you are on the bench, then your job is to do two things: Help the starters to shine, and prepare yourself to be a starter in the future. You can do that by cultivating an attitude of service and teachability, and by doing whatever you can to learn and grow.

If you are a starter, then you should perform at your best for the sake of the team, and you should honor the people on the bench. You do that by acknowledging the value of their contribution and by helping prepare them to start someday. If you are not already mentoring a teammate on the bench, start doing so right away.

BECOMING A BETTER TEAM LEADER

If you lead your team, you are responsible for making sure the revolving door moves in such a way that the players who are joining the team are better than those who are leaving. One way you can facilitate that is to place high value on the good people already on the team.

Every team has three groups of players. In this chapter I described the *starters,* who directly add value to the organization or who directly influence its course, and the *bench players,* who indirectly add value to the organization or who support the starters. The third group is a core group within the starters that I call the *inner-circle members.* Without these people the team would fall apart. Your job is to make sure each group is continually developed so that bench players are able to step up to become starters, and starters are able to step up to become inner-circle members.

If you're not sure who the inner-circle members are on your team, then try this exercise: Write the names of the people on your team who are starters. Now determine the people you could most easily do without. One by one, check off the names of the people whose loss would hurt the team least if they left. At some point you will end up with a smaller group of people without whom the team would be dead. That's your inner circle. (You can even rank the remaining people in order of importance.)

It's a good exercise to remind you of the value of people on the team. And by the way, if your treatment of those people doesn't match their value, you run the risk of losing them and having your revolving door work against you.

COMPANION ONLINE RESOURCE

Learn more about how the Law of the Bench uniquely applies to you.

Take the FREE Law of the Bench assessment at **LawsOfTeamwork.com**.

13

THE LAW OF IDENTITY

Shared Values Define the Team

At least one day a year, I try to bring together everyone in my organization. Early in INJOY's history, that was easy. Back in 1985 when we founded the company, Dick Peterson, who is now the company's COO, and I could get together on a moment's notice with his mother-in-law, Erma (our only employee), and the four or five volunteers who helped us (two of whom were our wives). Even ten years later we were still a fairly small outfit. The entire company could meet around one large conference table.

Today things are different. Now we have to rent a hall to accommodate all of our employees, but we still make the effort to get together. In fact, it's more important for us to do that now than it ever was before. Because of our size and the diversity of operations, the people on our team have a tendency to get disconnected from one another. And it becomes increasingly difficult for the leaders in the organization to maintain a personal connection with everyone.

DEFINING THE TEAM

Maybe you've experienced the disconnectedness that often accompanies rapid growth in an organization. Granted, with slightly more than two hundred employees, ours is not a large company, but it is big enough to experience growing pains. Where the team was once defined almost entirely through relationships, it now needs something more to keep it together. That's where the Law of Identity comes into play: *Shared values define the team.* Even if some members of a team don't share common experiences or have a personal relationship with one another, they can possess a cohesiveness that defies the size of the team. What it takes is a common vision (the Law of the Compass) and shared values. If everyone embraces the same values, team members can still have a connection to one another and to the larger team.

> *Just as personal values influence and guide an individual's behavior, organizational values influence and guide the team's behavior.*

We've all seen teams that have a common goal yet lack common values. Everyone on the team has different ideas about what's important. The result is chaos. Eventually the team breaks down if everyone tries to do things his own way. That's why team members need to be on the same page. Just as personal values influence and guide an individual's behavior, organizational values influence and guide the team's behavior.

THE VALUE OF VALUES

Values can help a team to become more connected and more effective. Shared values are like . . .

Glue

When difficult times come—and they do for every team—values hold people together. Look at a marriage, for example. It's easy for a couple to stay together when they are feeling the flush of love and everything is going smoothly. But eventually the passion that drew them together fades. And adversity comes. What keeps the people who stay married together? It's their values. Their values are more important than their feelings. They value their marriage so highly that they are willing to fight *for* the relationship. If two people don't have that mind-set going into the wedding, then their chances of staying together are pretty slim.

The same is true for any other team. If the players don't know what their values are—and live them out—their chances of working as a unit and reaching their potential are very small.

A Foundation

All teams need stability to perform well and to grow. Values provide a stable foundation that makes those things possible. This is true for just about any kind of relationship to grow. For example, if you are trying to build a relationship with someone from another culture, you begin by looking for the things you have in common. If you are trying to make a sale with a new customer, you look for common ground. The same is true when it comes to team building. You need something to build on, and values make the strongest foundation.

A Ruler

Values also help set the standard for a team's performance. In the corporate world, the values are often expressed in a mission statement or set of guidelines for doing business. But sometimes a company's stated values and its real values don't match up.

> *Values help set the standard for a team's performance.*

Author and management expert Ken Blanchard emphasizes, "Lots of companies claim they have a set of core values, but what they mean is a list of generic business beliefs that everyone would agree with, such as having integrity, making a profit, and responding to customers. Such values have meaning only when they are further defined in terms of how people actually behave and are rank-ordered to reveal priority." And they function as a measure of expectations and performance when they are genuinely embraced.

A Compass

Do you remember the television show *Dallas* from the 1980s? The main character was J. R. Ewing, a notoriously dishonest businessman. His character code for living can be summarized by something he said in an episode of the show: "Once you give up your ethics, the rest is a piece of cake." To a person with no values, anything goes.

I think we live in a time when people are searching for standards to live by. When individuals embrace strong values, they possess a moral compass that helps them make decisions. The same is true for people in an organization. When the team identifies and embraces a set of values, then in a month, a year, or a decade, no matter how much circumstances change or what challenges present themselves, people on the team still know it's moving in the right direction and make good decisions.

A Magnet

A team's values attract people with like values to the team. Think about some of the teams we've examined in previous chapters. What kinds of people are drawn to Habitat for Humanity? People who want to see substandard housing eliminated. What kinds of people are attracted to Enron? People who value innovation and organizational flexibility.

In *The 21 Irrefutable Laws of Leadership*, the Law of Magnetism states, "Who you are is who you attract." That law is as true for teams as it is for leaders. People attract other like-minded people.

An Identity

Values define the team and give it a unique identity—to team members, potential recruits, clients, and the public. What you believe identifies who you are.

THE VALUES OF THE INJOY GROUP

When I brought together all of the employees of The INJOY Group for our annual meeting this year, I wanted to emphasize our values. I think our team members see them acted out every day, but I wanted to give everyone a common language for the values to help ensure our alignment with them. To do that, I taught a lesson on those values.

Communication of the team's values is the place to start with the Law of Identity. A team cannot share values if the values have not been shared with the team. Allow me to acquaint you with the six core values that I shared with The INJOY Group so that you have a sense of what I mean.

1. The Personal Growth of Each Team Member

I am a strong believer in potential. Every day I work to develop my own, and I encourage everyone in my sphere of influence to do the same. How do people work to develop their potential? They start by making personal growth a priority.

Personal growth has been a major theme of my life. When I was a kid, my father used to pay me and my siblings to read books that would improve us. He also sent us to con-ferences. As I got older, reading books, listening to instructional tapes, and attending conferences became regular practices for me. Later, as I sought the key to organizational growth, I discovered another reason to promote personal growth because I found that the way to grow any organization is to grow the people in that organization.

> *A team cannot share values if the values have not been shared with the team.*

To promote personal growth in my organization, we encourage people to become members of a mentoring group. We also send people to our own conferences and to other types of training. We provide books, tapes, and other personal-growth tools. And I per-sonally spend time every month mentoring and developing the top leaders of the organization. When we or an employee discovers that the person would flourish in a different position or division of the company, we encourage him to explore new possibilities and make a change. You can't stand in the way of your employees' growth and still hope to grow your organization.

2. The Priority of Adding Value to Others

The INJOY Group exists to add value to people. That is our primary mission. First, we do that with the people in our own organization. But we also do it for our customers and clients. It's the reason we develop and provide consulting, training, and resources to organizations and individuals across the country and around the world. The day we can't add value to people is the day we close our doors.

3. The Power of Partnership

One of my favorite quotes comes from Mother Teresa, who observed, "You can do what I cannot do. I can do what you cannot do. Together we can do great things." That's a succinct way to describe partnership.

> "You can do what I cannot do. I can do what you cannot do. Together we can do great things."
>
> —MOTHER TERESA

It took me almost forty years to discover that I can't do everything. (You probably learned that sooner than I did; my high energy, low IQ, and endless optimism got the better of me for years!) That's when I realized the power of partnership. Over the years, our organization has learned more and more about working with others. Now partnership is the way we choose to accomplish our mission. Dave Sutherland, the CEO of The INJOY Group, likes to remind everyone, "Partnership begins the moment that a leader realizes we add value to him, and it ends when his vision is accomplished."

In recent years, we have expanded our partnership to include strategic alliances with other organizations. These partnerships have enabled The INJOY Group to train thousands of leaders in nearly a dozen countries overseas and to give away tens of thousands of books every year to people in developing countries.

I've come up with an acronym that describes what partnership means to me. As your partner, we promise to . . .

Put your needs first in every situation.

Add value to your personal leadership.

Recognize we serve a common goal.

Tailor our services to meet your need.

Never take for granted the trust placed in us.

Embody excellence in everything we do.

Respect everyone's uniqueness.

As individuals and as an organization, we can be good partners if we can remember each element.

4. The Practice of Raising Up and Developing Leaders

Everything rises and falls on leadership. That's why I have dedicated the past twenty years of my life to teaching leadership. That's also why I spend so much time finding and developing leaders. The single greatest way to impact an organization is to focus on leadership development. There is almost no limit to the potential of an organization that recruits good people, raises them up as leaders, and continually develops them.

> *The single greatest way to impact an organization is to focus on leadership development.*

5. *The Proper Stewardship of the Organization*

Any organization that wants to continue fulfilling its mission must learn to be a good steward of its resources. There are three primary ways we do that in our company: managing our assets to get the most out of them, placing our people strategically so they can give and receive as much as possible, and giving of ourselves to worthy causes. If we can do all three of these things, then we are maximizing the use of all the resources we have.

6. *The Purpose of Glorifying God*

The INJOY Group is an organization made up primarily of Christians, and our roots are in helping churches and pastors to reach their potential. Because of our heritage and our strong convictions, we believe that everything we do should honor God.

Undoubtedly the values of your organization will be different from ours. And that's as it should be. Your values should reflect the people on the team and their leader. What's important is that you go through the discovery process and embrace the team's values. Once you do, you will better understand your team, its mission, and its potential. Never forget that *shared values define the team.* That's the Law of Identity.

VALUES ADD VALUE TO YOUR TEAM

If you've never really thought about how your team's values can reveal its identity and increase its potential, go through the following process with your team:

- *Articulate the values.* Spend some think time or bring together a group of key team members to articulate the team's values. Then put them on paper.

- *Compare values with practices.* Then watch the team in action. You want to make sure the values you identify match the ones you're living. The alignment of the stated values and the behavior of team members boosts the team's energy and effectiveness. But if they are out of alignment, then the team will suffer.

- *Teach the values.* Once you settle what the right values are, you need to teach them to everyone on the team. Do it clearly, creatively, and continually.

- *Practice the values.* Values have no value if you don't put them into practice. If you discover teammates whose actions don't match the team's values, help them to make the changes necessary to align themselves with the rest of the team.

- *Institutionalize the values.* Weave the team's values into the fabric of the team. For example, my friend Bill Hybels, senior pastor of Willow Creek Community Church, identifies "community" as one of the core values of his church. To reinforce that value, the first third of every leadership meeting—whether it is staff, elders, or the board—is dedicated to building and maintaining the personal relationships among the members of that group.

- *Publicly praise the values.* The most fundamental management truth I've ever learned is that what gets rewarded gets done. If you praise and honor the people who epitomize the values of the team, those values get embraced and upheld by other members of the team. There is no better reinforcement.

If you are the leader of your team, it is especially important that you take your team through this process. Left to themselves, with no help to embrace the values you know to be fundamental, team members will create an identity of their choosing. For better or worse, the values of the most influential people on the team will become the team's values. However, by implementing each of the steps I outlined and continuing to repeat them over time, you will find that the culture of your organization will begin to change, and your people will embrace a new identity that you help them find. And once they develop a common team identity, they will work together better, even as the organization grows and changes.

> *The most fundamental management truth I've ever learned is that what gets rewarded gets done.*

NO PLACE LIKE HOME

When I moved to Atlanta, I became acquainted with an organization that has developed its unique identity and fosters a strong sense of teamwork despite being a huge company. That organization is Home Depot.

Now, I am not a do-it-yourselfer. What's the opposite of handy? Handless? Manually challenged? Whatever it is, that describes me. Then there's my son, Joel Porter. He never met a tool he didn't like, and if a thing can be fixed, he will find a way to do it. When he was thirteen years old, we let him create a workshop in a room adjacent to our garage. He put in a workbench, installed fixtures, and wired the room. A friend of ours who used to be a contractor said Joel had put enough power in that small room to light up an entire house!

After our arrival in Atlanta, Joel found himself a job at Home Depot, and he couldn't have been happier. Every day he would come home and tell us about the company, what he did that day, and the values the company held dear.

Intrigued, I did some research of my own. I discovered that the company was founded by Bernie Marcus and Arthur Blank. They opened their first store in Atlanta in June of 1979 after both men had been fired fourteen months earlier from Handy Dan, a home improvement chain located in the western part of the United States. For years, Marcus, a man with considerable retail experience and leadership talent, had possessed a vision for a national chain of huge one-stop home improvement stores. His idea was to offer the widest selection of products at the lowest prices with the best customer service possible.

BUILDING HOME DEPOT

Getting the company off the ground required the two men to keep plugging away, slowly expanding the business, opening more stores, and attracting first-rate people. Marcus said, "We are only as good as our people—especially the men and women working in our stores every day . . . That's why we believe a sure way of growing this company is to clearly state our values and instill them in our associates."[1]

The right leaders with the right values have attracted the right people to make the company a blockbuster. In 1979, they started with four stores. In 1999, Home Depot had 775 stores, 160,000 employees, and $38.4 billion in annual sales.[2]

Values truly are at the heart of Home Depot's success. Marcus explained,

A set of eight values has been our bedrock for the past twenty years. Although they were not put in writing until 1995, these values—the basis for the way we run the company—enabled us to explode across the North American landscape and will be the vehicle for reaching our ambitious goals in the international marketplace . . .

- *Excellent customer service.* Doing whatever it takes to build customer loyalty.

- *Taking care of our people.* The most important reason for The Home Depot's success.

- *Developing entrepreneurial spirit.* We think of our organizational structure as an inverted pyramid: Stores and customers are at the top and senior management is on the bottom.

- *Respect for all people.* Talent and good people are everywhere, and we can't afford to overlook any source of good people.

- *Building strong relationships with associates, customers, vendors and communities.*

- *Doing the right thing, not just doing things right.*

- *Giving back to our communities as an integral part of doing business.*

- *Shareholder return.* Investors in The Home Depot will benefit from the money they've given us to grow our business.[3]

These values have made the company a great place for people to work. For example, from the day Home Depot opened, the company has offered employees stock options rather than bonuses. That kind of treatment has made more than one thousand of its employees millionaires!

Joel Porter has since left his job at Home Depot. He now works for The INJOY Group in a technical capacity as our studio production manager. But he will always have a heart for Home Depot. Why? Because the company has an identity he respects. It has *shared values, and the values define the team.* That's the impact their organization had on him, and that's the impact the Law of Identity can have on you and your team.

TEAMWORK THOUGHT

If your values are the same as the team's, you become
more valuable to the team.

BECOMING A BETTER TEAM MEMBER

If you want to add value to your team and help it reach its potential, then you need to share in its values. First, make sure that you know what they are. Then, examine your values and goals in comparison to them. If you can wholeheartedly buy into the team's values, commit yourself to aligning yourself with them. If you can't, then your misalignment will be a constant source of frustration to you and your teammates. And you might want to think about finding a different team.

BECOMING A BETTER TEAM LEADER

As the leader of an organization, you have responsibilities when it comes to the team's values. I recommend that you proceed by following these steps:

- Know the values that the team should embrace.

- Live the values.

- Communicate the values to the team.

- Obtain buy-in of the values through aligned behavior among teammates.

Remember, the process takes time. Getting your people to buy in can be especially difficult. But the better leader you are, the more quickly they will buy into you. And the more quickly they buy into you, the more rapidly they will buy into the values you communicate. (To explore this leadership concept in more depth, read the Law of Buy-In in *The 21 Irrefutable Laws of Leadership*.)

COMPANION **ONLINE** RESOURCE

Learn more about how the Law of Identity uniquely applies to you.
Take the FREE Law of Identity assessment at **LawsOfTeamwork.com**.

THE LAW OF COMMUNICATION

Interaction Fuels Action

When Gordon Bethune took over Continental Airlines in 1994, the company was a mess. It had suffered through ten changes in leadership in ten years. It had gone through bankruptcy proceedings twice. Its stock value was at a pitiful $3.25 a share. It had not made a profit in a decade. Customers were flocking away from the airline, and those who did use Continental were rarely happy because in the words of Bethune, their planes "came and went as they happened to" with no predictability. That's not what business travelers and vacationers are looking for in an airline!

TRYING TIMES FOR THE TEAM

In his book, *From Worst to First*, Bethune described the state of Continental when he arrived:

In the years leading up to 1994, Continental was simply the worst among the nation's 10 biggest airlines . . . For example, DOT [the Department of Transportation] measures those 10 largest airlines in on-time percentage . . . *Continental was dead last.* It measures the number of mishandled-baggage reports filed per 1,000 passengers. *Continental was worst.* It measures the number of complaints it receives per 100,000 passengers on each airline. Continental was last. And not just last—in 1994, *Continental got almost three times as many complaints as the industry average* and more than 30 percent more complaints than the ninth-best airline, the runner-up in lousy service. We had a real lock on last place in that category . . . We weren't just the worst big airline. *We lapped the field.*[1]

When a company is that bad, the employees can't help being affected. Morale at Continental was abysmal. Cooperation was non-existent. Communication was at an all-time low. Employees had been lied to so often and so thoroughly that they didn't believe anything they were told. According to Bethune, they had learned one survival strategy: Duck. "That's what I joined in 1994," commented Bethune, "a company with a lousy product, angry employees, low wages, a history of ineffective management, and, I soon learned, an incipient bankruptcy, our third, which would probably kill us."[2]

TRYING TO TURN AROUND THE TEAM

Bethune's goal was to save Continental, but he knew that to do it, he would have to change the culture of the company. The key would be communication. He knew that positive interaction could turn the company around. If he could win the communication battle, he believed he could get the employees to work together again for the good of the team, the customers, and the stockholders.

His first step was to open up the executive offices to the rest of the team. When he began working for Continental, the twentieth-floor suite occupied by top management in Houston was like a fortress. Its doors were locked, the area was surveyed by lots of security cameras, and nobody could enter the area without a proper ID. It wasn't exactly inviting. Bethune literally propped open the doors and hosted open houses for employees to break down the intimidation factor between leaders and the rest of the team.

The next thing he did was to work to break the old bureaucracy that had developed over the years. At Continental, rules and manuals had taken the place of communication and the use of judgment. The chief symptom of that mind-set was the nine-inch-thick book of rules for employees that had come to be known as the "Thou Shalt Not" book. It was so detailed that it dictated what color pencil an agent was supposed to use on a boarding pass. In a significant gesture, CEO Bethune, along with Continental President Greg Brenneman, gathered employees in the parking lot, dropped the manual in a trash can, doused it with gasoline, and burned it![3] The message was clear. Everything at Continental was going to change.

COMMUNICATION CULTURE

Continental didn't change overnight. In fact, as Bethune and Brenneman laid out their "Go Forward Plan," employees were skeptical. But the leaders kept meeting with the people, committed themselves to being honest with them, and maintained their patience. If the news was good, they told the people. If the news was bad, they still told them. They put up bulletin boards in every employee area that showed two things: (1) their ratings for the last year according to the Department of Transportation rating guidelines; and (2) daily news updates from the company. They created a weekly voice-mail message to everyone on the team. They also put lots of communication in writing, using a monthly employee newsletter called *Continental Times and Continental Quarterly*, which they mailed to every employee's home. They put news wire–style LED displays by every coffee and soda machine. They even created 800-number hot lines for questions and information that could be accessed by any employee from anywhere in the world.

> *Bethune's communication policy was— and is—simple: "Unless it's dangerous or illegal for us to share it, we share it."*

A company that had been characterized by distrust and lack of cooperation became a place where communication was pervasive. Bethune's communication policy was—and is—simple: "Unless it's dangerous or illegal for us to share it, we share it."[4] It took time, but eventually the company began to turn. Employees started to trust their leaders. They began to work with and trust one another. And for the first time in more than a decade, the employees of Continental functioned as a team.

Today, Continental's service is among the best in its industry. Employee morale is high. And the company is profitable. In 1994, the year Bethune took over, the company *lost* $204 million. In 1995, it made a *profit* of $202 million. The next year it doubled. As of April 2001, Continental had posted twenty-four consecutive profitable quarters in an industry where many of its competitors are struggling to stay in the black. The company's stock has split twice, and each share is worth more than ten times the value it had in 1994.

WHAT'S IN A WORD?

Communication wasn't the entire reason for Continental's success. But without good communication, the company most likely would have continued on autopilot right into its third (and final) bankruptcy. Creating positive change in an organization requires communication. *Interaction fuels action.* That is the power of the Law of Communication.

> *Effective teams have teammates who are constantly talking to one another.*

Only with good communication can a team succeed—it doesn't matter whether that team is a family, a company, a ministry, or a ball club. Effective teams have teammates who are constantly talking to one another. Communication increases commitment and connection; they in turn fuel action. If you want your team to *perform* at the highest level, the people on it need to be able to talk to and listen to one another.

COMMUNICATION MATTERS

When people don't communicate effectively, the result can often be comical. Years ago, I came across the following illustration that conveys what I mean. It is made up of a series of memos on a college campus:

President to Academic V.P.: Next Thursday Halley's Comet will appear over this area. This is an event which occurs only once every 75 years. Call the Division Heads and have them assemble their professors and students on the athletic field and explain this phenomenon to them. If it rains, then cancel the observation and have the classes meet in the gym to see a film about the comet.

Academic V.P. to Division Chairmen: By order of the President, next Thursday Halley's Comet will appear over the athletic field. If it rains, then cancel classes and report to the gym with your professors and students where you will be shown films, a phenomenal event which occurs only once every 75 years.

Division Chairman to Professors: By order of the Phenomenal President, next Thursday Halley's Comet will appear in the gym. In case of rain over the athletic field the President will give another order, something which occurs every 75 years.

Professor to Students: Next Thursday the President will appear in our gym with Halley's Comet, something which occurs every 75 years. If it rains the President will cancel the comet and order us all out to our phenomenal athletic field.

Student Writing Home to Parents: When it rains next Thursday over the school athletic field, the phenomenal 75-year-old President will cancel all classes and appear before the whole school in the gym accompanied by Bill Halley and the Comets.

Scott Adams, the creator of the Dilbert comic strip, has masterfully described an organization where everyone does his best to undermine communication. The boss sends an employee to work for a year on a project that has been canceled, then later demotes the person for wasting so much time. Members of the marketing department continually think up harebrained products and promote them to the public; then they ask the engineers to produce them on an impossible timetable. The higher up in the organization people are, the more clueless they are. Thinkers are punished, the lazy are rewarded, and every decision is arbitrary. The comic strip is hilarious. What's sad is that too many American workers identify with it.

If you've ever been on a team where teammates never let one another know what's going on, then you know how frustrating poor communication can be. The team gets stuck because nobody knows what the real agenda is. Important tasks remain uncompleted because each of two team members believes the other one is taking care of it—or people duplicate others' work. Departments within the organization fight because each believes it is being sabotaged by the other.

In the book *Empowered Teams*, authors Richard Wellins, William Byham, and Jeanne Wilson state, "Communication refers to the style and extent of interactions both among members and between members and those outside the team. It also refers to the way that members handle conflict, decision making, and day-to-day interactions."

A Different Picture of Communication

An excellent example of the complexity—and importance—of good communication can be seen by watching a professional football team in the half minute prior to a play. When one play ends, the offensive team has only forty seconds to get itself ready for the next play. In that time, the quarterback first decides if there is enough time for the team to huddle. If there is, he calls the team members together and gives them the play. If there isn't, he communicates that he will call the play using a code at the line of scrimmage.

For many plays at the professional level, the team will line up with players in one formation and then move them around before the play to try to confuse the defense. If time is short, the quarterback will communicate to the players that they should skip the extra steps and just line up in the formation that will be used to run the play.

As the eleven offensive players approach the line, each is doing two things: assessing what the defense is doing, and paying attention to teammates for communication cues. The linemen who will be blocking pay attention to what kinds of players the other team has in the game and where they are positioned. The center, who hikes the ball to the quarterback, is usually responsible for calling out the blocking scheme to his teammates based on the defense.

Meanwhile, the quarterback is assessing the defense. If he thinks the play he has called in the huddle will fail against the defense, he is likely to use a few words to call an alternate play at the line of scrimmage. If the defense is lined up in such a way that the original play will work, but the blocking scheme of the running backs behind him is likely to fail, then he can change their blocking assignments.

At the same time, the quarterback, the running backs, and the receivers are watching the defense to see if they are about to do anything unusual, such as sending extra players after the quarterback to tackle him in a blitz. If the offensive players do see a blitz coming, then, without a word, the receivers and running backs change their assignments to a predetermined Plan B for that play, and they hope that everyone on the team made the same assessment.

Football is an extremely complex sport. The casual observer has no idea so much communication is going on before every play.

Sometimes it's subtle. Players call out things in code. They use hand signals. One player may simply point and communicate a lot of information to another teammate. And sometimes a quarterback and a receiver will just give each other a look and communicate enough information to make it possible for them to score on the play.

COMMUNICATION ON YOUR TEAM

Communication on your team may not look anything like what happens on a football field. But the success of your team and the ability of your team members to work together are just as dependent on good communication. Allow me to give you some guidelines that will help your team to improve in this area. Every team has to learn how to develop good communication in four areas.

1. From Leader to Teammates

John W. Gardner observed, "If I had to name a single all-purpose instrument of leadership, it would be communication." Perhaps you are familiar with my books on leadership; then you know that I believe everything rises and falls on leadership. What I haven't mentioned before is that leadership rises and falls on communication. You must be able to communicate to lead others effectively.

> "If I had to name a single all-purpose instrument of leadership, it would be communication."
>
> —JOHN W. GARDNER

If you lead your team, give yourself these standards to live by as you communicate to your people:

- *Be consistent.* Nothing frustrates team members more than leaders who can't make up their minds. One of the things that won the team over to Gordon Bethune was the consistency of his communication. His employees always knew they could depend on him and what he said.

- *Be clear.* Your team cannot execute if the members don't know what you want. Don't try to dazzle anyone with your intelligence; impress people with your straightforwardness.

- *Be courteous.* Everyone deserves to be shown respect, no matter what the position or what kind of history you might have with him. By being courteous to your people, you set the tone for the entire organization.

Never forget that because you are the leader, your communication sets the tone for the interaction among your people. Teams always reflect their leaders. And never forget that good communication is never one-way. It should not be top-down or dictatorial. The best leaders listen, invite, and then encourage participation.

2. From Teammates to Leader

Good team leaders never want yes-men. They want direct and honest communication from their people. Even autocratic movie mogul Sam Goldwyn quipped, "I want my people to speak up and be honest, even if it costs them their jobs."

I have always encouraged people on my team to speak openly and directly with me. When we hold meetings, they are often brainstorming sessions where the best idea wins. Often, a team member's remarks or observations really help the team. Sometimes we disagree. That's okay because we've developed strong enough relationships that we can survive conflict. Getting everything out on the table always improves the team. I never want to hear a teammate say, "I could have told you that wouldn't work." If you know it beforehand, that's the time to say it.

Besides directness, the other quality team members need to display when communicating with their leaders is respect. Leading a team isn't easy. It takes hard work. It demands personal sacrifice. It requires making tough and sometimes unpopular decisions. We should respect the person who has agreed to take on that role and show him loyalty.

3. Among Teammates

Author Charlie Brower remarked, "Few people are successful unless a lot of other people want them to be." In a team that desires to experience success, all team members must communicate for the common good. That means exhibiting the following qualities:

- *Being supportive.* Former NBA player Earvin "Magic" Johnson summed up support by paraphrasing President John F. Kennedy: "Ask not what your teammates can do for you. Ask what you can do for your teammates." Communication that is focused on giving rather than getting takes the team to a whole new level.

> *"Ask not what your teammates can do for you. Ask what you can do for your teammates."*
>
> —EARVIN "MAGIC" JOHNSON

- *Staying current.* Teammates who rehash old problems and continually open old wounds don't work together. And if they don't work together, they're sunk. As Babe Ruth remarked, "You may have the greatest bunch of individual stars in the world, but if they don't play together, the club won't be worth a dime."

- *Being vulnerable.* Teams are like little communities, and they develop only when the people in them don't posture with one another. In his book *The Different Drum,* psychiatrist M. Scott Peck observes, "If we are to use the word *community* meaningfully, we must restrict it to a group of individuals who have learned how to communicate honestly with each other, whose relationships go deeper than their masks of composure."

Teams succeed or fail based on the way that team members communicate with one another. Martin Luther King Jr. declared, "We must learn to live together as brothers or perish together as fools." If the interaction is strong, then the action teams take can be strong. *Interaction fuels action.* That's the essence of the Law of Communication.

4. Between the Team and the Public

For most teams, communication within the team isn't the only kind that's important. Most teams interact with outsiders in some way, whether the people are clients, customers, or the concerned public. When approached by people from outside the group, team members must remember three Rs; they need to be *receptive, responsive,* and *realistic.* If they receive communication from others gracefully, always respond in a timely fashion, and are realistic about setting and receiving expectations, they will do just fine. Outsiders will perceive that their concerns are being well received.

On the other hand, when it comes to communicating to people who are not on the team, the most important quality a team can display is unity. The more independent team members are, the more difficult that can be; it's not easy to get eagles to fly in formation. Yet the power of unity is incredible.

An old story that I heard when I lived in the Midwest was about a horse-pull at a country fair. That's an event where various horses compete to see which one can pull a sled with the greatest weight. One year, the champion horse pulled 4,500 pounds. The runner-up pulled 4,400. Wondering what the two stout horses might be able to pull together, a group of men yoked them together. They pulled more than 12,000 pounds—an increase of more than 33 percent over their individual efforts.

There's tremendous power in unity. One of the principles I always tell my team is that when we are brainstorming and planning, I want all the ideas and criticisms out on the table. We need an opportunity to hash things out. But once we leave the room, we must be united— even if we face opposition or criticism. We remain a strong team.

When it comes down to it, you spell cooperation "w-e." Working together means winning together. But no team works together unless it's communicating. It takes *interaction to fuel action*. That's just the way it works. That's the Law of Communication.

> *Working together means winning together.*

HANG TOGETHER OR HANG SEPARATELY

One of the most remarkable stories of communication and teamwork I've ever encountered occurred among the U.S. prisoners of war (POWs) who were detained in Vietnam. As American involvement in the war in Vietnam increased, so did the number of U.S. servicemen who were captured. Ultimately 772 servicemen, mostly pilots, were captured and imprisoned.

Most of the prisoners were held at the Hoa Lo prison, which the men called the Hanoi Hilton. There they suffered unspeakable torture and inhumane conditions. Most of them wasted away. It wasn't unusual for someone over six feet tall to weigh 120 pounds. But the worst part for most of the men was the forced solitude. Former POW Ron Bliss explained, "You get isolated. That's when the trouble begins. You have to communicate at virtually any cost. If you get caught and tortured for a little while, that's just the overhead. But you do it anyway."

The North Vietnamese captors at the Hanoi Hilton tried to defeat the POWs by breaking them physically, crushing their spirits, and keeping them isolated. If a man thought of himself as an abandoned individual, then he would give up hope. Jerry Driscoll, a POW who originally thought he might be released after a few months, was told by a fellow prisoner that it might be two years: "When I finally came to that realization that, my God, that's going to be a long time . . . it just kind of hit me all at once. And I just took my blanket and kind of balled it up and I . . . screamed with all this anguish that it's going to be that long. Two years. And when I was finished, I felt, *Oh, okay. I can do that. I can do two years.* Of course, as it turned out, it was two years, and it was two years after that, and two years after that, until it was about seven years in my case."

Taps for the Prisoners

Communication and connection with the other prisoners became necessary for the men to endure and survive. To make that communication possible, the prisoners devised an ingenious system. When four POWs—Carlyle Harris, Phillip Butler, Robert Peel, and Robert Shumaker—were held in the same cell for a time, they devised a tapping code that they could use to spell out words. When they were split up, they used it to communicate, and they taught the code to every prisoner they could. In a matter of months, nearly all of the prisoners knew the code and were using it. "The building sounded like a den of runaway woodpeckers," recalled former POW Ron Bliss.

The men would tap on the walls between cells or push a wire through a wall and tug on it using the code. They would sweep or shovel rhythmically, sending each other messages. They also developed hand signals and other ways of communicating. Ex-POW Thomas McNish observed, "We passed the equivalent of *War and Peace* several times over through different methods of communication."[5]

Even though the prisoners were kept separate from one another—and many men who "talked" all the time never saw the others' faces until they were released—they became a team. They worked together. They shared information. They supported one another. They became such a solid unit that they determined none of them would accept release until all of them could obtain it. The one person who did leave early, Seaman Douglas Hegdahl, accepted release only because he was given a direct order by Lt. Commander Al Stafford to accept it. And he was given the order for one reason: Hegdahl had memorized the 256 names of fellow prisoners, which the men wanted communicated to authorities back home.

Finally in January of 1973, a cease-fire was signed in Paris that made provision for the release of American POWs. They began coming home on February 12, and on March 29, the last prisoners left the

Hanoi Hilton. In all, 462 prisoners were released. That number might have been far fewer if they had not found—and fought for—a way to communicate with one another. But *interaction fuels action*. And their connection with one another fueled their ability to endure and to hold together as a team. That's the value of the Law of Communication.

TEAMWORK THOUGHT

Communication increases connection.

BECOMING A BETTER TEAM MEMBER

How committed are you to communicating with the other members of your team? Are you supportive of everyone, even the people who aren't your friends? Are you open and vulnerable, even if it's not pleasant? Are you holding a grudge against anyone on the team? If you are, you need to clear the air. If there are *any* barriers to good communication standing between you and another team member, you need to remove them. That is your responsibility.

BECOMING A BETTER TEAM LEADER

As the leader of an organization, you set the tone for communication. In this chapter, I mention that a leader's communication must be consistent, clear, and courteous. But leaders must also be good listeners. When leaders don't listen . . .

- They stop gaining wisdom.

- They stop "hearing" what isn't being said.

- Team members stop communicating.

- Their indifference spreads to other areas.

Ultimately, poor listening leads to hostility, miscommunication, and a breakdown of team cohesion.

Give yourself a 360-degree review. Ask for feedback concerning your listening skills from your boss or mentor, your colleagues, and your subordinates. If you don't get high marks from all of them, then quiet down, listen up, and work to become a better communicator.

COMPANION **ONLINE** RESOURCE

Learn more about how the Law of Communication uniquely applies to you.
Take the FREE Law of Communication assessment at **LawsOfTeamwork.com**.

THE LAW OF THE EDGE

The Difference Between Two Equally Talented Teams Is Leadership

T eams are always looking for an edge. I'm sure you've seen it. A ball team recruits new talent or develops new plays to beat a tough opponent—or even develops a whole new system to turn around a legacy of losing. Businesses invest in the latest technology, hoping to improve their productivity. Companies fire their ad agencies and hire new ones to launch a campaign, desiring to make gains on major competitors. Corporations cycle through the latest management fads like channel surfers through television reruns. Everyone is seeking the magic formula that will lead to success. The more competitive the field, the more relentless the search.

What is the key to success? Is it talent? Hard work? Technology? Efficiency? To be successful, a team needs all of these things, but it still needs something more. It needs leadership.

- *Personnel* determine the potential of the team.

- *Vision* determines the direction of the team.

- *Work ethic* determines the preparation of the team.

- *Leadership* determines the success of the team.

Everything rises and falls on leadership. If a team has great leadership, then it can gain everything else it needs to go to the highest level.

FINDING THE EDGE

Look at any team that has achieved great success, and you will find that it has strong leadership. What enabled General Electric to gain the respect of the corporate world? The leadership edge of Jack Welch. What sealed the victory of the United States in the Persian Gulf War? The leadership edge of Generals Norman Schwarzkopf and Colin Powell. What powered the Chicago Bulls to win six NBA championships? The leadership edge of Phil Jackson and Michael Jordan. That's why I say *the difference between two equally talented teams is leadership.* That's the Law of the Edge.

> *Look at any team that has achieved great success, and you will find that it has strong leadership.*

To get a clearer picture of the difference that leadership can make, think of the same players on the same team with different leadership. The Los Angeles Lakers are a notable example. During the late 1990s, they struggled despite having a very talented group of players, including Kobe Bryant, who many hoped would be the next Michael Jordan, and Shaquille O'Neal, the best center in the game. Both players were acquired in 1996, yet they continued to have major problems and never clicked as a team. In 1999, teammate Eddie Jones remarked, "Something isn't right with this team. We're all struggling to keep it together and with a team that has that much talent, this shouldn't be going on."[1]

The next year, the team brought in Phil Jackson, the man who had led the Chicago Bulls to six championships, to coach the Lakers. He kept the same team intact with few changes because he knew talent was not the issue. Of his three key players, O'Neal, Bryant, and Glen Rice, Jackson remarked,

> I think we have three of maybe the most talented players since the time of Kareem and Worthy and Magic. However, Baylor, West and Chamberlain [on the 1968–71 Lakers] outshone even those people. They were three of the greatest scorers in the game, and yet they couldn't win a championship. So yeah, we got the talent, we got the show, we got everything else—but how do you make all the pieces complement each other? That's really what my specialty is as a coach, to try to bring that to bear. And this team is learning that.[2]

Leadership is all about understanding players, bringing them together, and getting them to work together as a team to reach their potential. And Jackson provided it. In only one season, the team came together. In 2000, the Lakers won the NBA championship that everyone had believed they had the potential to win. They did it in the same city working under the same conditions and with the same players they'd had in previous years. The only thing that had changed was the leadership. That gave them the edge. *The difference between two equally talented teams is leadership.* That is the Law of the Edge.

NEED A LIFT?

With good leadership, everything improves. Leaders are lifters. They push the thinking of their teammates beyond old boundaries of creativity. They elevate others' performance, making them better than they've ever been before. They improve their confidence in themselves and each other. And they raise the expectations of everyone on the team. While managers are often able to maintain a team at its current level, leaders are able to lift it to a higher level than it has ever reached before. The key to that is working with people and bringing out the best in them.

- *Leaders transfer ownership for work to those who execute the work.* For a team to succeed, responsibility must go down deep into the organization, down to the roots. Getting that to happen requires a leader who will delegate responsibility and authority to the team. Stephen Covey remarked, "People and organizations don't grow much without delegation and completed staff work, because they are confined to the capacities of the boss and reflect both personal strengths and weaknesses." Good leaders seldom restrict their teams; they release them.

- *Leaders create an environment where each team member wants to be responsible.* Different people require different kinds of motivation to be their best. One needs encouragement. Another needs to be pushed. Another will rise to a big challenge. Good leaders know how to read people and find the key that will make them take responsibility for their part on the team. They also remember that they are responsible *to* their people, not *for* them.

- *Leaders coach the development of personal capabilities.* The team can reach its potential only if each individual on the team reaches his potential. Effective leaders help each player do that. For example, Phil Jackson is well known for giving his players books to read that will help them improve themselves, not just as basketball players, but as people.

- *Leaders learn quickly and encourage others to learn rapidly.* Leaders lift themselves to a higher level first; then they lift the others around them. Modeling comes first, then leadership. If everyone is improving, then the team is improving.

If you want to give a team a lift, then provide it with better leadership. The Law of the Edge works every time.

THE LAWS OF LEADERSHIP IMPACT THE TEAM

Leadership can improve a team and give it an edge in many ways, and the 21 laws from my book on leadership provide a useful summary. Good leaders . . .

1. Do not limit an organization as others do. (The Law of the Lid)

2. Have greater influence than others do. (The Law of Influence)

3. Value the process of developing people more than others do. (The Law of Process)

4. Prepare the team for the journey better than others do. (The Law of Navigation)

5. Communicate more effectively than others do. (The Law of E. F. Hutton)

6. Create momentum and lift the team to a higher level than others do. (The Law of the Big Mo)

7. Stand on a foundation of trust that is more solid than others' is. (The Law of Solid Ground)

8. Command greater respect than others do. (The Law of Respect)

9. Work on leadership issues earlier than others do. (The Law of Intuition)

10. Draw more leaders to themselves than others do. (The Law of Magnetism)

11. Connect with people better than others do. (The Law of Connection)

12. Bring stronger key people around them than others do. (The Law of the Inner Circle)

13. Reproduce more leaders than others do. (The Law of Reproduction)

14. Empower team members more than others do. (The Law of Empowerment)

15. Win with teams more than others do. (The Law of Victory)

16. Sell themselves and their vision to a greater degree than others do. (The Law of Buy-In)

---

17. Establish priorities more effectively than others do.
    (The Law of Priorities)

18. Understand and use timing more effectively than others do.
    (The Law of Priorities)

19. Give up their personal agendas more than others do.
    (The Law of Sacrifice)

20. Grow leaders and organizations faster than others do.
    (The Law of Explosive Growth)

21. Leave a legacy that lasts longer than others do.
    (The Law of Legacy)

Good leaders do things just a little bit better than others do. The result is usually victory. That's the Law of the Edge.

TURNING THE TABLE ON THE TABLES

Leadership is the key to the Law of the Edge, but I don't want you to get the idea that the responsibility for leadership always falls on one person. Although most teams have a designated leader who is ultimately responsible for the oversight of the team, the actual leadership of the team is usually shared.

I find that when it comes to leadership, many people tend to see it in one of two ways. The first I call *the myth of the head table*. It's the notion that on a particular team, one person is always in charge in every situation. It's the idea that this particular individual permanently occupies the "head table" in the organization and that everyone else always takes a subordinate role to him. For example, here is an illustration that might have been written by someone who subscribes to the myth of the head table:

> As everyone knows, an executive has practically nothing to do except . . .
>
> To decide what is to be done;
>
> To tell somebody to do it;
>
> To listen to reasons why it should not be done, why it should be done by somebody else, or why it should be done in a different way;
>
> To follow up to see if the thing has been done, only to discover that it has not;
>
> To inquire why;
>
> To listen to excuses from the person who should have done it;
>
> To follow up again to see if the thing has been done, only to discover that it has been done incorrectly;
>
> To point out how it should have been done;
>
> To conclude that as long as it has been done, it may as well be left where it is;
>
> To wonder if it is not time to get rid of a person who cannot do a thing right;
>
> To reflect that the person probably has a spouse and large family, and that certainly any successor would be just as bad—or maybe worse;
>
> To consider how much simpler and better the thing would have been done if one had done it oneself in the first place;
>
> To reflect sadly that one could have done it right in twenty minutes, and as things turned out, one has had to spend two days to find out why it has taken three weeks for somebody else to do it wrong.

The idea that one person is always doing all the leading is false. The same person should not always lead the team in every situation. The challenge of the moment often determines the leader for that challenge because every person on the team has strengths that come into play. Let me illustrate this point. Even though I lead The INJOY Group as its founder, I don't always lead the team. Other people on the team have gifts, skills, and abilities that I do not possess. When we moved our offices—along with the employees, their equipment, our supplies and computers, our information and communication systems—the job required sophisticated navigating and incredible planning skills.

The most obvious person to lead the team was Frank Hartman, a logistical thinker, exceptional planner, and detailed administrator. Frank created the plan for the move. He had the authority and responsibility of managing the process—and of leading all of the people, including the CEO and other officers of the organization. And he did a wonderful job. We didn't lose a single day of productivity at the office during the move. Nobody else on our team could have pulled it off as effectively. I handed the ball off to Frank, and he successfully led us—and fulfilled the Law of the Edge.

> *Everyone is important, but everyone isn't equal.*

The other misconception about leadership takes the opposite extreme. I call it the *myth of the roundtable*. It's the belief that everyone on the team is equal, all opinions count the same, and a team can function without leadership. That isn't true either. A team that tries to function like a democracy never gets anything done.

Everyone is important, but everyone isn't equal. The person with greater experience, skill, and productivity in a given area is more important to the team in that area. GE CEO Jack Welch's opinion carries more weight than the person who packs boxes on the assembly line. The NBA's Michael Jordan is worth more money than the guard who sits on the bench. That's the way it is. That doesn't mean that Jack and Michael have more value as *human beings*. In the eyes of God, everyone is loved equally. But when it comes to leading the team, somebody needs to step forward.

GIVING THE TEAM A HEAD START

In essence, leadership is like a running head start for the team. Leaders see farther than their teammates. They see things more quickly than their teammates. They know what's going to happen and can anticipate it. As a result, they get the team moving in the right direction ahead of time, and for that reason, the team is in a position to win. Even an average runner can win a 100-meter race against a world-class sprinter if he has a 50-meter head start.

The greater the challenge, the greater the need for the many advantages that leadership provides. And the more leaders a team develops, the greater the edge from leadership. If you want to win and keep winning for a long time, train players on the team to become better leaders.

The edge gained from good leadership is quite evident in sports, but the power of leadership carries over into every field. The business that is run by a top-notch leader often finds its market niche first and outperforms its rivals, even if the rivals possess greater talent. The nonprofit organization headed by strong leaders recruits more players, equips them to lead, and serves a greater number of people as a result. Even in a technical area such as engineering or construction, leadership is invaluable in ensuring the team is successful.

GOLDEN OPPORTUNITY

The Law of the Edge was at work in one of the most extraordinary feats of engineering in the world: the Golden Gate Bridge. Completed in 1937, the bridge had the longest main span of any suspension bridge in the world until the construction of the Verrazano Narrows Bridge was finished in New York City in 1964. If you've been to San Francisco, then you've seen how beautiful and impressive the Golden Gate Bridge is. But the story of its construction is even more impressive.

The concept of a bridge spanning the Golden Gate—the opening to San Francisco's bay—was proposed as early as 1872, although nobody thought it was really possible. The idea wasn't brought up again and taken seriously until 1916. The reason people wanted a bridge was simple: San Francisco's growth and expansion were being hindered by its location since it was surrounded on three sides by water. Plenty of open land lay to the north, but getting to it was hard. Even though Marin County lay only about a mile north across the strait, getting there required a circuitous drive of one hundred miles around San Francisco's huge bay area. The only other alternative was to take a ferry across the gap, but at peak times, drivers had to wait in line for hours to catch the ferry.

Building a bridge across the Golden Gate Strait looked as if it would never happen. The physical and technological challenges of the project were overwhelming. The entrance of the bay experienced strong ocean currents and battering winds. The depth of the channel, which reached more than three hundred feet at points, would make construction very difficult. On top of that, any bridge that would be built had to be high enough to allow large ships to navigate beneath it. Engineers from around the country estimated that a bridge would cost as much as $250 million. (At that time, the value of every piece of property in the entire city of San Francisco totaled only $375 million!)

ENTER A LEADER

Then along came Joseph B. Strauss. He was the owner of an engineering firm that had built more than four hundred bridges. But more important than his experience were his astonishing vision and powerful leadership. He believed he could build a bridge spanning the Golden Gate for $25 million. In 1921, Strauss put together preliminary designs for a bridge and began to gather support for the project among the leaders of the counties adjoining San Francisco. He promoted the bridge tirelessly. In the beginning, his influence was unofficial. But in time, after the formation of the Golden Gate Bridge and Highway District, he was named chief engineer of the proposed project.

If it hadn't been for a leader like Strauss, the bridge never would have been built. For twelve years, he fought every imaginable obstacle and opponent to the project. When the San Francisco political machine (including the city's chief engineer, Michael O'Shaughnessy) opposed him, he met with leaders and citizens in every county to raise grassroots support. When the Army Corps of Engineers and the War Department (which controlled the land on both sides of the strait) threatened to withdraw approval, Strauss went to Washington and persuaded the secretary of war to guarantee the government's cooperation. When the Golden Gate Bridge and Highway District experienced a severe cash flow problem, Strauss met with Amadeo P. Giannini, founder of Bank of America. In just a few hours he was able to persuade Giannini to buy bonds immediately to keep the project going—

and commit to buy more the next time they were offered. Strauss overcame powerful special interest groups, environmentalists, labor problems, and the ravages of the Great Depression, which hit in the middle of the process. His energy and influence were astounding.

A LEADER WHO DIDN'T GET IN HIS OWN WAY

One of Strauss's greatest strengths was his ability to attract good leaders and engineers. To make the project successful, he brought in the best bridge designers in the world. When he realized that his original design for the bridge was inadequate and could endanger the project, he abandoned it and relied on his leaders to create something better. "Strauss had an unusual ability," remarked author John Van der Zee, "to locate and draw to him men of greater abilities than his own, men who would accept his leadership."[3]

Strauss was a leader's leader, and no matter what difficulty was thrown at him, he handled it. He was a natural leader who understood how to influence others. Van der Zee observed, "Strauss was, if anything, stronger at marketing and promoting ideas than he was at conceiving them. He seemed to know instinctively whom to reach, whom to get to and persuade, who were the decision makers, the people who mattered in any given situation."[4]

FINALLY BREAKING GROUND

In 1933, construction finally began on the bridge. Again, Strauss hired the best engineers he could find to oversee construction.

That was no small task. The team who built the bridge put in 25 million hours of work on it.[5] But the actual construction of the bridge seemed almost easy by comparison to what had been necessary before the process could begin. When the bridge was completed, Strauss remarked that it had taken him two decades to convince people that the bridge was feasible, but only four years to actually build it! And he completed it just in time. He died at age sixty-eight—the year after the bridge was finished.

Look behind the scenes of any major undertaking, and you will always find a strong leader. If Joseph Strauss hadn't taken personal responsibility for the creation of the Golden Gate Bridge—and dedicated himself to it wholeheartedly—then it wouldn't have been built. That's the reality of the Law of the Edge. It takes a leader if a team wants to realize its potential and reach its goals. That's why I say that *the difference between two equally talented teams is leadership.*

TEAMWORK THOUGHT

Everything rises and falls on leadership.

BECOMING A BETTER TEAM MEMBER

You don't have to be *the* leader to be *a* leader on your team. Begin the process of improving your leadership skills today. Do the following:

- Acknowledge the value of leadership.
- Take personal responsibility for your leadership growth.

• Put yourself on a leadership development program.

• Find a leadership mentor.

Once you have added value to yourself, you will be able to add value to—and influence—others to help your team.

BECOMING A BETTER TEAM LEADER

If you are *the* leader of your team, then the best thing you can do for your teammates is to follow the example of Joseph Strauss. Add other leaders to the team.

You can do that in two ways. First, attract the best leaders you can—people whose talent and potential are greater than your own. Second, develop the people already on the team. The stronger the leadership of the team, the greater the team's potential for success. Never forget: Everything rises and falls on leadership.

COMPANION **ONLINE** RESOURCE

Learn more about how the Law of the Edge uniquely applies to you.

Take the FREE Law of the Edge assessment at **LawsOfTeamwork.com**.

THE LAW OF HIGH MORALE

When You're Winning, Nothing Hurts

I t's an image most Americans will never forget: gymnast Kerri Strug being carried in the arms of Coach Bela Karolyi to the podium to receive her gold medal along with her six teammates in the 1996 Summer Olympic Games in Atlanta. It was a landmark moment. It was the first time the women's gymnastics team from the United States had won the gold medal, but that isn't why people will remember it. Although it was a stick-in-your-mind image—the tiny eighty-seven-pound Strug being cradled by a big bear of a man who is considered the greatest gymnastics coach in history—it will be remembered primarily because it is the perfect picture of the Law of High Morale.

A First for the Team

Even if you didn't see it on television as I did, you probably know the story. In a sport dominated by the Russian and Romanian teams, the United States team was actually ahead during the Olympic Games. The Russians had opened strong, but after the first rotation of events, the Americans were in first place. As the athletes competed in each event, the U.S. team's lead continued to grow—not by a lot but steadily. As the teams went into the final event—the floor exercise for the Russians and the vault for the Americans—all the U.S. team had to do was to finish solidly, and the gold medal would be theirs.

The second to last vaulter for the U.S. was Dominique Moceanu, usually a smooth performer. Much to everyone's surprise, on her first attempt she landed on her bottom instead of her feet, which gave her a very low score. Fortunately, in women's vault, each athlete gets a second attempt, and only the better of the two scores counts. But, unbelievably, Moceanu missed her second attempt with the same results.

Although Moceanu's performance was unexpected, the situation wasn't desperate. The U.S. still had one athlete left: Kerri Strug, who had received the highest scores in the vault during U.S. Olympic trials. One good vault from her, and the gold medal would belong to the team. When Strug tried to land her first vault, however, her feet weren't positioned quite right. She, too, slipped and fell. Worse yet, she injured herself, and she still needed to complete another vault for the team.

The situation was desperate. After the fact, some commentators remarked that the U.S. could have won without Strug's second vault. But at that moment, Russian gymnast Rozalia Galiyeva was still to compete in the floor exercise. U.S. coach Bela Karolyi was concerned that a high score by the Russian would cost the Americans their hard-fought victory.

Strug knew what she had to do. She needed to land her vault—the final attempt of the final event of the women's team competition. "Give me one last vault," Karolyi encouraged her. "Give me one last good vault."

NOT A FIRST FOR STRUG

Every athlete who makes it to the highest levels knows what it means to play through pain. Kerri Strug was no different. Besides all the normal strains, sprains, and bruises, in the past she had recovered from a torn stomach muscle and a serious back injury received in a fall on the uneven parallel bars. Karolyi said of her, "She is just a little girl who was never the roughest girl . . . always a little shy, always standing behind someone else. But sometimes this is the person with the biggest ggrrrrr."[1]

A gymnast has only thirty seconds to complete her second vault after the scores from the first one have been tabulated. In those moments, Strug focused herself. She later remembered, "I knew something was wrong with me. I heard something snap. I kept telling myself not to fall on the vault or the gold would slip away and all that hard work and effort would fall apart in a few seconds. I just said a little prayer and asked God to help me out."[2]

PAIN OR GAIN?

What Strug didn't know then was that two ligaments in her left ankle had torn during her first vault. But that didn't matter. She flew down the runway, hit the beat-board, sprang off the vault with her hands, and went flying through the air. Miraculously, she landed solidly on both feet. Then, she felt excruciating pain. Standing on one foot, she quickly saluted the judges, then crumpled to the floor. She landed her vault, she got her score, and the entire team received its gold medal.

After that, the girl who had always been in the background, who had never been the star of her gym, became the star of the Olympic team. Everyone seemed to appreciate the sacrifice she made. Sports journalist E. M. Swift wrote,

> All she knew, beyond the certainty of the gold medal, was that she had injured herself too badly to compete in the individual all-around competition two days later, a goal she'd clung to for the past four years. This was her moment of greatest triumph, also her moment of greatest disappointment. Her will had found a way to block out the pain for a few crucial seconds, but it had exacted a punishing price. She had literally sacrificed herself for the team.[3]

Strug's own words were direct and simple: "When you do well, you think it's worth it. When you sacrifice so much and you finally do well, it feels really good."[4] In other words, *when you're winning, nothing hurts.* That is the Law of High Morale.

TAKING THE TEAM HIGHER

The Law of High Morale may ring a bell with you because the phrasing of the law was inspired by the words of Joe Namath, the quarterback who helped the New York Jets win the Super Bowl in 1969.

Like any champion, he understood that there is an exhilaration that comes from winning. That feeling can be so strong that it sustains you through the discipline, pain, and sacrifice required to perform at the highest level.

That's what Kerri Strug felt. As she faced that final vault, she knew that her performance would help her team win. And that knowledge empowered her to come through for the team when it mattered most. Perhaps that's why George Allen, who coached the Washington Redskins in the early 1970s, said, "Every time you win, you're reborn; when you lose, you die a little." It's ironic, but if you play hurt, you can put the team in the position to win. And if you win, nothing hurts.

> *It's ironic, but if you play hurt, you can put the team in the position to win. And if you win, nothing hurts.*

Really high morale helps the team to perform at its best. High morale can be a crucial difference maker. When a team has high morale, it doesn't just have to deal with whatever circumstances get thrown at it. It creates its own circumstances.

- The *fund-raiser* knows that under the right circumstances, people love to give.

- The *teacher* knows that under the right circumstances, students love to grow.

- The *leader* knows that under the right circumstances, people love to follow.

- The *coach* knows that under the right circumstances, players are able to win.

High morale is one of the essentials to creating the right circumstances for any team to perform at the highest level.

High Morale Is Great . . .

If the team is winning, then morale is high. And if morale is high, then the team is in a position to win. So which comes first: high morale or winning? I believe that high morale usually comes first. Why? Because high morale magnifies everything positive that is happening for a team.

1. High Morale Is the Great Exaggerator

When an entire team is positive and all the players feel good about themselves, *everything* seems good. Preparation seems to proceed more smoothly. Every break seems to go your way. The small victories seem sweet, and the big ones make you feel almost invincible. The stars of the team deliver at crunch time, and even the bench players seem to be playing beyond their usual capabilities.

Some people call such a time a winning streak or a stretch of good luck. But it's really just high morale. In sports, during times of high morale, everybody jumps onto the bandwagon as a fan. In big business, people buy the company's stock. In entertainment, magazines and television networks ask for interviews—and producers pay top dollar for the team's services. Has the team changed from talentless to talented overnight? Is the team really as good as its press? Probably not. The team is enjoying the great exaggerator at work.

2. High Morale Is the Great Elevator

When a team possesses high morale, the performance of its people goes to a whole new level. The team focuses on its potential, not its problems. Team members become more committed. And everyone finds it easier to be unselfish. Team members are confident, and that confidence helps them to perform at a higher level.

When a team is losing, the opposite effect occurs. Players focus on their problems. Everyone's level of commitment goes down. The team repels others rather than attracts them. And everyone starts to look out for himself rather than his teammates. When you're losing, everything hurts.

3. High Morale Is the Great Energizer

High morale gives a team energy. Players become like the Energizer bunny: They keep going and going. No mountain seems too high. No project seems too difficult. No race seems too long. Their enthusiasm builds along with their energy, and the team develops a momentum that is almost unstoppable.

4. High Morale Is the Great Eliminator

Because of the momentum and energy that come with it, high morale also becomes the great eliminator. While a team that is losing and experiencing poor morale can be hurt by even the most minor problem, a team with high morale will keep right on going even when faced with a huge obstacle or otherwise disabling setback. Problems just seem to disappear—no matter how big they are.

5. High Morale Is the Great Emancipator

Something else that high morale does for a team is to free it up. Winning creates breathing room. A good team with high morale will use that breathing room to take risks and try out new ideas, new moves, new concepts that it otherwise wouldn't. It stops to ask questions that it otherwise might not. And doing these things yields creativity and innovation. In the end, high morale releases the team to reach its potential.

The Four Stages of Morale

You may be saying, "Okay, I agree. *When you're winning, nothing hurts.* High morale is great for the team. How in the world do we get it?" Let me tell you. If you are a player, then you need to have a good attitude, always give your best, and support the people on the team—players and leaders alike. If you have little influence, then exert what influence you have by modeling excellence.

However, if you're one of the team's leaders, then you have more extensive responsibilities. You need to model excellence, but you also need to do more. You need to help the people you lead to develop morale and momentum to create a winning team. The key to knowing what to do can be found in the four stages of morale.

Stage 1: Poor Morale–The Leader Must Do Everything

Nothing is more unpleasant than being on a team when nobody wants to be there. When that is the case, the team is usually negative, feels lethargic, or has no hope. That is often the atmosphere found in a team that is losing.

If you are in that situation, then do the following:

- *Investigate the situation.* Start by addressing what the team is doing wrong. Begin by fixing what's broken. That alone won't give the team high morale, but it will stop giving players reasons to have poor morale.

- *Initiate belief.* A team will change only when people believe in themselves. As the leader, you must initiate that belief. Show people you believe in yourself and them.

- *Create energy.* The desire to change without the energy to change just frustrates people. To bring a greater level of energy to the team, you need to be energetic. Work with energy long enough, and someone on the team will eventually come alongside you and join you. Then another person will. Eventually the energy will spread.

- *Communicate hope.* The deepest need of players at this stage is hope. As Napoleon Bonaparte said, "Leaders are dealers in hope." Help them to see the potential of the team.

> *"Leaders are dealers in hope."*
>
> —NAPOLEON BONAPARTE

In stage one, the only way to get the ball rolling is to start pushing it yourself. As the leader, you can't wait for anyone else to do it.

Stage 2: Low Morale—The Leader Must Do Productive Things

In the beginning, any movement is a noteworthy victory. But to create positive morale, you need to pick up some speed. You need to be productive. After all, you can't steer a parked car! Get the team moving.

- *Model behavior that has a high return.* People do what people see. The best way for them to learn what you expect of them is to model it yourself.

- *Develop relationships with people of potential.* To get any team going in the right direction, you need players who can produce. At this stage, your team may have some producers. If it does, develop relationships with them. If it doesn't, then find the people who have the potential to be productive, and start with them. Don't ask too much of them too soon. Leaders touch a heart before they ask for a hand. That's why you want to begin by building relationships.

- *Set up small victories and talk teammates through them.* Nothing helps people grow in skill and confidence like having some wins under their belts. That's what you want to give the people on your team. Once again, begin with the people who have the most potential. Their small victories will help less talented team members to gain confidence and succeed.

- *Communicate vision.* As I've already explained in the Law of the Compass, vision gives team members direction and confidence. Keep the vision before your team continually.

Once you've got the team really moving, then you can begin to steer.

Stage 3: Moderate Morale—The Leader Must Do Difficult Things

Do you remember what it was like when you first got your driver's license? Maybe before you received it, you enjoyed just sitting in the driver's seat of a car and imagining what it would be like to drive. Later, when you had your license and you were allowed to take out the car, just going for a drive was probably a thrill. It didn't really matter where you went. But as you got older, just driving wasn't enough. Having a destination became significant.

The same is true with a team. Getting the team together and moving add up to an accomplishment. But where you're going matters. To change from simply *moving the team* to *moving the team in the right direction,* you must do the difficult things that help the team to improve and develop high morale. You need to . . .

- *Make changes that make the team better.* You already understand the Law of the Chain. Just remember that leaders are responsible for minimizing the damage any team member can do because of weakness or attitude, and for maximizing the effectiveness of all team members by placing them in their proper niches. Often these actions require tough decisions.

- *Receive the buy-in of team members.* It's one thing to cast vision to the team. It's another to get your teammates to buy in. Yet to build higher morale, you must do that. The teammates must buy into you as a leader, embrace the values and mission of the team, and align themselves with your expectations. If you can do all of that, you will be able to take the team where it needs to go.

- *Communicate commitment.* Part of the process of getting people to buy in comes from showing them your commitment. The Law of Buy-In from *The 21 Irrefutable Laws of Leadership* says that people buy into the leader, then the vision. If you have consistently demonstrated high competence, good character, and strong commitment, you have laid the foundation for your people to buy in.

- *Develop and equip members for success.* Nothing builds morale like success. Most people are not capable of achieving success on their own. They need help, and that is one of the primary reasons for anyone to lead them. If you invest in your teammates, then you help them and the team succeed.

The two toughest stages in the life of the team are the first stage, when you are trying to create movement in a team that's going nowhere, and the third stage, when you must become a change agent. These are the times when leadership is most needed. And stage three is the make-or-break time for a leader. If you can succeed in stage three, then you will be able to create high morale on your team.

Stage 4: High Morale–The Leader Must Do Little Things

In stage four, your job as a leader is to help the team maintain high morale and momentum.

- *Keep the team focused and on course.* High morale leads to winning, and winning maintains morale. That's why it's important to keep team members focused. If they lose focus or get off course, then they'll stop winning. And remember, the farther you intend to go, the greater the impact of an error in direction. If you want to cross a street, being a degree or two off course doesn't hurt you. If you want to cross the ocean, miscalculating by a few degrees can get you into a lot of trouble.

- *Communicate successes.* Knowing what they're doing right helps people stay on track. You can indicate that by communicating the team's successes. Nothing boosts morale like winning and then celebrating it.

- *Remove morale mashers.* Once the team is rolling in the right direction, keep it rolling. The Law of the Big Mo from *The 21*

Irrefutable Laws of Leadership says that momentum is a leader's best friend. Leaders see before others do, so they need to protect the team from the things that will hurt the team.

- *Allow other leaders to lead.* A leader who prepares other team members to lead and then turns them loose to do it accomplishes two things. First, he uses the momentum the team already has to create new leaders for the team. It's easier to make new leaders successful if they are part of a successful team. Second, he increases the leadership of the team. And that makes the team even more successful. A leader who continually does that can create a cycle of success that feeds the team's high morale.

The process of building high morale takes strong leadership, and it takes time. When I think of someone who was a master at that process, I think of Ronald Reagan. When he took office as president of the United States in 1981, morale in the country was at the lowest it had been since the Great Depression. People had lost faith in the American government following Watergate. The threat of nuclear war with the Soviet Union was never far from people's thinking. Inflation was out of control. Oil prices were up. And interest rates were off the charts. People could not have been more discouraged.

Ronald Reagan helped people to

> *Four Stages of Morale:*
> *1. Poor Morale—*
> *The leader must do everything.*
> *2. Low Morale—*
> *The leader must do productive things.*
> *3. Moderate Morale—*
> *The leader must do difficult things.*
> *4. High Morale—*
> *The leader must do little things.*

believe in the country again. Under his presidency, the economy revived, the cold war ended, the Berlin Wall fell, and people believed in themselves and their country again.

HIGH MORALE AT HOME

You don't need to have the power of a president or the ability of an Olympic athlete to practice the Law of High Morale. You can apply the principle to your business, your volunteer service, or even your family. In fact, when the Law of High Morale is working at its best, the leader boosts the morale of the team, and the team boosts the morale of the leader. That's the way it should be. *When you're winning, nothing hurts.*

> *When the Law of High Morale is working at its best, the leader boosts the morale of the team, and the team boosts the morale of the leader.*

Let me tell you about a team where the members continually inspire one another and build up one another to such an extent that their morale is high and they keep winning despite the pain they feel. They are the father-and-son team of Dick and Rick Hoyt.

When Rick Hoyt was born in 1962, his parents possessed the typical excited expectations of first-time parents. But then they discovered that during Rick's birth, his umbilical cord had been wrapped around his neck, cutting off the oxygen to his brain. Later, Rick was diagnosed with cerebral palsy. "When he was eight months old," his father, Dick, remembers, "the doctors told us we should put him away—he'd be a vegetable all his life."[5] But Rick's parents wouldn't do that. They were determined to raise him like any other kid.

An Uphill Battle

Sometimes that was tough. Rick is a quadriplegic who cannot speak because he has limited control of his tongue. But Rick's parents worked with him, teaching him everything they could and including him in family activities. When Rick was ten, his life changed; engineers from Tufts University created a device that enabled him to communicate via computer. The first words he slowly and painstakingly punched out were, "Go Bruins." That's when the family, who had been following the NHL's Boston Bruins in the play-offs, found out Rick was a sports fan.

In 1975, after a long battle, the family was finally able to get Rick into public school, where he excelled despite his physical limitations. Rick's world was changing. It changed even more two years later. When Rick found out that a fund-raising 5K race (3.1 miles) was being put on to help a young athlete who had been paralyzed in an accident, he told his father that he wanted to participate.

Dick, a lieutenant colonel in the Air National Guard (who has since retired), was in his late thirties and out of shape. But he agreed to run and push his son in a modified wheelchair. When they crossed the finish line (second to last), Dick recalls, Rick flashed "the biggest smile you ever saw in your life." After the race, Rick wrote out this simple message: "Dad, I felt like I wasn't handicapped." After that day, their lives would never be the same again.

Working Together

What does a father do when his son, who has never been out of a wheelchair, says that he loves to race? He becomes his boy's hands and feet. That's the day "Team Hoyt" was born. Dick got Rick a more sophisticated racing chair. Then the quadriplegic teenager and the out-of-shape dad began running together—and not casually. Before long, they were training seriously, and in 1981, they ran in their first Boston Marathon together. Since then, they haven't missed a Boston Marathon in twenty years.

After four years of running marathons, the two decided that they were ready for another challenge: triathlons, which combine swimming, cycling, and running. That was no small challenge, especially since Dick would have to learn how to swim! But he did. Dick explained, "He's the one who has motivated me because if it wasn't for him, I wouldn't be out there competing. What I'm doing is loaning Rick my arms and legs so he can be out there competing like everybody else."[6]

Of all the races in the world, one is considered the toughest—the Ironman Triathlon in Hawaii. The race consists of three back-to-back legs: a 2.4-mile swim, a 112-mile bike race, and a full marathon run of 26.2 miles. It's an excruciating test of stamina for any individual. In 1989, Dick and Rick competed in the race together. For the swimming portion, Dick towed a small boat with Rick in it. Then he biked for the 112 miles with Rick in a seat on his bicycle's handlebars. By the time they got to the running leg, Dick was exhausted.

But it's in such situations that the Law of High Morale kicks in. All Dick had to do was to think of the words of his son:

When I'm running, my disability seems to disappear. It is the only place where truly I feel as an equal. Due to all the positive feedback, I do not feel handicapped at all. Rather, I feel that I am the intelligent person that I am with no limits.[7]

When you're winning, nothing hurts. By continuing to run, Dick would be winning for his son, and that's what makes all the training and pain worthwhile. Dick loaded Rick into his running chair, and off they went to finish the Ironman. The pair finished the race in a little over thirteen hours and forty-three minutes—a very strong time.

Since then, Rick has earned his college degree, and he works at Boston University helping to design computer systems for people with disabilities. And of course, he still competes with his father, who is now more than sixty years old. As of March 2001, Team Hoyt had completed a total of 731 races. They had run 53 marathons and 135 triathlons, including 4 races at Ironman distances. And they will keep running. "There is nothing in the world that the both of us can't conquer together," says Dick.[8] He should know. For almost twenty-five years, he and his teammate have been reaping the rewards of the Law of High Morale.

TEAMWORK THOUGHT

When you do good, you feel good—when you
feel good, you do good.

BECOMING A BETTER TEAM MEMBER

If you want to reap the rewards of the Law of High Morale, you can't wait until your morale is high to begin performing. You need to act your way into feeling, not feel your way into acting. Begin by performing at a level of excellence appropriate for someone who is experiencing a winning season. Your dedication and enthusiasm will help your performance—and will inspire some of your teammates.

BECOMING A BETTER TEAM LEADER

If you are a leader on your team, then you need to figure out what kind of morale your team is currently experiencing:

- *Poor morale:* The team is dead in the water and negative.

- *Low morale:* The team is making some progress, but it is not cohesive and confident.

- *Moderate morale:* The team is experiencing some wins and beginning to believe in itself, but some hard decisions need to be made to take it to the next level.

- *High morale:* The team is performing close to its potential, it's winning, and it just needs to be kept on track.

Once you've determined the stage of your team, then apply the guidelines in the chapter so that you can take the team (or your area of it) to the next stage.

COMPANION **ONLINE** RESOURCE

Learn more about how the Law of High Morale uniquely applies to you.

Take the FREE Law of High Morale assessment at **LawsOfTeamwork.com**.

THE LAW OF DIVIDENDS

Investing in the Team Compounds Over Time

He's one of the greatest team builders in all of sports, yet you've probably never heard of him. Here is a list of these impressive accomplishments:

- Forty consecutive basketball seasons with at least twenty wins

- Five national championships

- Number one ranking in his region in twenty of the last thirty-three years

- Lifetime winning percentage of .870

His name is Morgan Wootten. And why have most people never heard of him? Because he is a *high school* basketball coach!

When asked to name the greatest basketball coach of all time, most people would respond with one of two names: Red Auerbach or John Wooden. But do you know what John Wooden, the UCLA coach called the Wizard of Westwood, had to say about Morgan Wootten? He was emphatic in his appraisal: "People say Morgan Wootten is the best high school coach in the country. I disagree. I know of no finer coach at any level—high school, college or pro. I've said it elsewhere and I'll say it here: I stand in awe of him."[1]

That's a pretty strong recommendation from the man who won ten NCAA national championships and coached some of the most talented players in the game, including Kareem Abdul-Jabbar. (By the way, when Kareem was in high school at Power Memorial Academy, his team lost only one game—to Morgan Wootten's team!)

No Plan to Be a Team Builder

Morgan Wootten never planned to coach a team. He was a decent athlete in high school, but nothing special. However, he was an excellent talker. When he was growing up, his ambition was to be an attorney. But when he was a nineteen-year-old college student, a friend tricked him into accepting a job coaching baseball, a game he knew little about, to kids from an orphanage. The team had no uniforms and no equipment. And despite working hard, the boys lost all sixteen of their games.

During that first season, Wootten fell in love with those kids. When they asked him to come back and coach football, he couldn't refuse them. Besides, he had played football in high school, so he knew something about it. The orphanage team went undefeated and won the Washington, D.C., Catholic Youth Organization (CYO) championship. But more important, Wootten began to realize that he wanted to invest his time in children, not in court cases.

Even that first year he made a difference in the lives of kids. He remembers one boy in particular who had started stealing and kept being brought back to the orphanage by the police. He described the boy as having "two and a half strikes against him already." Wootten let the boy know he was headed for trouble. But he also took the boy under his wing. Wootten recalled,

> We started spending some time together. I took him to my house and he'd enjoy Mom's meals. He spent weekends with us. He became friends with my brother and sisters. He's still in Washington today and doing quite well and known to a lot of people. Anyone would be proud to call him their son. He was bound for a life of crime and jail, however, and maybe a lot worse, until someone gave him the greatest gift a parent can give a child—his time.

Giving of himself to the people on his teams is something Wootten has done every year since then. NCAA basketball coach Marty Fletcher, a former player and assistant under Wooten, summarized his talent this way: "His secret is that he makes whomever he is with feel like the most important person in the world."[2]

CREATING A DYNASTY

It wasn't long before Wootten was invited to become an assistant coach at a local powerhouse high school. Then with a couple of years' experience under his belt, he became head coach at DeMatha High School.

When he started at the school in 1956, Wootten was taking over a bunch of losing teams. He called together all of the students who wanted to play sports at DeMatha, and he told them:

> Fellas, things are going to change. I know how bad DeMatha's teams have been during these last few years, but that's over with. We're going to win at DeMatha and we're going to build a *tradition* of winning. Starting right now . . . But let me tell you how we're going to do it. We're going to outwork every team we ever play . . . With a lot of hard work and discipline and dedication, people are going to hear about us and respect us, because DeMatha will be a winner.[3]

That year, the football team won half of its games, which was quite an accomplishment. In basketball and baseball, they were division champions. His teams have been winning ever since. DeMatha has long been considered a dynasty.

On October 13, 2000, Wootten was inducted into the Naismith Basketball Hall of Fame in Springfield, Massachusetts. At that time, his teams had amassed a record of 1,210–183. Over the years, more than 250 of his players have won college scholarships. Twelve players from his high school teams went on to play in the NBA.[4]

It's Not About Basketball

But winning games and honors isn't what excites Wootten most. It's investing in the kids. Wooten says,

> Coaches at every level have a tendency to lose sight of their purpose at times, especially after success arrives. They start to put the cart

---

before the horse by working harder and harder to develop their teams, using their boys or girls to do it, gradually forgetting that their real purpose should be to develop the kids, using their teams to do it.[5]

Wootten's attitude reaps rewards not only for the team, but also for the individuals on the team. For example, for a twenty-six-year stretch, every single one of Wootten's seniors earned college scholarships—not just starters but bench players too. Penn State assistant coach Chuck Swenson observed, "Even if you know a kid isn't a great player, if he's a DeMatha player, he'll help your program. With Morgan, you know you're getting a quality kid, who will make good grades and work hard for you."[6] Gary Williams, head coach of the University of Maryland, agreed about the quality of the players: "His players are so fundamentally sound, do so many things right, that they may not improve as much as kids in another program who haven't been as well coached . . . These aren't raw talents: They're refined ones."[7] What's remarkable is that these comments describe *high school* students, not college players or pros.

Investing in the team compounds over time. Morgan Wootten invests in his players because it is the right thing to do, because he cares about them. That practice has made his players good, his teams successful, and his career remarkable. He is the first basketball coach to have won 1,200 games at any level. Developing people pays off in every way. That is the power of the Law of Dividends.

GREAT INVESTORS

Throughout the chapters of this book, you've read about people who have dedicated themselves to investing in the people on their teams. And those investments pay all kinds of rich dividends. Gordon Bethune's investment of trust has paid off by keeping Continental in business and saving the jobs of its fourteen thousand employees. The investment of Bernie Marcus and Arthur Blank is paying dividends to the employees who own Home Depot stock, including one thousand employee-millionaires. The investment of Jeff Skilling at Enron is paying dividends in the formation of new industry initiatives by leaders in the company. And Lilly Tartikoff's investment in people is paying dividends in cancer research. Usually the time, money, and effort required to develop team members don't change the team overnight, but developing them always pays off. *Investing in the team compounds over time.*

> *The time, money, and effort required to develop team members don't change the team overnight, but developing them always pays off.*

How to Invest in Your Team

I believe that most people recognize that investing in a team brings benefits to everyone on the team. The question for most people isn't *why*, but *how*. Allow me to share with you ten steps you can take to invest in your team. You can implement these practices whether you are a player or coach, employee or employer, follower or leader. There is always someone on the team who can benefit from what you have to offer. And when everyone on the team is investing, then the benefits are like those of compound interest. They multiply.

Here is how to get started:

1. Make the Decision to Build a Team . . . This Starts the Investment in the Team

It's said that every journey begins with the first step. Deciding that people on the team are worth developing is the first step in building a better team. That requires *commitment*.

> *Deciding that people on the team are worth developing is the first step in building a better team.*

2. Gather the Best Team Possible . . . This Elevates the Potential of the Team

As I've previously mentioned, the better the people on the team, the greater the potential. There's only one kind of team that you may be a part of where you *shouldn't* go out and find the best players available, and that's family. You need to stick with those teammates through thick and thin. But every other kind of team can benefit from the recruitment of the very best people available.

3. Pay the Price to Develop the Team . . . This Ensures the Growth of the Team

When Morgan Wootten extended himself to benefit the kid who had two-and-a-half strikes against him, he and his family had to pay a price to help that boy. It wasn't convenient or comfortable. It cost them in energy, money, and time.

It will cost you to develop your team. You will have to dedicate time that could be used for personal productivity. You will have to spend money that could be used for personal benefit. And sometimes you will have to set aside your personal agenda. But the benefit to the individuals—and the team—is worth the price. Everything you give is an investment.

4. Do Things Together as a Team . . . This Provides Community for the Team

I once read the statement, "Even when you've played the game of your life, it's the feeling of teamwork that you'll remember. You'll forget the plays, the shots, and the scores, but you'll never forget your teammates." That is describing the community that develops among teammates who spend time doing things together.

> Even when you've played the game of your life, it's the feeling of teamwork that you'll remember.

The only way to develop community and cohesiveness among your teammates is to get them together, not just in a professional setting but in personal ones as well. There are lots of ways to get yourself connected with your teammates, and to connect them with one another. Many families who want to bond find that camping does the trick. Business colleagues can socialize outside work (in an appropriate way). The *where* and *when* are not as important as the fact that team members share common experiences.

5. Empower Team Members with Responsibility and Authority . . . This Raises Up Leaders for the Team

The greatest growth for people often occurs as a result of the trial and error of personal experience. Any team that wants people to step up to a higher level of performance—and to higher levels of leadership—must give team members authority as well as responsibility. If you are a leader on your team, don't protect your position or hoard your power. Give it away. That's the only way to empower your team.

6. Give Credit for Success to the Team . . . This Lifts the Morale of the Team

Mark Twain said, "I can live for two months on one good compliment." That's the way most people feel. They are willing to work hard if they receive recognition for their efforts. That's why Napoleon Bonaparte observed, "A soldier will fight long and hard for a bit of colored ribbon." Compliment your teammates. Talk up their accomplishments. And if you're the leader, take the blame but never the credit. Do that and your team will always fight for you.

> "I can live for two months on one good compliment."
>
> —MARK TWAIN

7. Watch to See That the Investment in the Team Is Paying Off . . . This Brings Accountability to the Team

If you put money into an investment, you expect a return—maybe not right away, but certainly over time. How will you know whether you are gaining or losing ground on that investment? You have to pay attention to it and measure its progress.

The same is true of an investment in people. You need to observe whether you are getting a return for the time, energy, and resources you are putting into them. Some people develop quickly. Others are slower to respond, and that's okay. The main outcome you want to see is progress.

8. Stop Your Investment in Players Who Do Not Grow . . . This Eliminates Greater Losses for the Team

One of the most difficult experiences for any team member is leaving a teammate behind. Yet that is what you must do if someone on your team refuses to grow or change for the benefit of teammates. As I mentioned in the Law of the Chain, that doesn't mean that you love the person less. It just means you stop spending your time trying to invest in someone who won't or can't make the team better.

9. Create New Opportunities for the Team . . . This Allows the Team to Stretch

There is no greater investment you can make in a team than giving it new opportunities. When a team has the possibility of taking new ground or facing new challenges, it has to stretch to meet them. That process not only gives the team a chance to grow, but it also benefits every individual. Everyone has the opportunity to grow toward his or her potential.

10. Give the Team the Best Possible Chance to Succeed . . . This Guarantees the Team a High Return

James E. Hunton says, "Coming together is a beginning. Keeping together is progress. Working together is success." One of the most essential tasks you can undertake is to clear obstacles so that the team has the best possible chance to work toward success. If you are a team member, that may mean making a personal sacrifice or helping others to work together better. If you are a leader, that means creating an energized environment for the team and giving each person what he needs at any given time to ensure success.

> *Where there's a will there's a way; where there's a team, there's more than one way.*

Investing in a team almost guarantees a high return for the effort because a team can do so much more than individuals. Or as Rex Murphy, one of my conference attendees, told me: "Where there's a will there's a way; where there's a team, there's more than one way."

MY PERSONAL INVESTMENT—AND RETURN

Once you have experienced what it means to invest in your team, you will never be able to stop. Thinking about my team—about how the teammates add value to me as I add value to them—brings me abundant joy. And just like my investment and their return, my joy continues to compound.

I value everyone on my team, and if I could, I would tell you about every person. But since that isn't possible, I want to at least acquaint you with key players in my inner circle:

- Larry Maxwell (fifty-four years). He loves me unconditionally. He has taken The INJOY Group to a whole new level. Asks great questions. Keeps our team focused. Protects me. He's my big brother!

- Margaret Maxwell (thirty-seven years). My wife. She knows me so well, loves me so much. Her partnership has allowed me to go to a higher level. Our journey together is my greatest joy.

- Dan Reiland (nineteen years). He was my executive pastor for many years. Now as a consultant, he helps pastors with my heart and experience plus his wisdom and perspective. He is a pastor's best friend and mine!

- Dick Peterson (eighteen years). He follows up on all the details of my company. I open the door, and he closes it. I start a sentence, and he finishes it!

- Tim Elmore (fifteen years). He teaches my leadership material better than I do. He gives me leadership material better than my own.

- Linda Eggers (fourteen years). She knows my strengths and weaknesses. Represents me so well. Answers the team's questions better than I would and much more quickly.

- Charlie Wetzel (eight years). He shapes the lives of more people than anyone else on my team. He takes my ideas, lessons, and outlines and turns them into books. From there, they multiply.

- Dave Johnson (seven years). He stewards The INJOY Group's resources to extend its impact around the globe. He is a financial wizard who loves and understands me.

- Kevin Small (seven years). He has unlimited energy and unlimited potential. Sees an opportunity a mile away. I love pouring myself into him. The return is huge!

- Dave Sutherland (seven years). He is my number one guy. He's the man. A great thinker. He can grow the company without me. When I give him the ball, it's always a touchdown.

- Kirk Nowery (five years). He represents me so well and loves pastors and local churches. Every night he tells the story of how we can add value through ISS. Every night we get that opportunity.

- Doug Carter (five years). He loves to share the mission of EQUIP (my nonprofit organization) with others. He helps businesspeople go from success to significance. He has taken me to a whole new level.

At this stage of my life, everything I do is a team effort. When I first started teaching seminars, I did everything. Certainly there were other people pitching in, but I was just as likely to pack and ship a box as I was to speak. Now, I show up and teach. My wonderful team takes care of everything else. Even the book you're reading was a team effort.

My team is my joy. I would do anything for the people on my team because they do everything for me:

> My team makes me better than I am.
> My team multiplies my value to others.
> My team enables me to do what I do best.
> My team gives me more time.
> My team represents me where I cannot go.
> My team provides community for our enjoyment.
> My team fulfills the desires of my heart.

If your current team experiences are not as positive as you would like, then it's time to increase your level of investment. Building a team for the future is just like developing a financial nest egg. It may start slowly, but what you put in brings a high return— similar to the way that compound interest works with finances. Try it and you will find that the Law of Dividends really works. *Investing in the team compounds over time.*

TEAMWORK THOUGHT

Is the team's investment in you paying off?

BECOMING A BETTER TEAM MEMBER

Are you giving a good return for what your teammates are investing in you? Think about the opportunities you have received and the positive learning experiences to which you've been exposed. Have you seized all of them enthusiastically, or have you allowed many of them to slip by?

If you've been lackadaisical about pursuing growth opportunities, then change your attitude today. Grow all you can, and determine to give the team a good return on its investment in you.

BECOMING A BETTER TEAM LEADER

As a leader, you, more than anyone else, determine the environment of your organization and whether your people are investing in others. Begin by institutionalizing investment and making it a part of your organization's culture. Encourage growth. Set aside time and money for investment in the team. And take on the responsibility for investing in your core leaders. The more leaders you have on the team and the further developed they are, the greater the dividends.

COMPANION **ONLINE** RESOURCE

Learn more about how the Law of Dividends uniquely applies to you.

Take the FREE Law of Dividends assessment at **LawsOfTeamwork.com**.

AFTERWORD

A lot of people talk about team chemistry. You hear it often in sports. Analysts will say, "That team certainly had the talent, but they weren't able to develop the chemistry. That's why they didn't perform the way everyone expected."

You may have noticed that there is no Law of Chemistry in this book, and that may have been a disappointment to you. But let me tell you why that concept isn't one of the 17 Indisputable Laws of Teamwork.

Chemistry isn't something you can create with one skill or implementation of a single technique. Chemistry develops when you are able to implement *all* of the Laws of Teamwork. The more laws you put into practice, the greater the chemistry your team will develop. Each time a player finds his niche on the team, it helps to create positive chemistry. Each time a weak link is replaced by a better player from the bench, it creates better chemistry. When a catalyst steps up to the plate and makes something happen for the first time, or when a leader finds a way to help the team perform at a higher level, it creates good chemistry. When players finally count on one another, it makes the chemistry better. Every time another law comes to life for the team, the chemistry gets that much better—and the team gets that much stronger.

I hope you have enjoyed learning about the Laws of Teamwork. More important, I hope they will help you develop the team of your dreams. Embrace them and you will empower your team. That is my promise to you!

NOTES

Chapter 1

1. Brandon Tartikoff and Charles Leerhsen, *The Last Great Ride* (New York: Turtle Bay Books, 1992), 60.
2. "OncoLink: An Interview with Lilly Tartikoff," <www.oncolink.upenn.edu>.

Chapter 2

1. Frye Gaillard, *If I Were a Carpenter: Twenty Years of Habitat for Humanity* (Winston-Salem, NC: John F. Blair, 1995).
2. "The History of Habitat," <www.habitat.org>.

Chapter 3

1. "Bush Nominates Powell as Secretary of State," 17 December 2000.
2. Colin Powell with Joseph E. Persico, *My American Journey* (New York: Random House, 1995), 28.

3. Michael Hirsh and John Barry, "Leader of the Pack," *Newsweek* <www.newsweek.com>, 25 December 2000.

4. "Town Hall Meeting: January 25, 2001," <www.state.gov>.

5. "Packing Parachutes," audiotape excerpt, <www.charlieplumb.com>.

6. "Charlie Plumb's Speech Content," <www.charlieplumb.com>.

Chapter 4

1. "Mount Everest History/Facts," <www.mnteverest.com>.

2. James Ramsey Ullman, *Man of Everest: The Autobiography of Tenzing* (London: George G. Harrap and Co., 1955), 178.

3. Ibid., 250.

4. Ibid., 255.

5. Jim Lovell and Jeffrey Kluger, *Lost Moon: The Perilous Voyage of Apollo 13* (Boston: Houghton Mifflin, 1994), 159–60.

6. W. David Compton, *Where No Man Has Gone Before: A History of Apollo Lunar Exploration Missions* (Washington DC: NASA SP-4214, 1989).

7. Ullman, *Man of Everest*, 227.

Chapter 5

1. "Quick Answers to the Most Frequently Asked Questions," <www.oilspill.state.ak.us/history>.

2. "Exxon's Appeal of the Valdez Oil Spill $5 Billion in Punitive Judgement," <www.exxon.mobil.com>.

3. Danny Cox with John Hoover, *Leadership When the Heat's On* (New York: McGraw-Hill, 1992), 69–70.

4. John Carl Roat, *Class-29: The Making of U.S. Navy SEALs* (New York: Ballantine Books, 1998), 192.

5. Ibid., 7.

6. Ibid., 223.

Chapter 6

1. "The President Suits Up for Practice," <www.cbs.sportsline.com>.

2. "The History of the 'I Have a Dream' Program," <www.ihad.org>.

Chapter 7

1. Greg Farrell, "Building a New Big Blue," <www.usatoday.com>, 23 November 1999.

2. "IBM Wants Business Partners to Focus on Growth," <www.findarticles.com>, 2 March 1999.

3. Farrell, "Building a New Big Blue."

4. Michelle Marchetti, "IBM's Marketing Visionary," *Sales and Marketing Management,* September 2000, 55.

5. Proverbs 29:18 KJV.

6. Dan Westell, "HNG Purchase Gives Internorth New Scope," *Wall Street Journal,* 16 July 1985, <bis.dowjones.com>.

7. Thomas A. Stewart, "Taking Risk to the Marketplace," *Fortune,* 6 March 2000, <www.fortune.com>.

8. Gary Hamel, "Inside the Revolution: Take It Higher," *Fortune,* 5 February 2001, <www.fortune.com>.

9. "100 Best Companies to Work For," <www.fortune.com>.

Chapter 8

1. John C. Maxwell, *The Winning Attitude* (Nashville: Thomas Nelson, 1993), 24.

2. Pat Riley, *The Winner Within* (New York: Berkley Publishing Group, 1994), 41, 52.

Chapter 9

1. "Interview with Stacey Loizeaux."
2. John C. Maxwell, *The 21 Irrefutable Laws of Leadership: Follow Them and People Will Follow You* (Nashville: Thomas Nelson, 1998), 58.
3. Barry J. Gibbons, *This Indecision Is Final: 32 Management Secrets of Albert Einstein, Billie Holiday, and a Bunch of Other People Who Never Worked 9 to 5* (Chicago: Irwin Professional Publishing, 1996).
4. Colossians 3:23–24.
5. Roat, *Class-29: The Making of U.S. Navy SEALs*, 135–36.
6. "Statement of FBI Director Louis J. Freeh on the Arrest of FBI Special Agent Robert Philip Hanssen," <www.fbi.gov>, 20 February 2001.
7. Walter Pincus and Brooke A. Masters, "U.S. May Seek Death Penalty Against Accused Spy Hanssen," <www.washingtonpost.com>, 28 March 2001.
8. "Core Values," <www.fbi.gov>, 30 March 2001.
9. "Statement of FBI Director Louis J. Freeh on the Arrest of FBI Special Agent Robert Philip Hanssen."
10. William A. Cohen, *The Art of the Leader* (Englewood Cliffs, NJ: Prentice Hall, 1994).

Chapter 10

1. Stephen Franklin, "Founder a Force in Retail, Civic Affairs," <www.chicagotribune.com>, 29 December 2000.
2. "End of the Line," <www.nytimes.com>, 29 December 2000.
3. "Historical Chronology—1925: Opening Retail Stores," <www.sears.com>, 15 March 2001.
4. Allan Cox, *Straight Talk for Monday Morning* (New York: John Wiley & Sons, 1990).

5. John C. Maxwell, *The 21 Indispensable Qualities of a Leader: Becoming the Person Others Will Want to Follow* (Nashville: Thomas Nelson, 1999), 144–45.

6. Robert Newall, "History Comes Alive in Valley Forge," <www.vaportrails.com>, 11 March 2001.

Chapter 11

1. Michael D. Eisner with Tony Schwartz, *Work in Progress* (New York: Random House, 1998), 171.

2. John Taylor, *Storming the Magic Kingdom: Wall Street Raiders and the Battle for Disney* (New York: Knopf, 1987), 14.

3. Eisner, *Work in Progress*, 235.

4. "The Walt Disney Company Annual Report 2000: Financial Review," <www.disney.go.com>, 28 March 2001.

5. Adam Cohen, "eBay's Bid to Conquer All," *Time*, 5 February 2001, 48.

6. "Company Overview," <pages.ebay.com>, 12 March 2001.

Chapter 12

1. John Wooden with Jack Tobin, *They Call Me Coach* (Chicago: Contemporary Books, 1988), 104.

Chapter 13

1. Bernie Marcus and Arthur Blank with Bob Andelman, *Built from Scratch: How a Couple of Regular Guys Grew The Home Depot from Nothing to $30 Billion* (New York: Times Business, 1999), xvi–xvii.

2. "Company Information," <www.homedepot.com>, 11 April 2001.

3. Marcus and Blank, *Built from Scratch*, xvii.

Chapter 14

1. Gordon Bethune with Scott Huler, *From Worst to First: Behind the Scenes of Continental's Remarkable Comeback* (New York: John Wiley and Sons, 1998), 4.
2. Ibid., 6.
3. Thomas A. Stewart, "Just Think: No Permission Needed," *Fortune,* 8 January 2001, <www.fortune.com>.
4. Bethune, *From Worst to First,* 211.
5. "Return with Honor," *The American Experience,* <www.pbs.org>, 22 February 2001.

Chapter 15

1. Mike Kahn, "Harris' Deletion No Surprise," <www.cbs.sport-sline.com>, 24 February 1999.
2. Mike Rowland, *Los Angeles Magazine,* June 2000, <www.findarti-cles.com>.
3. John Van der Zee, *The Gate: The True Story of the Design and Construction of the Golden Gate Bridge* (Lincoln, NE: Backinprint.com, 2000), 50.
4. Ibid., 42.
5. Craig A. Doherty and Katherine M. Doherty, *The Golden Gate Bridge* (Woodbridge, CT: Blackbirch Press, 1995), 17.

Chapter 16

1. Johnette Howard, "True Grit," <sportsillustrated.cnn.com>, 24 July 1996.
2. Ibid.
3. E. M. Swift, "Carried Away with Emotion," <sportsillustrated.cnn.com>, 8 December 1996.
4. "Not Just the Wink of an Eye," <www.strug.com>, 30 March 2001.

5. David Tereshchuk, "Racing Towards Inclusion," <www.teamhoyt.com>, 14 March 2001.

6. "Father-Son Duo Are World Class Competitors, Despite Odds," <www.cnn.com>, 29 November 1999.

7. Ibid.

8. Ibid.

Chapter 17

1. Don Banks, "Teacher First, Seldom Second, Wootten has Built Monument to Excellence at Maryland's DeMatha High," *St. Petersburg Times*, 3 April 1987, <www.dematha.org>.

2. John Feinstein, "A Down-to-Earth Coach Brings DeMatha to New Heights," *Washington Post*, 27 February 1984, <www.dematha.org>.

3. Morgan Wootten and Bill Gilbert, *From Orphans to Champions: The Story of DeMatha's Morgan Wootten* (New York: Atheneum, 1979), 24–25.

4. William Plummer, "Wooten's Way," *People*, 20 November 2000, 166.

5. Wootten and Gilbert, *From Orphans to Champions*, 12–13.

6. Feinstein, "A Down-to-Earth Coach Brings DeMatha to New Heights."

7. Ibid.

How Can You Be A More Successful Team Leader?

John C. Maxwell has the resources for you!

STEP 1	Assess Your Team Leadership Skills

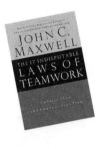

Take the FREE online assessment at **www.LawsOfTeamwork.com**. You will immediately see a snapshot of your leadership ability and how well you create and lead teams.

STEP 2	Start With The Basics

Spend 17 days reading *The 17 Indisputable Laws of Teamwork*. Read one chapter each day to understand the foundations for building and leading solid teams.

Leadership expert John C. Maxwell encourages readers to explore and enhance their teamwork skills. John examines how a group of individuals can come together and succeed by outlining principles for building, enhancing, and working as a team.

These principles can be used in any business, family or organization. No matter who you are, if you learn and apply the laws, your teamwork capacity will increase and your efforts will be multiplied.

The INJOY Group™
A Lifelong Partner Dedicated to Lifting Your Potential

The INJOY Group™, founded in 1985 by Dr. John C. Maxwell, dedicates itself to adding value to individuals and organizations across America and around the world. It accomplishes its mission by forging lasting partnerships that foster personal growth and organizational effectiveness.

The INJOY Group™ consists of . . .

INJOY® Resources—Equipping People to Succeed

INJOY® Conferences—Empowering Leaders to Excel

INJOY Stewardship Services®—Energizing Churches to Raise Funds for Financing the Future

EQUIP™—Affecting Leadership Development in Emerging Countries, American Urban Centers, and Academic Communities

Each year, The INJOY Group™ partners with tens of thousands of people, dozens of church denominations, and countless business and non-profit organizations to help people reach their potential.

To learn more about Dr. John C. Maxwell or any division of The INJOY Group™, visit us at:

www.INJOY.com

Books by Dr. John C. Maxwell
Can Teach You How to Be a REAL Success

RELATIONSHIPS
Be a People Person (Victor Books)
Becoming a Person of Influence (Thomas Nelson)
The Power of Influence (Honor Books)
The Power of Partnership in the Church (J. Countryman)
The Treasure of a Friend (J. Countryman)

EQUIPPING
Developing the Leaders Around You (Thomas Nelson)
Partners in Prayer (Thomas Nelson)
The Success Journey (Thomas Nelson)
Success One Day at a Time (J. Countryman)

ATTITUDE
Be All You Can Be (Victor Books)
Failing Forward (Thomas Nelson)
The Power of Thinking (Honor Books)
Living at the Next Level (Thomas Nelson)
Think On These Things (Beacon Hill)
The Winning Attitude (Thomas Nelson)
Your Bridge to a Better Future (Thomas Nelson)
The Power of Attitude (Honor Books)

LEADERSHIP
The 21 Indispensable Qualities of a Leader (Thomas Nelson)
The 21 Irrefutable Laws of Leadership (Thomas Nelson)
The 21 Most Powerful Minutes in a Leader's Day (Thomas Nelson)
Developing the Leader Within You (Thomas Nelson)
The Power of Leadership (Honor Books)
The 17 Indisputable Laws of Teamwork (Thomas Nelson)
The 17 Essential Qualities of a Team Player (Thomas Nelson, Jan. 2002)